Framework FOCUS

KS3 Classbook

Terry Hudson

Letts Educational

4 Grosvenor Place

London

SW1X 7DL

School enquiries: 01539 564910

Parent & Student enquiries: 01539 564913

email: mail@lettsed.co.uk

website: www.educational.com

Text © Terry Hudson 2003

First published 2003
05/101007

ISBN 978 1 84085 459 6

British Library Cataloguing in Publication Data

A catalogue record for this book is available from the British Library.

Commissioned by Helen Clark

Project management by Vicky Butt and Julia Swales

Cover design by Ken Vail

Design, editorial and layout by Hart McLeod, Cambridge

Production by PDQ

Printed in Dubai

Acknowledgements

Cover photo Alfred Pasieka/Science Photo Library

p.11 fig 3a, J.C. Revy/SPL; p.15 fig 2, Frank Spooner; p.18 fig 2, Rick Hall/SPL; p.20 fig 1, Bruce Coleman; p.21 fig 2a, Bruce Coleman; p.22 fig 1, Bruce Coleman; p.23 fig 2, SPL; p.27 fig 2, Robert Llewellyn/ImageState/Alamy; p.32 fig 1, Astrid & Hans-Frieder Michler/SPL; p.34 fig 1, Art Directors and Trip; p.37 fig 2, Spectrum Colour Library; p.38 fig 1, Pictor ImageState; p.39 fig 3, Frank Spooner; p.40 fig 1, Frank Spooner; p.44 fig 1a, Frank Spooner; p.44 fig 1b Art Directors and Trip; p.52 fig 2, Frank Spooner; p.56 fig 1, Alamy; p.57 fig 7, Eye Ubiquitous; p.59 fig 1, Frank Spooner; p.61 fig 3, Spectrum Colour Library; p.62 fig 1, Pictor /ImageState; p.64 fig 1, Eye Ubiquitous; p.65 fig 3, Spectrum Colour Library; p.66 fig 1, Richard Noble; p.72 fig 3, Frank Spooner; p.75 fig 3a Williams Renault; p.75 fig 3b, Eye Ubiquitous; p.76 fig 1, David Nunak/SPL; p.77 fig 4, NASA/SPL; p.78 fig 1, NASA/SPL; p.80 fig 2, David Nunak/SPL; p.86 fig 1, Spectrum Colour Library; p.92 fig 2, Biophoto Associates/SPL; p.97 fig 3, D. Phillips/SPL; p.98 fig 1, Art Directors and Trip; p.100 fig 1, Matt Meadows & Peter Arnold Inc/SPL; p.101 fig 2, Dr Jeremy Burgess/SPL; p.106 fig 1, Corbis; p.108 fig 1, Spectrum Colour Library; p.108 fig 2 both, Bruce Coleman; p.111 fig 2, Planet Earth; p.118 fig 2, Art Directors and Trip; p.123 fig 2, Spectrum Colour Library; p.123 fig 3, Jonathon Blair/Corbis; p.126 fig 1, Bill Ross/Corbis; p.126 fig 2, Greg Probst/Corbis; p.127 fig 4, Grafton Marshall Smith/Corbis; p.128 fig 1, Spectrum Colour Library; p.131 fig 2, Worldwide Picture Library/ Alamy; p.131 fig 3, Imagina The Image Maker/Alamy; p.132 fig 1 Spectrum Colour Library; p.132 fig 3, Planet Earth; p.135 fig 3, Sandro Vannini/Corbis; p.136 fig 1, Art Directors and Trip; p.142 fig 1, Eye Ubiquitous; p.143 fig 1 Sciencephotos/Alamy; p.143 fig 4, Mark Gibson/Corbis; p.145 fig 3, NASA/SPL; p.146 fig 1, Spectrum Colour Library; p.150 fig 1, Alex Bartel/ SPL; p.151 fig 3, BUPA; p.152 fig 1, Stone/Getty Images; p.155 fig 3, Jerome Wexler/SPL; p.158 fig 1, Superstock; p.158 fig 3, CNRI/SPL; p.159 fig 5, Eye Ubiquitous; p.161 fig 4, Deep Light Productions/SPL; p.165 fig 5, Art Directors and Trip; p.170 fig 2, ImageState/Alamy; p.171 fig 1, Doug Wilson/Alamy; p.171 fig 2, Frank Spooner; p.173 fig 4, Holt Studios; p.174 fig 1, Frank Spooner; p.175 fig 3, Hulton Getty; p.177 fig 2, SPL; p.179 fig 4, robertharding.com; p.181 fig 3 both, Matt Meadows & Peter Arnold/SPL; p.183 fig 1, Frank Spooner; p.191 fig 2, Holt Studios International Ltd/ Alamy; p.193 fig 2, Gunter Marx/Corbis; p.195 fig 2, Magnum; p.201 fig 4, Kevin Schafer/Corbis; p.204 fig 1, Rex Features; p.206 fig 1, Art Directors and Trip; p.206 fig 2, Art Directors and Trip; p.208 fig 2, Simon Fraser/SPL; p.209 fig 3, George McLeod; p.209 fig 4, Rosenfeld Images Ltd/SPL; p.210 fig 1, SPL; p.211 fig 4, Corbis; p.211 fig 5, robertharding.com/Alamy; p.212 fig 1, David Hoffman Photo Library/Alamy; p.212 fig 2, Peter Downing/Manchester Evening News; p.214 fig 1, Oscar Burriel/SPL; p.216 fig 1, Sciencephotos/Alamy; p.219 fig 2, Still Pictures; p.220 fig 1, Raoul Minsart/Corbis; p.221 fig 3, S.I.N/Alamy; p.222 fig 1, Eye Ubiquitous; p.226 fig 1, ImageState/Alamy; p.227 fig 4, Jerry Lodriguss/SPL; p.228 fig 1, Worldwide Picture Library/Alamy; p.229 fig 3 Sciencephotos/Alamy; p.230 fig 1, Art Directors and Trip; p.230 fig 2, NOAA/SPL; p.231 fig 3, NASA/SPL; p.232 fig 1, Pete Saloutos/Corbis; p.234 fig 1, Duemo/Corbis; p.235 fig 3, Brand X Pictures/Alamy; p.236 fig 1, ImageState/Alamy; p.237 fig 3, ImageState/Alamy; p.237 fig 4, Brandon Cole Marine Photography/Alamy; p.238 fig 1, Caterpillar; p.242 fig 1, Frank Spooner.

Year 7 contents

Year 8 contents

Year 9 contents

Introduction to Year 7 topics

Biology (pages 8–31)

The first part of the Year 7 topics is designed to help you to understand life processes and living things. It is divided into four sections. Each section covers a unit from the Scheme of Work for Science.

Cells

In this section you will learn that living things are made up of cells. You will also learn that cells can be organised into tissues and organs. The spreads will give you opportunities to explore cell structure and learn about the vital functions carried out by cells. Plant and animal cells will be discussed and you will learn how cells grow and divide to make new cells.

Reproduction

The second section covers ideas about human reproduction. You will learn the names and functions of the different parts of the reproductive organs. Also, you will study how eggs are fertilised by sperm and how a foetus grows in the womb. The units also cover the birth of babies and how young people develop into adulthood.

Environment and feeding relationships

In this section you will learn to identify different habitats and to explain how the animals and plants in habitats are specially adapted. You will also study food chains and food webs to show feeding relationships within an environment.

Variation and classification

This section will give you opportunities to explore variation within and between species. You will study how this variation is the result of environmental or inherited factors. This section also explains the importance of classifying living things and gives you opportunities to identify some of the main taxonomic groups of animals and plants.

Chemistry (pages 32–55)

The second part of the Year 7 topics is designed to help you to understand materials and their properties. It is divided into four sections. Each section covers a unit from the Scheme of Work for science.

Acids and alkalis

In this section you will learn about some common acids and alkalis and be able to classify solutions as acidic, alkaline or neutral. You will be able to describe the use of indicators and the pH scale. The unit also covers the uses of acids and alkalis and you will be able to explain what happens when a solution is neutralised.

Simple chemical reactions

This section will give you opportunities to identify some new materials formed during chemical reactions. In particular you will study burning and some reactions of acids in which a gas is made. As part of this work you will learn how to test for hydrogen and carbon dioxide. You will learn that burning is a chemical reaction involving air or oxygen and that oxides are produced.

Particle model of solids, liquids and gases

This unit of work encourages you to explain differences between solids, liquids and gases by using the particle model. You will learn how to use the particle model to explain phenomena such as expansion and mixing of liquids.

Solutions

In this section you will be able to learn more about the particle theory and use this to explain how substances dissolve. You will classify some solids as soluble or insoluble and be able to explain what a saturated solution is. The work then encourages you to separate mixtures using distillation and chromatography. You will also learn about the conservation of mass.

Physics (pages 56–81)

The third part of the Year 7 topics is designed to help you to understand physical processes. It is divided into four sections. Each section covers a unit from the Scheme of Work for Science.

Energy resources

In this section of the book you will learn that fuels release energy when they burn and that we can use this energy for many things. You will study fossil fuels and the idea that some fuels are renewable and others are not. The unit will encourage you to appreciate that conservation of fuels is important. You will also study energy transfers within a range of systems, including living things.

Electric circuits

This unit of work will allow you to develop your earlier ideas of electric circuits. You will be able to use the concepts of electric current and energy transfer to explain how circuits work. You will be able to state that current is the same at all points in a series circuit and divides along the branches in a parallel circuit. Also, you will be able to explain resistance.

Forces and their effects

This section helps you to build on your earlier work on forces and how forces can be measured. You will go on to explore friction and air resistance and explain the difference between mass and weight. The work also covers the concept of speed and how it can be measured.

The Solar System and beyond

This section will help you to develop your understanding of the Sun and Moon and to allow you to use models to explain eclipses, the phases of the Moon and seasonal changes. You will be able to describe the relative positions of the planets and compare their conditions to those on Earth. In addition, you will be able to state that stars are light sources but planets and other objects are seen because they reflect light.

1 How living things are organised

In this section of the book you will have opportunities to:
- Review the seven processes of life
- Explain that similar specialised cells may be grouped together to form tissues and that tissues form organs.

With a partner.
Make a list of ten objects around you and then try to classify them as either 'living', 'once living' or 'not living'. Discuss and then write down a list of 'rules' you used to help you to decide.

The processes of life

Study tip

Some people remember the seven processes by using the first letters of the processes and arranging them as MRS NERG.

It is easy to decide whether most objects are living or not. A brick is obviously not living and never has been. A dog running around is obviously alive. But what about a leaf that has fallen from a tree? To answer a question like this we need to think about what all living things must do to be alive.

All living things must carry out seven processes to stay alive

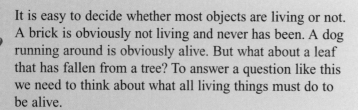

1. All living things move. **Movement** is an important part of life.   M
2. All living things obtain energy from their food by a process called **respiration**.   R
3. All living things respond to their **environment**. They therefore require **sensitivity**.   S
4. All living things obtain food by a process called **nutrition**.   N
5. All living things rid themselves of waste materials by a process called **excretion**.   E
6. All living things get old and die. Replacements are made by the process of **reproduction**.   R
7. All living things grow. **Growth** is another important function of living things.   G

Your teacher will divide the class into seven groups and allocate each group one of the seven processes above. Each group should then imagine an animal that is not able to carry out the process they have been allocated. Make notes describing what would happen to the animal. A spokesperson will feed back to the class.

Single-celled organisms

The simplest living organisms have just one **cell**. An organism made up of just one cell is called **unicellular** or **acellular**. A single cell needs to be good at everything. It needs to be an 'all-rounder'.

A single cell cannot grow bigger than a certain size. If it becomes too big, chemicals cannot move through it quickly enough (see Fig 1). Most unicellular organisms are so small that you need a microscope to see them. An amoeba is one example.

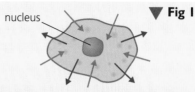

▼ **Fig 1**

nucleus

Materials can reach all parts of the cell. Waste materials can leave easily.

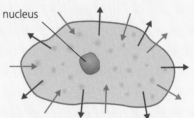

nucleus

Materials have difficulty reaching all parts of the cell. Waste materials cannot leave easily.

Multicellular organisms

Bigger organisms need to have more than one cell working together (see Fig 2). Plants and animals made up of more than one cell are called **multicellular**. Some of their cells can become **specialised** to do particular jobs (see Units 3 and 4). However, when an organism becomes more complicated its cells need to be carefully organised.

Cells are often grouped together. Groups of cells of the same type carrying out the same task are called **tissues**. Two examples are nerve and muscle.

Different tissues can work together to carry out more complicated jobs. Groups of tissues working together are called **organs**. One example is the heart, which is made up of muscle tissue, nerve tissue and connective tissue.

Groups of organs work together as an **organ system** within an **organism**. The heart works together with arteries, veins and capillaries to form the **circulatory system** (see Unit 42). Other examples are the **reproductive system** (see Unit 5) and the **digestive system** (see Unit 40).

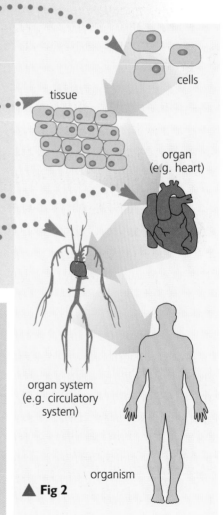

cells

tissue

organ
(e.g. heart)

organ system
(e.g. circulatory system)

organism

▲ **Fig 2**

REVIEW

- Work on your own to complete this activity.
  - ○ Take a clean piece of paper. Without looking at your classbook, try to write down the seven processes of life.
  - ○ Next, write down how an amoeba would carry out each process.
  - ○ Finally, write down which organs and tissues of your body help carry out the seven processes of life.

  You are going to do a small home survey. At home, make a list of five things that are living and five things that are non-living. Explain which rules you used to help you to decide.

2 Cells in detail

KEY IDEAS

In this section of the book you will have opportunities to:
- Explain the similarities and differences between plant and animal cells.

STARTER

In a group.
Collect some small objects from around the room. What size is the smallest object? Look at the objects using a hand lens. How much bigger do they look? Now look at your hand using the hand lens. Why do you think you cannot see any cells?

Microscopes

▶ **Fig 1**

A microscope can magnify objects much more than a hand lens. A typical light microscope is shown in Fig 1. Without a microscope your eyes can see objects as small as 0.1mm. With a light microscope it is possible to see objects tens, hundreds or even thousands of times smaller than this. This allows us to see cells.

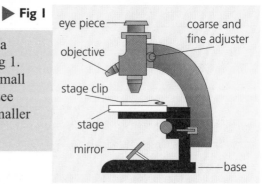

eye piece — coarse and fine adjuster
objective
stage clip
stage
mirror
base

What are cells?

Cells are the building blocks of living things, or **organisms**. They are often called the basic unit of life. Cells come in thousands of different shapes and sizes but they all have the same basic jobs to do. They must all be able to:

obtain energy from foods
⇩
make new chemicals for the organism
⇩
control their own chemical reactions
⇩
reproduce to make new cells
⇩
keep their contents together and safe from the environment.

ACTIVITY

With a partner.
- List four functions of a cell.
- Discuss what would happen if the cell was unable to carry out each of these functions.

These special roles are carried out by different parts of the cell.

Animal and plant cells

Animal and plant cells are made up of **cytoplasm**, a **nucleus** and a **cell membrane**.

The cytoplasm is the liquid part of the cell. Chemicals in the cytoplasm can break down molecules to release energy. They can also join small molecules together to make larger ones. The chemicals made in the cytoplasm break down food and build proteins and other important chemicals.

The nucleus is the cell's control centre. It contains **genetic material** that allows the nucleus to control the chemical reactions taking place in the cytoplasm. The nucleus is also responsible for cell reproduction.

The cell membrane is the outer skin of the cell. This is a thin and flexible covering that keeps the cell contents together. The cell membrane also controls the movement of chemicals in and out of the cell. Some chemicals can pass through easily and others cannot. The membrane is therefore described as **selectively** or **partially permeable**.

Plant cells are surrounded by a thick, rigid **cell wall** made of **cellulose** and contain a space called a **vacuole** filled with watery sap. They also contain structures called **chloroplasts** filled with a green chemical called **chlorophyll**. Chlorophyll allows plant cells to use energy from sunlight to make small chemical molecules (Units 85 and 86).

▼ **Fig 2** Typical animal and plant cells.

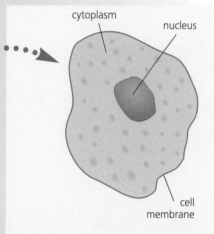

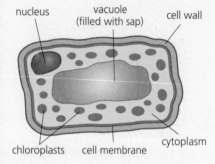

▼ **Fig 3** Typical animal and plant cells.

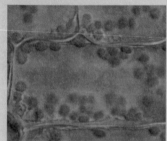
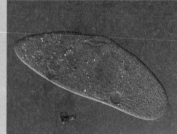

Making new cells

Cells reproduce by growing and then dividing in two. This is called **cell division**. The genetic material in the nucleus allows the cell to make an exact copy of itself. The genetic material in the nucleus copies itself and then each copy splits into two. When the rest of the cell divides each new cell has an exact copy of the original genetic material. This is how the tissues of your body are repaired.

▼ **Fig 4** Cell division.

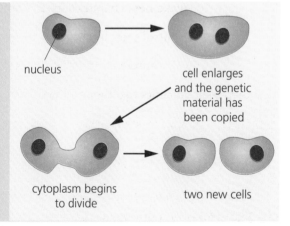

REVIEW
- In a group.
  - Make a poster showing a fully labelled plant cell.
  - Circle any of the parts you would expect to see in a plant and an animal cell.
  - Draw a square around the parts you would only expect to find in a plant cell.

3 Some specialised cells

KEY IDEAS

In this section of the book you will have opportunities to:
- Explain that some animal and plant cells are specialised to carry out special jobs
- Describe how sperm and egg cells are adapted.

STARTER

With a partner.
Make a list of five different tissues found in animals and plants. What roles do each of these tissues carry out? Finally, discuss with a partner what the cells in these tissues might look like.

Each to its own job

Multicellular animals are made up of many cells. These cells are not all the same. Some are adapted or specialised to do special jobs within the organism. They work together like a team to share the job of living. This is called **division of labour**.

Some cells and their special jobs are shown in Fig 1.

Animal epithelial cells

Epithelial cells cover outer surfaces such as skin and inner surfaces such as mouth and intestines. Epithelial cells need to protect the organism from wear and tear and chemicals. They must also allow substances to pass into and out of the organism. Epithelial cells divide rapidly so that any lost cells can be replaced. Many of them are flat so that they can be arranged like tiles on a roof. Some make protective oils or mucus. Some have surface hairs called **cilia** that wave backwards and forwards to move particles that could harm the organism. Dust particles in the lungs are removed in this way. These are called ciliated epithelial cells.

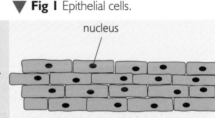

▼ **Fig 1** Epithelial cells.

nucleus

epithelial cells in skin tissue

dust particles   cilia

ciliated epithelial cells in the nose

ACTIVITY

With a partner.
- Imagine you are explaining about epithelial cells to a younger person.
- Write down how you would describe how these cells are specially adapted to do their job.

Cells specialised for reproduction

Some animal cells are specialised for reproduction. Egg and sperm cells play a vital role in the reproduction of animals. Eggs, or **ova** (singular, **ovum**),

Connections

This unit builds on work you have already done on cells. It will help you to understand how plant and animal cells can be specialised to carry out important jobs. It will lead on to work on cells in other units.

contain one half of the genetic material needed to make a new organism. They also contain a food store that makes them amongst the largest cells known.

Sperm cells contain the other half of the genetic material needed to make a new organism. Unlike ova, they do not have a large food store. A sperm cell is adapted for swimming. The head contains the genetic material and energy. The tail drives the sperm through liquid towards an ovum.

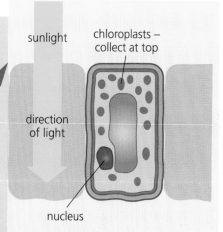

▶ **Fig 2** Human ovum and sperm.

Plant cells are specialised too

Cells in leaves

Plant leaves contain many cells adapted to carry out photosynthesis (Unit 86). **Palisade cells** are especially well designed for this. These cells contain many chloroplasts filled with chlorophyll and form a layer just beneath the upper protective covering of the leaf. When the Sun shines on the leaf the energy from the sunlight passes directly into them. They are also tall and arranged in regular rows, to help the sunlight to shine deep inside.

Some plant cells are specialised for reproduction. Flowering plants have an **ovary** that produces the female sex cell or **ovules**. The male sex cells, or **pollen**, are produced in the **anther** at the top of the **stamen**. A pollen grain landing on the sticky stigma grows a long **pollen tube** down the style. The genetic material from the pollen grain passes down the tube and fertilises the ovule.

▲ **Fig 3** Palisade cells.

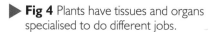

▶ **Fig 4** Plants have tissues and organs specialised to do different jobs.

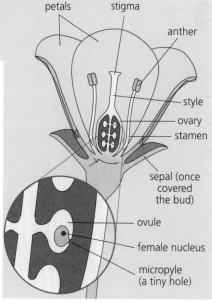

4 Reproduction and human development

KEY IDEAS

In this section of the book you will have opportunities to:
- Describe the important emotional and physical changes that occur as humans change from being children to being adults
- Understand that the changes are part of preparing for reproduction.

STARTER

On your own.
Make a list of the things you are able to do now that you could not do as a baby. With a partner, share your ideas and make a combined list. Discuss why babies need so much care.

Sexual reproduction

Humans reproduce by a process called sexual reproduction. In sexual reproduction genetic material from the male is combined with genetic material from the female. The genetic material from the male is carried in cells called sperm. The genetic material from the female is in the egg. Babies are born with sex organs already formed but they are not ready to work yet. Before sexual reproduction can take place human males must be able to produce sperm and females must be able to produce eggs. This will not happen until they are almost old enough to take on the responsibility of bringing a new life into the world.

Puberty

The stage of life when human sex organs begin to work is called **puberty**. Puberty generally starts between 11 and 15 years old for a girl and between 13 and 15 years old for a boy. Everyone is different so it may occur before or after these ages. During this important stage of life many changes take place in young men and women.

The changes at puberty are controlled by **sex hormones**. Hormones are chemical messengers that are produced by glands and carried in the blood. Some of the important changes are shown in Fig 1. Many of the differences between males and females are called **secondary sexual characteristics**. These visible changes start to develop at the same time as the female sex organs start producing eggs and the male sex organs start producing sperm. The period of time when secondary sexual characteristics develop after puberty is known as adolescence. Adulthood is usually reached in the late teens or early twenties. Boys may continue growing up to the age of 23. Girls may continue growing up to the age of 20.

ACTIVITY

With a partner.
- Make a list of the changes that occur in males and females during puberty.
- Compare your list with a partner's.

Physical changes

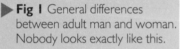

Both girls and boys change shape. A girl develops breasts and her body shape softens. A boy's shoulders broaden and his penis grows larger and can become erect. A boy's voice becomes deeper and facial hair starts to grow. Boys and girls grow pubic hair around their sex organs. At some point a girl will start to menstruate. Boys and girls may also suffer from spots.

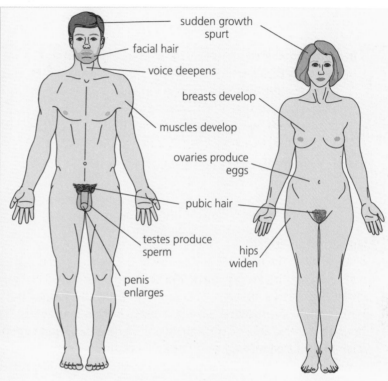

sudden growth spurt

facial hair

voice deepens

breasts develop

muscles develop

ovaries produce eggs

pubic hair

testes produce sperm

hips widen

penis enlarges

▶ **Fig 1** General differences between adult man and woman. Nobody looks exactly like this.

Emotional changes

As they grow, adolescents become more independent from their parents. They begin to think and act for themselves, become more aware of people of the opposite sex, and take on more responsibility for their actions. These changes can be exciting but they can also be confusing and difficult.

▶ **Fig 2**

- With a partner.
  - Discuss some of the things you will legally be able to do when you are an adult that you cannot do now.
  - How do developments during puberty and adolescence help you to cope with these responsibilities?
  - List some reasons why you think adolescence is an exciting but a confusing time for many people.

5 The reproductive system and fertilisation

KEY IDEAS

In this section of the book you will have opportunities to:
● Identify and name the reproductive organs of humans
● Describe how sperm cells and egg cells meet.

STARTER

With a partner.
Write down how sperm and egg cells are specially adapted to carry out their jobs.

The reproductive system

Sperm and egg cells are also called sex cells or **gametes**. Sperm cells are male gametes and eggs or ova are female gametes. The organs that produce gametes and bring them together are called the reproductive or **sex organs**. The sex organs make up the reproductive system.

Fertilisation in water

Animals that live in water, such as fish, can shed their eggs or sperm into the water and let them mix there. This is called **external fertilisation**. Land animals cannot do this because sperm cells need to swim to an egg. Most land animals, including humans, solve this problem by arranging for the egg and sperm to meet inside the female's body, where the new organism will also grow. This is called **internal fertilisation**.

The human male

The human body is too warm for sperm cells to survive. This is why the **testes**, where sperm are made, need to be kept outside the body in a bag of skin called the **scrotum**. The testes also make sex hormones. The penis is made of soft, spongy tissue that can fill with blood and become hard and erect.

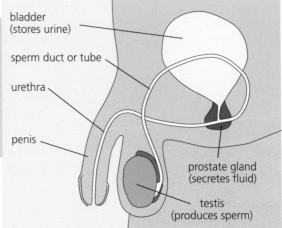

▶ **Fig 1** Human male reproductive system.

The human female

The ova are made in two ovaries. Ovaries also produce female sex hormones. When an egg is released it passes into the nearest **fallopian tube**. This is where it may be fertilised by a sperm cell. The egg travels on down the fallopian tube to the womb or **uterus**. If it has been fertilised by a sperm it stays here.

ACTIVITY

With a partner.
- Draw and label the male and female reproductive organs.
- Clearly mark onto the drawings where sperm and egg cells are produced.

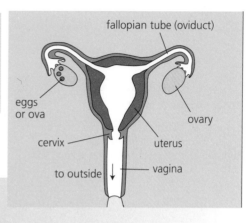

▶ **Fig 2** Human female reproductive system.

Sexual intercourse

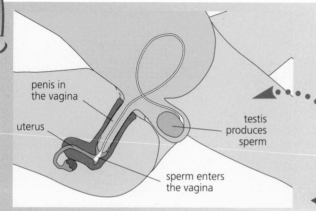

◀ **Fig 3**

The vagina is a tube lined with muscle. It links the uterus with the outside of the body. When it is erect the male penis can enter the female vagina (see Fig 3). During sexual intercourse more than 300 million sperm cells may enter the female at one time. Only about 100 will reach the egg. Only one can enter an egg.

Fertilisation

When a sperm cell enters an egg, the surface of the egg changes to prevent any more sperm from entering. Each egg can only be fertilised by a single sperm. This is when the genetic material from the male and female combine. The fertilised egg now has a complete set of genetic material to make a new human. The fertilised egg contains genetic material from two different people. This means that the new baby will have a mixture of characteristics from both parents. The mixture is different for each individual. It makes each person unique.

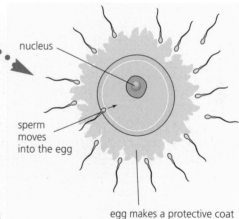

▶ **Fig 4**

REVIEW

- In a group.
  - Imagine you are going to give a presentation to your class explaining sexual reproduction.
  - Design four overhead projector transparencies or powerpoint pages to help you.
  - These visual aids should contain clear text and drawings.

  Carry out research to find examples of animals that use internal fertilisation and some that use external fertilisation. In each case, try to discover what happens to the young after they are born or hatched.

6 Pregnancy and birth

Growth of the baby

As the fertilised egg cell moves down the fallopian tube it starts to divide into more cells. When it reaches the uterus it is a ball of cells. The ball of cells buries itself in the soft wall of the uterus. The thick lining provides food and protection. Here, the developing ball of cells carries on growing into an **embryo**. When a woman is carrying an embryo she is pregnant. Her **menstrual cycle** stops. No new eggs are released and the uterus keeps its lining to protect her embryo. The uterus is not much bigger yet. As the embryo grows the uterus will become much bigger. It is filled with fluid called **amniotic fluid** and this helps to cushion and protect the baby.

▶ **Fig 1** Development of a human embryo.

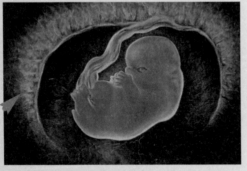

▲ **Fig 2** The embryo floats safely inside the uterus.

The placenta

After six weeks the embryo is approximately 1 cm long. It now has a brain and a beating heart and floats in a sac filled with fluid. A close link is formed between the embryo and the uterus to supply the embryo with food and oxygen. This is called the **placenta**. Here the mother's blood and the embryo's blood flow in capillaries side by side.

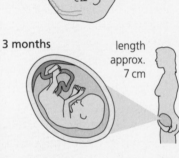

6 weeks — length approx. 1 cm

7 weeks — length approx. 2.5 cm

3 months — length approx. 7 cm

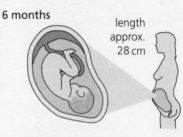

6 months — length approx. 28 cm

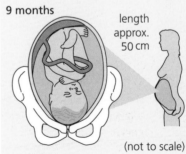

9 months — length approx. 50 cm

(not to scale)

Food and oxygen can pass from the mother's blood into the embryo's blood. At the same time waste materials can pass in the other direction. The blood of the baby does not mix with the blood of its mother. Only food, oxygen, waste products and some other chemicals are exchanged.

After two months the embryo becomes a **foetus** (or fetus). It grows too big to stay buried in the uterus lining but is still connected to the placenta by a tube called the **umbilical cord**.

Not only useful materials can pass through the placenta from the mother to the embryo. If the mother smokes or drinks alcohol then harmful substances can be given to the embryo. Many other substances, including viruses and drugs, can also be very harmful to the developing embryo. It is also important that mothers eat a healthy diet. They need extra vitamins and essential minerals such as calcium.

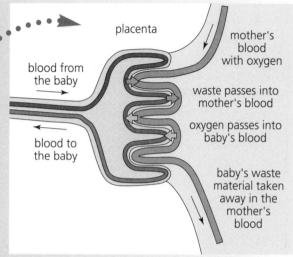

▲ **Fig 3** Some drugs can enter the baby's blood together with food and oxygen.

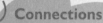
ACTIVITY

In a group.
- Discuss how the embryo is protected and fed within the uterus.

The birth

Approximately nine months after fertilisation the baby is ready to be born. It has usually turned round so that the head is ready to emerge first. First the opening of the uterus, called the **cervix**, relaxes. The bag of fluid around the baby may now burst. Gradually, powerful muscles in the uterus wall begin to contract to push the baby out. Eventually the baby is born through the vagina. After it is born the baby's umbilical cord will be sealed and then cut to separate it from the placenta. The stub will eventually form the belly button or navel. The uterus pushes the placenta out a little while after the baby, which is why it is often called the 'afterbirth'. Once born, the baby can be fed milk from the mother's **mammary glands** in the breasts. Not only is this milk full of **nutrients**, but also antibodies that protect against disease.

Connections

This unit builds on your work on life cycles at Key Stage 2 and is linked to work on cells. The work will help you to understand further work on health and how your body works.

REVIEW

- In a group.
  ○ Describe the life story of a fertilised egg, using the following words in the correct order:
  vagina; fallopian tube; placenta; foetus; embryo; uterus; cervix; umbilical cord.

7 Habitats

KEY IDEAS

In this section of the book you will have opportunities to:
- Explain that different habitats have different plants and animals living in them
- Describe how animals and plants are adapted to live in their own habitats.

STARTER

On your own.
Write down three examples of habitats. In your own words, write a definition of the words habitat, community and ecosystem. At the end of this unit, check your definitions.

Organisms and their surroundings

The type of place where an organism normally lives is called its **habitat**.

A tiny habitat is called a **microhabitat**. A crack in a rock may be a microhabitat within the general habitat of a beach. The collection of plants and animals in a habitat make up a **community**. A community and its environment together form an **ecosystem**. Environmental factors include light, **temperature**, acidity and moisture content.

Habitats

A habitat must supply everything that an organism needs to survive. There must be oxygen, food, water and shelter. Rotting leaves provide food and shelter for many small creatures. The same habitat supplies small creatures for bigger creatures to eat. Living things alter habitats by living in them. The rotting leaves are changed by the insects that feed on them and push them around. Even the rot is caused by microorganisms that live there.

▲ **Fig 1** The forest floor habitat contains hundreds of microhabitats.

Ponds, rivers, beaches, rock pools and soil are all different habitats and there are hundreds more. Different habitats support different animals and plants. An animal that lives in a tree may not be able to live in a pond. Sometimes different habitats support the same animals at different stages of their lives.

A dragonfly grows up in a pond but eventually comes out of the water to hunt in the air.

ACTIVITY

On your own.
- List five microhabitats that you may find in a garden habitat.
- Compare your list with a partner.
- Now try to write down the names of some of the animals and plants that live in these microhabitats.

Competition

The different species of animals and plants in a habitat use it in different ways. Each one occupies a different niche. Two species fighting for the same niche would be in **competition**. When two species compete, one generally drives the other out. A beach may support many different birds. There may be curlews feeding on animals that burrow under the sand and plovers picking animals from the surface of the sand (see Fig 2). Both species live within the same habitat but they do not compete for the same food.

▲ **Fig 2a** Curlew.

b Grey plover. ▶

Adaptation

Animals and plants are adapted to their habitat. A fish can breathe underwater. A limpet clings to a seashore rock. Conifers have thin shiny leaves so that heavy snow can slide off without breaking their branches.

The lives of animals and plants in a habitat may be closely connected. Some animals eat plants, others eat smaller animals. Being adapted to a habitat may mean protecting yourself from being eaten at the same time as finding food for yourself.

The dog whelk (see Fig 3) feeds on other shellfish. Dog whelks on exposed shores have thinner shells than dog whelks on sheltered shores. This may seem mysterious until you also discover that crabs eat dog whelks. Crabs cannot survive on exposed shores with big waves. The thick shell of the dog whelk protects it from crabs rather than the environment. Even though the dog whelk is a **predator** itself, it needs to keep itself safe from other predators.

▶ **Fig 3** Dog whelk

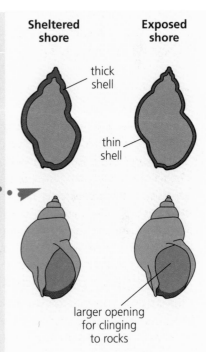

Sheltered shore   Exposed shore

thick shell

thin shell

larger opening for clinging to rocks

REVIEW

- In a group.
  - Identify five different habitats around your school or home and list some of the animals and plants that live there.
  - How do these living things interact with one another and with their environment?

Produce some creative writing to describe how you think humans would look if we had spent a million years adapting to life underground instead of above ground.

8 Adapting to change

KEY IDEAS

In this section of the book you will have opportunities to:
- Explain how organisms are adapted to survive daily changes in their habitat
- Explain that organisms are adapted to survive seasonal changes in their habitat.

STARTER

On your own.
In many countries the winters are cold and harsh. Write down some of the ways that animals and plants have adapted to survive such winters.

Change

Regular changes occur daily or seasonally in most habitats. Some habitats also suffer occasional changes, such as drought or forest fire. Organisms need adaptations to help them to survive both regular and occasional changes.

Daily changes

Each morning the Sun rises and daylight begins. Every evening the level of light falls until it becomes dark. Living things adapt to the pattern of light and dark in many ways.

Most animals and plants are more active during the day. They are **diurnal**. Some are more active at night. They are **nocturnal**. Being nocturnal can keep small animals safe from predators that hunt in daylight. Some predators specialise in hunting at night. A bat uses sound to hunt nocturnal insects. An owl uses sensitive ears and large eyes. It is specially adapted to see a warm body moving in dim light.

Flowers attract insects for pollination. Many bee-pollinated flowers open in sunlight and close at night. Moth-pollinated flowers may only open at night. These flowers are often strongly scented to attract moths. Plants can also turn their leaves towards the Sun to gather more light for photosynthesis.

▲ **Fig 1** Sunflowers are so sensitive to light that the flowerheads follow the Sun as it crosses the sky.

ACTIVITY

On your own.
- Make a list of some of the ways that plants have adapted to changes that take place during the day.
- How is a sunflower adapted for pollination?

Seasonal changes

Tropical regions of the world do not have seasons. The climate there is warm all the year round.

Northern or southern regions can be very cold in winter and very warm in summer. Plants and animals there must adapt to these seasonal changes or they would not survive.

Many plants survive the winter by becoming **dormant**. Annual plants die after making seeds to survive the winter. Biennial plants survive for two years by making an underground food store and allowing their green parts to wither. The following year, the root can grow new leaves and a flower to make seeds. Perennial plants such as bulbs and trees can survive for many years by losing their leaves each winter and growing new ones in the spring.

▲ **Fig 2** Oak trees can survive more than a hundred winters by losing their leaves and becoming dormant.

Animals also have different ways to survive through the winter. Some invertebrates die after laying eggs that can survive the cold, like annual plants. Some spend the winter as a dormant pupa, like biennial plants.

Mammals and birds can survive cold weather but they cannot survive without food, and food is scarce in winter. Many birds simply fly to a warmer region. This is called **migration**. Some mammals hide away and sleep when food is scarce. This is called **hibernation**. Before hibernating an animal builds up a store of body fat to provide food and warmth during the winter. Animals that remain active through the winter also need extra fat and thick fur to protect them from the cold.

Heat and drought

Desert plants are specialised for collecting and storing water. Snails keep moisture in by withdrawing into their shells and sealing the entrance. Many desert animals hide underground during the day and come out to feed at night.

REVIEW

- In a group.
  - Think about seashore animals and plants. Twice everyday they are covered by the tide.
  - Make a list of the daily and seasonal changes they must be able to survive.

23

9 Food chains and food webs

In this section of the book you will have opportunities to:
- Explain what food chains and food webs are
- Describe what happens to the energy within a community of plants and animals.

In a group.
Think back to your earlier work on feeding relationships. Now discuss why a shortage of grass could cause foxes to be short of food and farmers to be pleased.

Food for life

Energy for life comes from the Sun. Green plants use sunlight to make food by photosynthesis. Animals cannot make their own food. They must feed on plants or other animals.

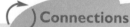 **Connections**

This unit builds on earlier work on habitats, food chains and food webs and leads on to further study of ecological relationships and how living things are interdependent.

Food chains

Green plants building their own food are called **producers**. Animals eating plants or other animals are called **consumers**. Consumers fall into three groups. Animals that eat green plants directly are called **primary consumers** or **herbivores**. Animals that eat herbivores are called **secondary consumers**. Animals that eat secondary consumers are called **tertiary consumers**.

The relationship between producers and consumers can be drawn as a chain. • • • • •

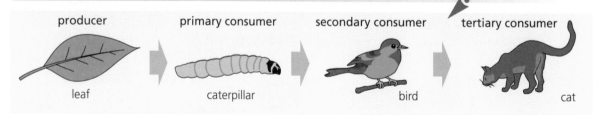

producer — leaf → primary consumer — caterpillar → secondary consumer — bird → tertiary consumer — cat

▲ **Fig 1** All four stages of production and consumption.

Food chains occur in every habitat. Fig 2 shows a pond habitat.

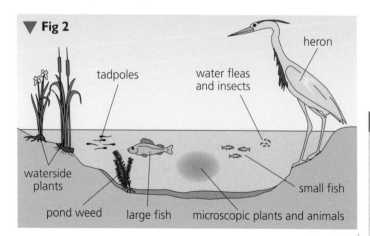

▼ **Fig 2**

heron
tadpoles
water fleas and insects
waterside plants
pond weed
large fish
microscopic plants and animals
small fish

ACTIVITY

On your own.
- Draw a food chain from the pond habitat.
- Identify the producers, primary consumers and secondary consumers in the chain.

Energy flow

When an animal eats a plant it uses the food to provide energy and raw materials. Some of the plant material is simply wasted. Some energy is given out as heat and some material is **egested**. Half of the grass a cow eats is used to provide energy. Less than half of the grass becomes part of the cow. Energy is lost or used up in this way at every stage in the food chain.

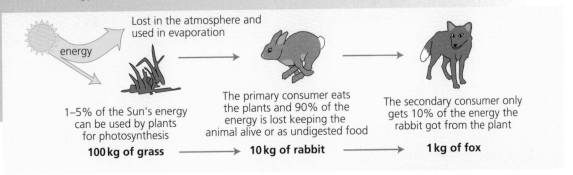

Lost in the atmosphere and used in evaporation

energy

1–5% of the Sun's energy can be used by plants for photosynthesis

The primary consumer eats the plants and 90% of the energy is lost keeping the animal alive or as undigested food

The secondary consumer only gets 10% of the energy the rabbit got from the plant

100 kg of grass ⟶ **10 kg of rabbit** ⟶ **1 kg of fox**

▲ **Fig 3** A lot of energy is lost as it passes down the food chain.

Food webs

The **food web** tells you more about a habitat than a food chain. The links between and across chains give a truer picture of the complex relationships between organisms in a habitat.

A food chain can only show a rabbit eating grass or a sparrowhawk eating sparrows. Rabbits also eat other plants. Sparrowhawks eat many other small birds.

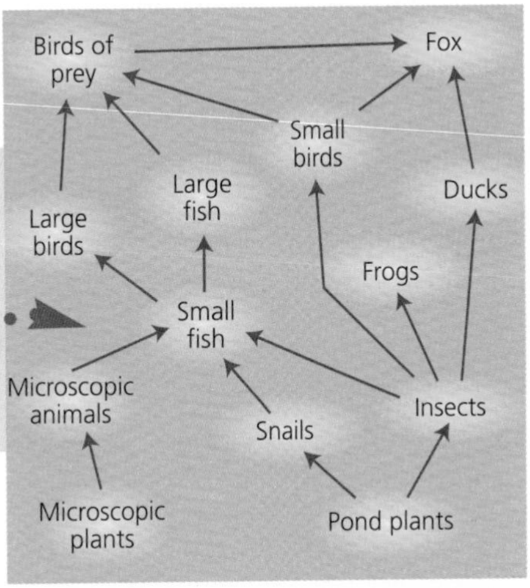

▶ **Fig 4** How many different chains can you trace in this food web?

Birds of prey — Fox
Small birds
Large fish
Ducks
Large birds
Frogs
Small fish
Microscopic animals
Insects
Snails
Microscopic plants
Pond plants

Marine food webs

▼ **Fig 5**

The **plankton** is a very important part of the marine food web (see Fig 5) because many of the living things in plankton are green plants. They are the main producers of the ocean. Without plant plankton there would be little life there, because all life depends on producers locking the Sun's energy into molecules that other living things can use for food.

plant plankton ⟶ animal plankton
larger fish
dead organisms sink to the sea floor
lobsters and crabs
small fish
shellfish   algae   starfish   anemones   filter feeders and worms

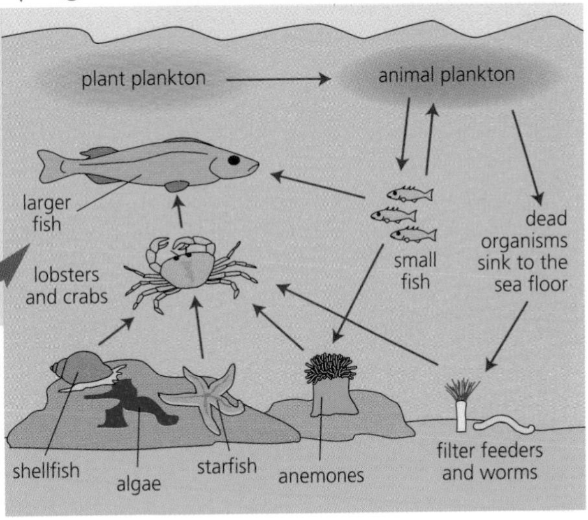

REVIEW
- In a group.
  - Work out and draw a food web to show some of the places where food chains in a garden habitat affect one another.

10 Variety of life

What is a species?

Although the people you know are different in many ways, they are also very similar. The most important similarity of all is that, even if they look quite different, male and female humans can reproduce and make children together. Animals that are as similar as this are called a **species**.

Variation within a species usually has limits. All the people in your class will have different sized feet but there is a limit for the largest and the smallest shoe size. The shoe sizes of a class of 13-year-old pupils are shown in Table 1 and Fig 1. Some people may think they have large or small feet but their size will fall within the normal range for people of their age. This normal range is called the **normal distribution**.

Shoe size	2	3	4	5	6	7	8	9
Number of people	1	1	4	7	8	4	2	2

▲ Table 1

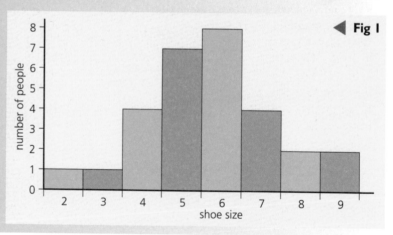

◀ Fig 1

Variation between species

Animals and plants from different species show more **variation** than animals from the same species. Two people will have more in common than a person and a bear. However, some species are very similar and it is thought that they could be closely related.

The causes of variety

Variation is caused by a combination of two factors.

Inherited variation

All of the genetic information that makes you a unique person has come from your parents. This information is carried as **genes** in the egg and the sperm. Genes are large molecules that are coded instructions for each characteristic of a living thing. When characteristics are passed from one generation to the next we say they are **inherited**. The mixing of genes to give unique characteristics is very important to a species. There is a chance that new and improved characteristics will appear.

Environmental variation

It is possible for two identical babies to be born. These are made from the same fertilised egg that splits. Such babies are called identical twins. However, there is no guarantee that the babies will continue to be identical in every way. For example, one baby may eat more than the other. Or perhaps one baby will become ill and not grow properly. The variation between the babies is nothing to do with genes. It has nothing to do with inheritance. It is outside influences that are having an effect on how the babies look. These outside influences are called environmental factors.

▲ **Fig 2** These identical twins are genetically identical. However, environmental factors could mean they start to look different in some ways.

- With a partner.
  - Make a list of some of the variations that may occur within a species.
  - Decide which of these you think are inherited and which are environmental.

🏠 Carry out a survey of hand span among your friends and family. Measure from the tip of the thumb to the tip of the little finger in each case. Use the results to produce a chart like Fig 1.

11 Classifying animals and plants

Classification

There are millions of different species of living things on Earth. Scientists have divided organisms into groups which make them easier to study and understand. The groups are organised according to the characteristics of the organisms they contain. First, all living things are placed in five main groups called **kingdoms**. Each kingdom is then divided into smaller and smaller groups. Placing an organism into a group is called **classification**. The process of describing, classifying and naming organisms is called **taxonomy**.

The five kingdoms

There are a lot of obvious differences between a horse and a tree. Horses and trees clearly belong to completely different kingdoms. One main kingdom is the animal kingdom and another is the plant kingdom (see Table 1).

The kingdoms can be further divided until each organism is classified to species level (see Fig 1). This is the smallest group in the classification of living things.

▶ **Table 1**

Kingdom	Types of organisms
prokaryotes	bacteria and some algae
protists	single-celled organisms
fungi	moulds, mushrooms and toadstools
plants	plants such as ferns, mosses, conifers and flowering plants – all green plants
animals	insects, worms, shellfish, birds, mammals – all multicelled animals

With a partner.
- Try to think up a way to remember the divisions used to classify living things.
- Perhaps you can think of a phrase using the first letter of each word.

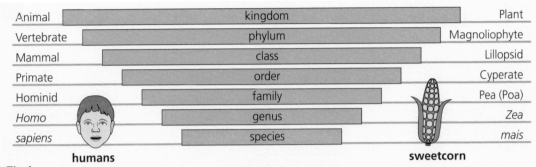

Animal	kingdom	Plant
Vertebrate	phylum	Magnoliophyte
Mammal	class	Lillopsid
Primate	order	Cyperate
Hominid	family	Pea (Poa)
Homo	genus	*Zea*
sapiens	species	*mais*
humans		**sweetcorn**

▲ Fig 1

The animal kingdom

Some animals have a backbone and others do not. This helps us to divide the animal kingdom into two main groups. Animals with backbones are called **vertebrates**. Animals without backbones are called **invertebrates**. Vertebrates include fish, snakes and people. Invertebrates include starfish, snails, worms and insects.

Then vertebrates are divided into five smaller classes. The main characteristics of each class are shown in Table 2.

▶ **Table 2**

Study tip

Remember, snakes have backbones even though they can bend easily. The vertebrae are designed to move easily.

Vertebrate class	Characteristics
fish	backbone, gills, live in water, scales, fins, streamlined body
amphibians	backbone, eggs laid in water, soft and wet skin, adults have lungs, adults can live on land and in water
reptiles	backbone, lay eggs with a shell, lungs, skin covered in dry scales
birds	backbone, lay eggs with a hard shell, lungs, feathers, wings
mammals	backbone, young develop inside the mother, young fed on milk from the mother, have lungs, hair or fur

REVIEW

● On your own.
  ○ Find a picture of a horse and a picture of a rose.
  ○ Study them carefully and try to classify them, step by step, as far as you can.
  ○ Search carefully for clues.

12 Identifying animals and plants

KEY IDEAS

In this section of the book you will have opportunities to:
- Explain that the plant kingdom can also be divided into smaller groups
- Describe how to use a key to identify and name living things.

STARTER

With a partner.
To help you to remember about keys, design a key that can be used to identify the people in your class.

The plant kingdom

The plant kingdom can also be divided into smaller and smaller groups. One of the main divisions is made according to whether a plant has a vascular system or not. Some very simple plants do not need a vascular system because they are small enough for water, food and gases to move around easily.

Vascular plants are divided into those that produce flowers and those that do not. A simplified classification for plants is shown below. Only the larger groups are shown. Each can be further divided down to the species level, as animals are.

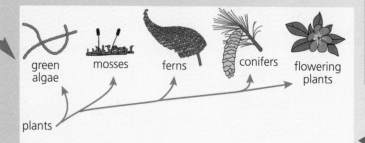

green algae   mosses   ferns   conifers   flowering plants

plants

◀ **Fig 1** Green plants.

 A warning about classification

The system of classification we use today has been made up and modified by scientists for generations. When new information is discovered, the system is changed and improved. Small changes are regularly made. An organism placed in one **genus** can be moved to another genus, or even put into a completely new family, when somebody notices something different about it.

Reviewing keys

There are far too many living things on Earth for any one person to learn all their names. It is impossible to memorise more than a small fraction of all the different insects or flowers. This can be a problem for scientists and other people interested in living things. It could take a long time just to memorise all the species that you might see during a short walk. Using a key is a short cut.

Connections

This unit builds on earlier work on keys at Key Stage 2 and will help you to understand later work on variation, interdependence and the environment.

Identification keys

You do not have to memorise every hill and street in your area in case you get lost. A map will help you to find out where you are and where you need to go. To help us find our way through the variety of life and identify living things we have never seen before we do not have a map, but we have keys. A **key** is a special chart or table that helps us to identify living things.

As you will know from your previous study, there are different types of keys. Some are in the form of a list of questions about the living thing you are trying to identify.

Another type of key is set out as a diagram rather than a list of questions, see Fig 2.

ACTIVITY

On your own.
Using a key to identify trees using their leaves can very useful. Why might this cause problems at certain times of the year? Other than studying the organism itself, what other clues can be used to identify it?

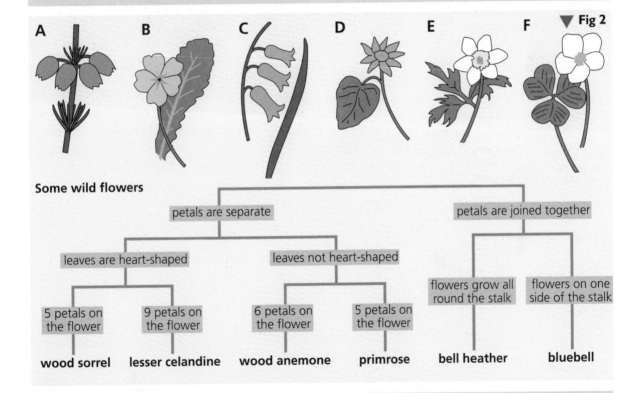

▼ Fig 2

Some wild flowers

- petals are separate
  - leaves are heart-shaped
    - 5 petals on the flower → **wood sorrel**
    - 9 petals on the flower → **lesser celandine**
  - leaves not heart-shaped
    - 6 petals on the flower → **wood anemone**
    - 5 petals on the flower → **primrose**
- petals are joined together
  - flowers grow all round the stalk → **bell heather**
  - flowers on one side of the stalk → **bluebell**

REVIEW

- In a group.
  - Look back at the class keys you designed at the start of this unit.
  - Discuss how they could be improved.
  - What type of keys did you select?

Collect some pictures of vertebrates from a magazine. Try to classify them into one of the vertebrate classes. Now design a key so that others can also identify the vertebrates.

13 Acids around us

KEY IDEAS

In this section of the book you will have opportunities to:
- Describe how acids are important to all living things
- Learn the names of some common strong and weak acids.

STARTER

In a group.
Try to make a list of acids that you have heard of. For each acid, discuss where it might be found and what it is used for. Write down your ideas and prepare to share them with the class.

Natural acids

Ants make an acid called formic acid. Its name comes from *Formica*, which is the Latin name for ant. They squirt this acid at their enemies. Some ants can also bite, which allows the acid to get under your skin. Formic acid can be used to remove **scale** from kettles and pans.

▲ **Fig I** Ants use acid to defend themselves.

Vinegar contains a natural acid called ethanoic acid. Before refrigeration was invented pickling was one of the most important methods of preserving food, especially vegetables. Living things are sensitive to acids. Pickling food in vinegar helps to preserve it by destroying microorganisms. It also helps to prevent chemicals in the food combining with oxygen, which might spoil the food. We also pickle vegetables and add vinegar to foods such as chips because we enjoy the flavour.

The hydrochloric acid in your stomach helps enzymes to digest proteins. Citric acid in fruit helps to prevent oxidation. Many fruits contain acids. These acids are often named after the fruit. You may find **ascorbic acid** named on food labels. This is Vitamin C. It is mainly added to food as a preservative. Preservatives that prevent oxidation are called **antioxidants**.

▼ **Table I** Some common acids.

Acid	Where found	Uses
citric acid	lemons, oranges and other citrus fruits	cooking and drinks
formic acid	ants and nettles	cleaning pans
ethanoic acid	vinegar	cooking and preserving food
hydrochloric acid	stomach	digestion and many uses in industry
nitric acid	manufactured from nitrogen gas; in acid rain	in fertilisers and explosives
sulphuric acid	manufactured using nitric acid; in acid rain	fertilisers, batteries, plastics and paints
carbonic acid	rainwater	fizzy drinks

Laboratory acids

The three common laboratory acids are hydrochloric acid, nitric acid and sulphuric (sulfuric) acid. They are used for many experiments. They are strong acids that must be handled carefully.

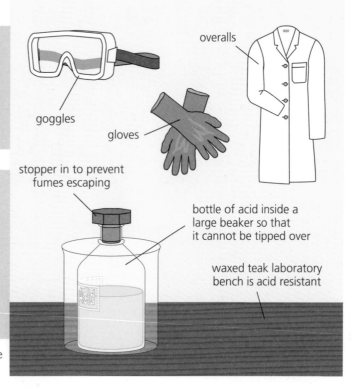

goggles

gloves

overalls

stopper in to prevent fumes escaping

bottle of acid inside a large beaker so that it cannot be tipped over

waxed teak laboratory bench is acid resistant

▶ **Fig 2** Acids must always be handled with great care.

ACTIVITY

In a group.
- Discuss what you have learned about acids.
- Write down five safety rules that you must follow when working with acids.
- Prepare to discuss your rules with the class.

Strong and weak acids

The difference between a strong acid and a weak acid is not how **dilute** it is.

A strong acid is strongly acid because the hydrogen it contains combines easily with other substances. This is a chemical property. Dilution is a physical property. Strong acids are **corrosive**. Sulphuric acid and nitric acid can corrode metal very quickly. Formic acid can take the scale off a kettle but it does not corrode the kettle.

REVIEW

- In a group.
  ○ Study Table 1 'Some common acids'.
  ○ Make a poster that shows the uses of acids as a series of pictures that can be put on display.
  ○ Include every acid in the table.

- On your own.
  ○ What is the name of the acid that ants make?
  ○ How does pickling food help to preserve it?

🏠 Carry out a survey of food and drink labels in your kitchen. Make a list of foods and drinks that contain acids. Name the acids in each. What is the reason for adding each named acid to each named food or drink?

14 Testing for acidity

KEY IDEAS

In this section of the book you will have opportunities to:
● Explain how indicators and the pH scale are used to classify solutions as acidic, alkaline or neutral.

STARTER

In a group.
Make a list of the names of the acids you have studied. Write down what the acids have in common. Discuss how acids can be handled safely. What warning symbols tell you that a substance is an acid?

Alkalis

Adding oxygen to a metal makes a metal **oxide**. Many metal oxides will not dissolve in water. They are insoluble. An **alkali** is a solution of a metal oxide in water. An insoluble metal oxide cannot become an alkali. Just as there are strong acids, there are also strong alkalis. Oxides of more reactive metals make stronger alkalis than oxides of less reactive metals. Alkalis are called hydroxides. An example is sodium hydroxide.

Indicators

Strong acids and strong alkalis are corrosive. How can we test them without harming ourselves? Luckily there is a simple way to test whether a solution is an acid or an alkali. Some plant juices change colour in different solutions. We can use them as **indicators**.

ACTIVITY

With a partner.
● Discuss why indicators are so useful.
● Write down your ideas and prepare to share them with the rest of the class.
● Remember to think about acids and safety.

pH number

▶ **Fig 1** Red cabbage becomes redder in acid vinegar **a** and bluer in alkaline tapwater **b**.

Indicators measure acid or alkali on a scale called **pH**. The full range of pH runs from 1 to 14. Numbers under 7 are acid and numbers above 7 are alkaline. The **neutral** point is at 7, in the middle.

It is very easy to make a simple indicator from red cabbage following the instructions given here.

1 Remove some leaves from a red cabbage and tear them up into small pieces.

2 Add the torn leaves to some water that has been boiled and allowed to cool slightly.

3 Stir the cabbage and water until the water becomes purple with sap from the leaves.

4 Filter the mixture and collect the purple liquid.

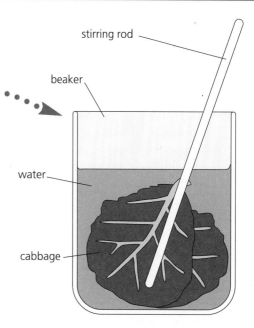

The purple liquid is the indicator. If it is added to an acid it will become redder. If it is added to an alkali it will become bluer.

Red cabbage juice can only tell you whether a solution is an acid or an alkali. Some indicators can tell you how acid or how alkaline a solution is. Some indicators may only work for a small range of pH but can show very tiny differences. These are useful where great accuracy is important.

One very useful indicator is called universal indicator. This is a mixture of indicators that change colour at different points on the pH scale. Universal indicator can show whether something is an alkali or an acid and how strong it is.

▶ **Fig 2** You can do this at home. The only problem you may have is 'hard' tap water. Hard water is alkaline so your indicator may start out blue. Boiling the water first can help.

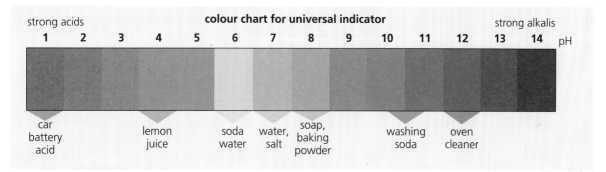

colour chart for universal indicator

strong acids
1 2 3 4 5 6 7 8 9 10 11 12 13 14 pH
strong alkalis

car battery acid | lemon juice | soda water | water, salt | soap, baking powder | washing soda | oven cleaner

▲ **Fig 3** Using universal indicator is an easy way to measure the pH of any solution.

REVIEW

- In a group.
  - Discuss exactly how you would test the pH of the soil in your local park.
  - Write your ideas down and prepare to discuss them with the rest of the class.
  - Would this test be any use to:
    a a gardener
    b a forester
    c the owner of a nearby factory?

Study tip

When using universal indicator some people find it helpful to remember the colour of acid by thinking of Red for Danger. Acids give low pH numbers and alkalis give high pH numbers.

15 Neutralisation

KEY IDEAS

In this section of the book you will have opportunities to:
- Explain what neutralisation means
- Describe some of the uses of neutralisation.

STARTER

In a group.
Think back to your work on pH indicators. List two acids and two alkalis. Discuss what you think might happen if an acid was carefully added to an alkali. Write down your ideas.

Acids and neutralisation

If you have been attacked by an angry ant you can take some of the pain away by rubbing calamine lotion or baking soda solution onto the sting. These are weak alkalis. They work by neutralising the acid.

Neutralisation

Adding an alkali to an acid (see Fig 1) changes the pH. Testing the solution with an indicator before and afterwards shows that the pH has been raised. If we do this carefully we can stop adding alkali at the exact point when the pH is 7. The solution is then neutral. This is neutralisation.

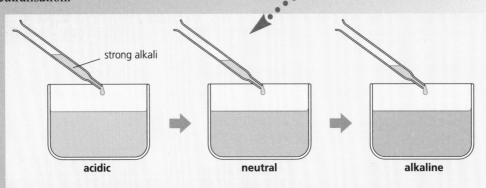

strong alkali

acidic   neutral   alkaline

◀ **Fig 1**

The chemistry of neutralisation produces a salt and water. We can show this in a shorthand way called a word equation. Word equations are covered in more detail in Unit 54.

acid + alkali → salt + water

For example, hydrochloric acid reacts with sodium hydroxide (alkali) to make sodium chloride (table salt) and water:

hydrochloric acid + sodium hydroxide → sodium chloride + water

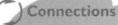

ACTIVITY

With a partner.
- Nettle stings contain formic acid.
- Discuss what you could rub on the sting to stop it hurting.
- Write down your reasons.

Acid indigestion

Your stomach contains hydrochloric acid. This helps you to digest your food. Your stomach wall is designed to cope with a normal amount but if more acid than usual is produced you may feel a burning pain. This is called **acid indigestion**. The acid can be neutralised with a weak alkali such as bicarbonate of soda. This is how many types of indigestion tablets work.

Treating soils

Plants are adapted to grow wherever there is a space. Some plants prefer acidic soil and others prefer alkaline soil. Soil with a pH just on the acid side of neutral is good for growing many garden plants.

An extremely acidic soil is not an easy place for plants to live. The reason why carnivorous plants exist is because it is difficult for plant roots to extract nutrients from strongly acidic soils. Carnivorous plants get nutrients such as nitrates and phosphates from the bodies of insects they trap.

Many food plants do not grow well in moderately acid soil. They cannot extract enough nutrients to produce a profitable crop. Farmers often add **lime** to acidic soil to neutralise it. Calcium oxide is called

▲ **Fig 2** Rhododendrons flourish where crops are hard to grow.

quicklime, from the old word for 'alive'. It fizzes when it meets water. Calcium hydroxide is called slaked lime. Its name comes from an old word meaning 'not thirsty'.

REVIEW

- In a group.
  - **Acid rain** is becoming more and more of a problem.
  - Discuss how lakes and rivers affected by acid rain could be improved.
  - Write down your ideas.
  - How might the treatment also cause problems?

The gardens of Nitric City have very acidic soil. Produce a short information leaflet for gardeners that explains how their acid soil can be neutralised to let them grow a greater variety of plants.

16 Physical and chemical changes

KEY IDEAS

In this section of the book you will have opportunities to:
- Explain some of the differences between physical changes and chemical changes
- Describe burning as an example of a chemical change.

STARTER

In a group.
Think about adding sugar to tea and acid to calcium carbonate. In both cases changes take place. Discuss the differences between the two changes. What happens to the chemicals in each case?

Physical changes

You see **physical changes** every day. All changes of state are physical changes. Dissolving sugar in a cup of tea is a physical change. A physical change happens when one

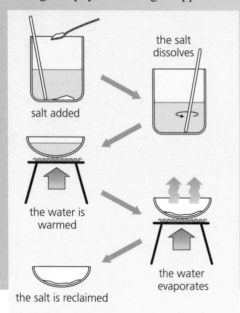

salt added

the salt dissolves

the water is warmed

the water evaporates

the salt is reclaimed

▲ **Fig 1** Very cold water becomes solid ice.

or more of the physical properties of a substance is changed. This means a substance may look and behave differently and be in a different form but it will still be the same chemical. When liquid water changes to ice its hardness, density, volume and appearance all become different but it is still the same chemical with the same chemical formula.

Physical changes are temporary and can easily be reversed. Water can easily be turned into ice and back again. If we add salt to water we can evaporate the water and get the salt back. These are physical changes.

◀ **Fig 2** The salt has simply dissolved. It still exists as salt in the water.

Chemical changes

When paper burns we see a total change. The paper gets very hot and turns to ash. What happens if we cool the ash? Does it change back into paper? Obviously the answer to that is no. The paper no longer exists. It has changed into new chemicals. This is an example of a **chemical change**.

ACTIVITY

With a partner.

● Discuss the difference between a chemical change and a physical change.

● Give two examples of chemical changes you have seen and write down why they are chemical changes and not physical changes.

◀ **Fig 3** The paper is changing into new chemicals.

Chemical reactions

A chemical change is a permanent change. New substances are made by a chemical reaction. There are different types of chemical **reaction**. Some examples are:

● iron and steel rusting
● sulphur burning in air
● limestone fizzing in acid.

Chemicals that react together in a reaction are called **reactants**. The new chemicals created are called the **products**.

All chemicals are made up of atoms. In a chemical reaction, atoms are rearranged into new patterns. Atoms are never broken down during chemical reactions. If we look at what happens when sulphur burns we can see where the atoms go.

If you start out with 100 grams of sulphur and then burn half of it you will have 50 grams of sulphur left. Where does the other half go? It may seem that the chemical reaction made half of the sulphur disappear. If this was possible then you would have performed a magic trick (see Fig 4).

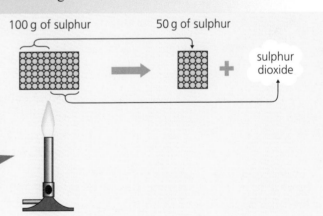

100 g of sulphur   50 g of sulphur

sulphur dioxide

▲ **Fig 4** The sulphur seems to disappear as it burns.

REVIEW

● In a group.
  ○ Think back to your starter activity.
  ○ Discuss how accurate your answers were.
  ○ How would you improve them?

17 Reactions with acids

KEY IDEAS

In this section of the book you will have opportunities to:
- Explain how acids react with metal oxides and carbonates.

STARTER

In a group.
Think back to your earlier work on the uses of acids. Which of these uses involve chemical reactions?

Acid reactions

▶ **Fig 1** Acid made this underground cavern.

The walls and roof of the cave in Fig 1 are made of limestone. Acids in rainwater have been reacting with the limestone for millions of years. Acidic rain has turned small cracks into large caves. This is a natural example of an acid reaction.

Acids and carbonates

Limestone is a chemical compound called calcium carbonate. Other carbonates include copper carbonate and magnesium carbonate. These are called **metal carbonates** because they contain a metal as well as the carbonate. An acid reacts with a carbonate by breaking it down into a salt, water and carbon dioxide gas. The carbon dioxide makes the reaction fizz. This is one way to find out if a substance is a carbonate.

The general word equation for the reaction is:

> acid + metal carbonate → metal salt + water + carbon dioxide

Here is a word equation for hydrochloric acid reacting with calcium carbonate:

> calcium carbonate + hydrochloric acid → calcium chloride + water + carbon dioxide

The acids in rainwater are weak and work very slowly to break limestone down. In time the limestone will be attacked, especially if it is exposed to extra acid from traffic fumes. Marble is another form of calcium carbonate. It is also slowly broken down by acid rainwater.

▼ **Fig 2** Limestone buildings are vulnerable to attack from acid rain.

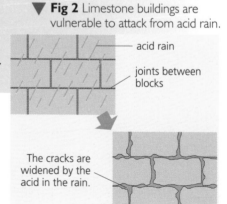

acid rain

joints between blocks

The cracks are widened by the acid in the rain.

ACTIVITY

On your own.
- Write a word equation for sulphuric acid reacting with copper carbonate.
- How would you know a reaction was taking place?
- Write down what you predict you would see.

Marble chips react with hydrochloric acid to make calcium chloride. Calcium chloride is a soluble salt. It dissolves away and allows the reaction to continue. If you try the same experiment with sulphuric acid instead of hydrochloric acid the reaction begins in the same way but then it stops. This is because calcium sulphate is insoluble. Instead of dissolving and going away, it stays and makes a protective layer around each chip. This separates the acid from the marble and stops the reaction.

Acids and metal oxides

When metal oxides are mixed with acids they react to make salts. The oxygen in the oxide joins up with the hydrogen in the acid to make water. So instead of visible bubbles of hydrogen a little extra water is quietly added to the solution.

metal oxide (base) +   acid   →   salt   + water
copper oxide   + sulphuric acid → copper sulphate + water

▼ **Fig 3** How acids react with four main groups of chemicals. Notice that salts are formed every time. Acid reactions are a very good way to make salts.

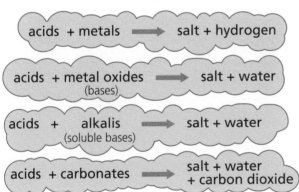

▼ **Fig 4** General properties of acids.

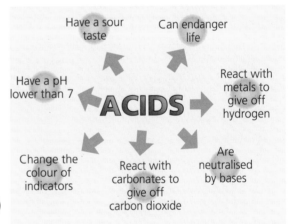

REVIEW

- In a group.
  ○ Discuss the acid reaction you have just studied.
  ○ Use this information to help you to work out three different ways of making copper sulphate.
  ○ Write down your ideas.

To help you to remember the reactions of acids make a large poster that shows how acids react with other chemicals. For each reaction try to write down one example. Finally, explain what each reaction has in common.

18 Testing the products

Carbon dioxide from marble

Marble is made of calcium carbonate. This reacts with hydrochloric acid to give off carbon dioxide. Carbon dioxide makes the reaction fizzy. The reaction also produces calcium chloride and water. The word equation for this is:

calcium carbonate + hydrochloric acid → calcium chloride + water + carbon dioxide

Testing for carbon dioxide

Carbon dioxide is a very important gas. Plants use it during photosynthesis and it is also a product of respiration. Carbon dioxide is also produced when fuels such as coal and wood burn. The carbon in the fuel combines with oxygen in the air and carbon dioxide is made.

Limewater is a solution of calcium hydroxide in water. When carbon dioxide is bubbled through limewater it combines with the calcium hydroxide to form calcium carbonate. This is a white solid and turns the clear limewater a milky white colour. This is used as a test for carbon dioxide.

calcium hydroxide + carbon dioxide → calcium carbonate + water

The apparatus commonly used to test for carbon dioxide is shown in Fig 1. • • • • • • •

ACTIVITY

With a partner.
● Plan an investigation to show that the gas dissolved in fizzy drinks is carbon dioxide.
● Draw the apparatus you would use.

Connections

This unit builds on earlier work on gases and reversible and irreversible changes at Key Stage 2. The work is linked to work on acids and alkalis and forms the basis for further work on chemical reactions in Year 9.

▼ **Fig 1** Testing for carbon dioxide.

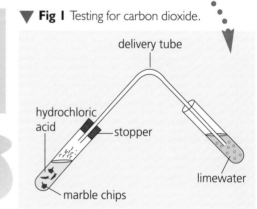

delivery tube

hydrochloric acid

stopper

limewater

marble chips

Testing for hydrogen

When metals react with acids a colourless gas is produced. This gas is hydrogen. That is why metals such as magnesium will fizz when added to acid. Hydrogen gas will burn. If it is mixed with air or oxygen first then it will explode. On a small scale this explosion is a small 'pop' sometimes described as a squeaky pop because of the noise it makes. This explosive property of hydrogen is used to identify it.

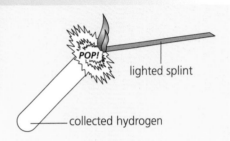

▶ **Fig 2** Testing for hydrogen.

Testing for water

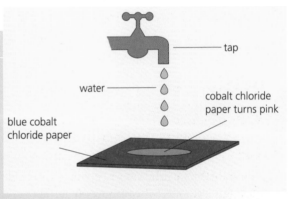

When water reacts with blue cobalt chloride paper it turns the paper pink (see Fig 3). This is used as an identification test for water. Using this test it has been discovered that water is produced when fuels such as coal and wood burn. This means that the products of burning are water and carbon dioxide. This is because the hydrogen and carbon in fuels combine with oxygen to make the oxides.

fuel + oxygen → carbon dioxide + water

▲ **Fig 3** Water reacting with blue cobalt chloride paper.

REVIEW

- In a group.
  - Imagine an unknown substance is added to an acid and a gas is produced.
  - Plan how you would test to identify whether the gas was hydrogen or carbon dioxide.
  - Write down the main points of your plan and prepare to discuss it with the rest of the class.

- Design an investigation to show that carbon dioxide and water are produced when a candle burns. Include a diagram and describe how the products would be tested.

Study tip

Draw a table that shows the name and test for the following substances: carbon dioxide, hydrogen and water. Cut the table up and mix up the parts. Now practise matching the correct test with each substance.

19 Solids, liquids and gases

KEY IDEAS

In this section of the book you will have opportunities to:
- Explain that there are three states of matter
- Describe the difference between solids, liquids and gases.

STARTER

In a group.
Think back to earlier work on solids, liquids and gases. Make a list of five solids, five liquids and five gases. Discuss why these substances look and feel so different. Write your ideas down.

Types of substances

Many substances occur naturally. Air, wood, rubber and rock are examples of **natural** substances. Plastic is not a natural substance. It is a **synthetic** substance made by people. Every substance, natural or synthetic, is either a solid, a liquid or a gas.

▶ **Fig I** Some solids, liquids and gases.

Properties of substances

The way a substance looks, feels or behaves is called a **property** of that substance.

The properties of a substance show whether it is a solid, a liquid or a gas (see Table 1). Some properties that we can test are:

hardness   density   compressibility

ease of flow   volume   shape

Property	Solid	Liquid	Gas
Volume	definite	definite	fills its container
Shape	definite	takes the shape of lower part of container	takes the whole container's shape
Density	high	medium	low
Ease of compression	very low	low	high
Ease of flow	nil	easy	easy

▲ **Table I**

Solids

Solids keep their shape. They are not easily compressed or squashed. Even a soft solid has the same volume when it is squashed. A solid never flows unless it has been ground up into powder. The physical properties of solids make many of them useful for building furniture, houses, and other solid structures.

Liquids

Liquids have a definite volume but no fixed shape. A liquid takes the same shape as its container. Liquids are difficult to compress but they do flow easily.

Gases

Gases have no fixed shape or volume. A gas spreads out to fill its container and also flows very easily. The reason why you can smell a person's scent soon after they come into a room is because the gases of the scent spread out to fill the room.

▼ Fig 2

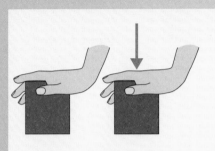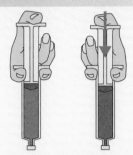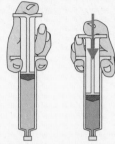

Solids have a fixed shape and are hard to compress

Liquids take on the shape of their container and are hard to compress

Gases take on the shape of their container and are easy to compress

Changes of state

Substances do not always stay in the same state (see Fig 3). Water can freeze into a solid called ice or boil in a kettle to become a gas called steam. These physical changes are called **changes of state**. Different substances change state at different temperatures.

▶ Fig 3

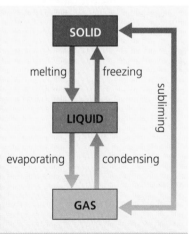

20 Particles and states of matter

KEY IDEAS

In this section of the book you will have opportunities to:
- Describe that substances are made up of tiny particles
- Explain that the way particles behave explains the differences between solids, liquids and gases.

STARTER

In a group.
You can smell some flowers from many metres away. Discuss how this might be possible.

States of matter

Substances can exist in three different states (see Unit 19). These states are solid, liquid and gas.

The particle theory

To explain how substances can exist in these three very different forms we must first look at what substances are made of. According to the particle theory, all substances are made up of very small **particles**.

Solid

The particles in a solid are arranged in regular patterns. They are very close together with little space between them. This is what gives a solid its fixed shape. The particles can vibrate but they cannot move far. This is why solids are dense.

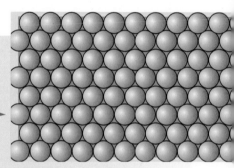

▲ **Fig 1** Particles in a sol

Liquid

The particles in a liquid are less tightly packed than particles in a solid. Because they are not arranged in a regular pattern they can move more easily. This is why liquids can flow and why they take the shape of any container they are poured into. When a liquid is heated it can expand more easily than a solid because the particles are not held together as firmly.

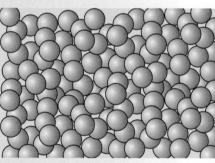

▲ **Fig 2** Particles in a liqu

Gas

The particles in a gas are not regularly arranged. They are widely spaced and move at great speeds in all directions. Gas particles are said to be in random motion. This is why gases have a low density and can flow easily. Gas particles do not hold on to each other very much. When you heat a gas it expands a great deal.

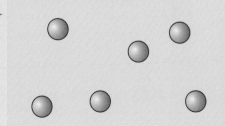

▶ **Fig 3** Particles in a gas.

With a partner.
- Think back to the starter activity.
- How does your explanation of the flowers fit in with particle theory?

Particles and changes of state

When you heat a solid, the particles in it start to vibrate faster. The closely packed particles start to break free from each other. This makes the solid melt into a liquid. If the substance is heated even more the particles move even faster until they are in random motion. Now the liquid has become a gas. This is called **evaporation**.

If you cool a gas down you force the particles to slow down. Eventually they are moving slowly enough and packed closely enough to be a liquid. This is called **condensing**. You can sometimes see invisible steam condense to visible water on a cold window pane.

If the liquid is cooled even more the particles slow down even more. Eventually the liquid will become a solid. This is called freezing. Water can do this in water-pipes on very cold days.

Changes of state therefore depend on how close the particles are in a substance and how quickly they are moving (see Fig 4).

▼ Fig 4

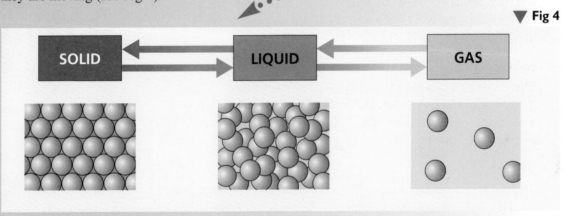

REVIEW
- In a group.
  - There are hundreds of everyday examples of changes of state.
  - Make a list of as many examples as you can.
  - Explain one of your examples by drawing a diagram of what happens to the particles.

21 Moving particles

KEY IDEAS

In this section of the book you will have opportunities to:
- Explain that the movement or diffusion of gases can be explained by particle theory
- Describe how particle theory can be used to explain gas pressure.

STARTER

In a group.
Discuss why a gas leak in one room can cause great danger throughout the whole house if the leak is not detected. Try to explain what is happening to the gas, using the particle theory.

Diffusion

If a drop of ink falls into a glass of water some of the ink particles will begin to spread out. Eventually all the water will be coloured. The spread of ink particles is called diffusion. Movement of particles is called **diffusion**.

Gases or **vapours** diffuse very easily because their particles are not fixed together and can move quickly in all directions. It is possible to watch a coloured gas diffusing. Bromine is a brown liquid at normal room temperature but becomes a brown gas if it is warmed up.

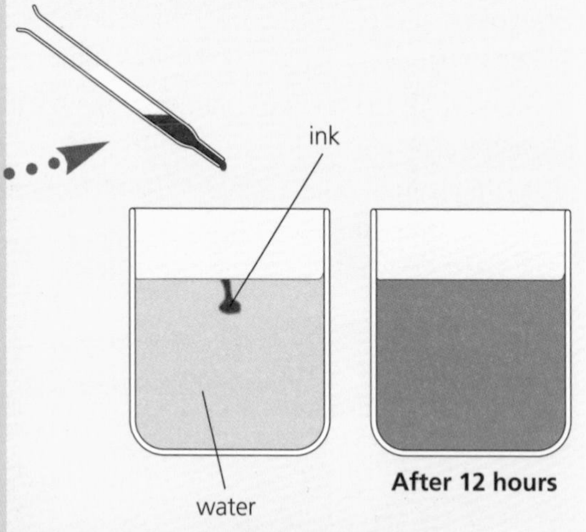

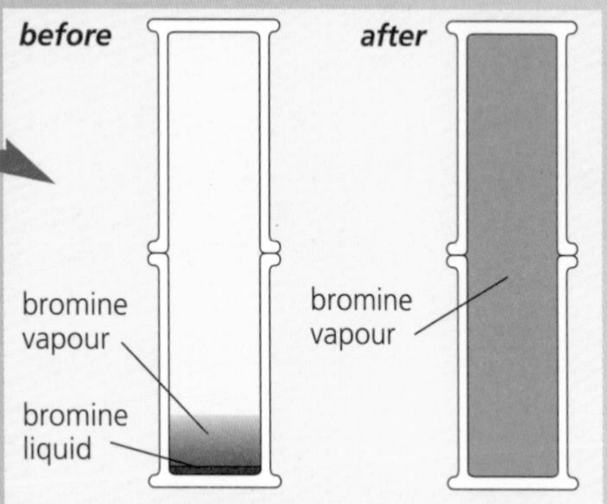

▼ **Fig 1** Ink particles gradually spread out into the water. This is diffusion.

ink

water

After 12 hours

before   *after*

bromine vapour

bromine vapour

bromine liquid

We can also detect the movement of scented gases. You can smell the scent of a flower from a distance because the particles of scent diffuse through the air from the flower to your nose. The scent is strongest near the flower, where the particles are most concentrated. Flower scents are important to moths. Some moths can catch the scent of just one particle and follow it back to the flower.

▲ **Fig 2 Caution:** bromine gas is poisonous.

Gas pressure

Particles of a gas are moving around very quickly. When a gas is put into a container the moving particles constantly crash against the sides (see Fig 3 opposite). The force of all these collisions creates pressure inside the container. If more gas is added then there will be more particles hitting the sides. The gas pressure will increase.

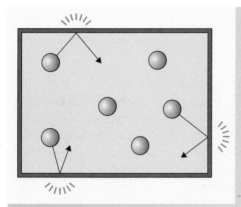

◀ **Fig 3**

Pressure can also be increased by heating particles up or squashing them into a smaller space. This is what happens inside a bicycle pump. The more you squash the air, the higher the pressure becomes. Eventually the air particles are squashed so tightly that they can be forced into a hard rubber tyre.

Gases are often stored by being squashed into small containers. The pressure inside these containers is very high because they hold so many gas particles.

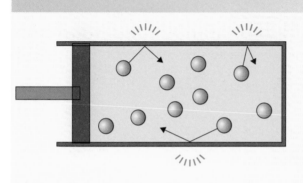
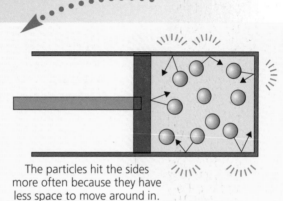

The particles hit the sides more often because they have less space to move around in.

▲ **Fig 4** Adding more particles or squashing particles into a smaller space will increase the gas pressure.

ACTIVITY

With a partner.
- Discuss where you would find examples of **a** diffusion and **b** gas pressure in everyday life?
- Which of them do you find most useful?
- Which can be potentially harmful, and why?

REVIEW

- In a group.
  o Look back at the starter activity.
  o How would you improve your answer now you know more about diffusion and particle theory?

  Carry out research to find examples of gases stored under pressure. What are the gases used for? How are the gases used and stored safely?

Connections

This work builds on your earlier work on solids, liquids and gases at Key Stage 2. This work on particles will help you to understand many ideas in Science, such as dissolving, expansion, digestion, and the formation of rocks.

22 Soluble and insoluble

KEY IDEAS

In this section of the book you will have opportunities to:
- Explain that some substances dissolve in water and others do not
- Explain that water is not the only liquid that can be used to dissolve things.

STARTER

In a group.
Make a list of substances that you think will dissolve in water. Now make a list of substances that you think will not dissolve in water. Present your results as a table.

Dissolving substances

If a solid will dissolve in a liquid we say that it is **soluble**. The liquid is called the **solvent** and the solid is called the **solute**. So if salt is dissolved in water, the water is the solvent and the salt is the solute. When a solute and a solvent are mixed they make a **solution** (see Fig 1). There are many different solvents and many different solutes.

▼ **Fig 1**

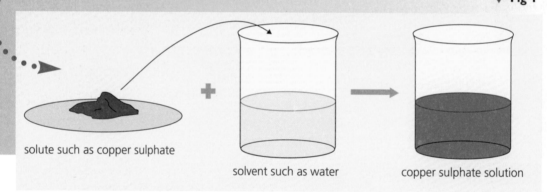

solute such as copper sulphate

solvent such as water

copper sulphate solution

Water as a solvent

Water is a very good solvent. It can dissolve many things. However, some things do not dissolve in water and others only dissolve slightly. They have different solubilities. The **solubility** of a substance is a measure of how well it will dissolve in a solvent. If it dissolves well it has a high solubility. Substances that do not dissolve in a solvent are called **insoluble**.

▶ **Table 1** Different chemicals have different solubilities.

Chemical	How many grams dissolve in 100 grams of water at 20°C
sodium chloride (salt)	36
sodium carbonate	22
calcium sulphate	0.2
sugar	211
sand	0

ACTIVITY

On your own.
- Study Table 1 on page 50. Place the chemicals in order of solubility, with the most soluble chemical at the top.
- Are any of the chemicals in the table insoluble in water?

Solvents other than water

Whether or not a substance will dissolve can depend on the solvent. Salt dissolves easily in water but it does not dissolve very well in alcohol. Candle wax does not dissolve in water but it will dissolve in some other solvents. Different solvents are used to dissolve different solutes. Solvents have many uses. Some are used to remove stains that water will not wash out. Others are used in nail varnish, glues, paints and correcting fluid. Many solvents are harmful and must not be breathed in or spilt on your skin.

▶ **Fig 2** Many of the old-fashioned solvents in paints and varnishes can make people ill. Some modern paints and varnishes use water as a solvent.

Dry cleaning

Some stains will not wash out in water. The stain is insoluble in water. Solvents other than water can be used. These are called **non-aqueous** solvents. The process is known as dry cleaning. The solvents used are expensive so they are recycled. Any dirty deposits or residue has to be removed otherwise the machine will clog with the substances washed off the clothes. The solvent can stay on the clothes for a while and this makes them smell strange after cleaning. However, the clothes are less likely to shrink.

REVIEW

- In a group.
  - Make a list of the words in bold on these two pages.
  - For each word try to agree an accurate definition.
  - Once you have done this make sure you each have a copy.
  - Prepare to discuss your definitions with the rest of the class.

Carry out research at home to identify some examples of non-aqueous solvents. Write down the name and the use of each solvent.

23 Particles and dissolving

KEY IDEAS

In this section of the book you will have opportunities to:
- Explain the link between temperature and dissolving
- Explain the formation of saturated solutions.

STARTER

In a group.
Discuss some of the ways that you would be able to speed up how quickly sodium chloride dissolves in water. Write your ideas down in the form of a plan for an investigation.

Conservation of mass

▼ Fig 1

If you add 10 grams of salt to a glass of water and give it a stir it will dissolve and become invisible. You can get it back by evaporating the water (see Fig 1). If you weigh the salt at the end, you will find that there are still 10 grams. None of it will have gone missing. When something stays the same we say that it is conserved. The mass of the salt was conserved through two physical changes. This is called **conservation of mass**.

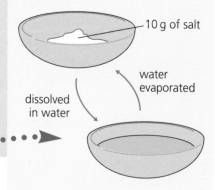

10 g of salt

water evaporated

dissolved in water

Temperature and solubility

You have probably noticed that sugar dissolves more quickly in hot water than in cold water. This is true for most solvents and solutes. The warmer the solvent is, the easier it is to dissolve the solute. It does not only dissolve more quickly. More solute dissolves in a warm solvent than in a cold solvent. This can be tested by trying to dissolve as much solute as possible in 100 grams of water at different temperatures. The results of this experiment are shown in Fig 2. You can see that more and more solute dissolves as the solvent's temperature rises. Some solvents do not act like this, but many do.

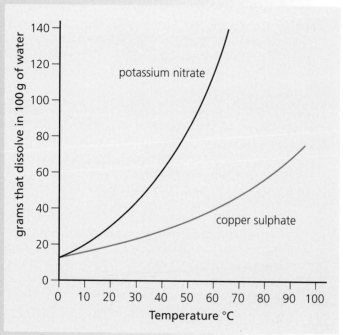

▶ **Fig 2** As the solvent's temperature rises, more of a solute will dissolve in it.

Salt is extracted from layers under the ground by pumping water down into it. The salty water (brine) rises to the surface and can be collected. Then the salt is removed by letting the water evaporate.

▼ **Fig 3** Extracting salt using hot water.

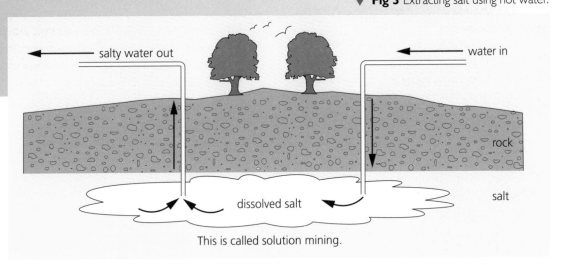

salty water out

water in

rock

dissolved salt

salt

This is called solution mining.

Saturated solutions

The solubility of a substance is measured by finding the maximum amount of the solute that will dissolve in a given amount of solvent at a certain temperature. Usually we record solubility as grams of solute per 100 g of solvent. As you have just seen, for many solutes increasing the temperature will increase solubility. After the solid completely dissolves, a solution can be cooled. Eventually, the solution is so cool that small crystals of the solid start to appear. They look like small snowflakes. The solution has become saturated. A saturated solution cannot dissolve any more solute.

ACTIVITY

With a partner.
- Discuss how you would make a saturated solution of sodium carbonate.
- What would happen if you tried to dissolve more sodium carbonate in the saturated solution?

Study tip

It will help you to remember what a saturated solution is if you make sure you understand that the word 'saturated' means that a substance is full of something. A saturated solution is full of solute.

REVIEW

- In a group.
  - Use your knowledge of particle theory to explain the following terms. Use diagrams to help you.
    a saturated solution
    b dilute solution
    c concentrated solution

24 Separating mixtures

In this section of the book you will have opportunities to:
- Explain how mixtures can be separated by a variety of methods
- Describe that the best separation method to choose depends on the type of mixture.

In a group.
Discuss how you might separate dry sand from a mixture of sand and salt. Make a note of your ideas.

Connections

This unit builds on earlier work on solids, liquids and separating mixtures at Key Stage 2. It is also related to your work on the particle model. This work will help you to understand later work on heating and cooling, digestion and rocks in Year 8 and the behaviour of gases in Year 9.

Separating mixtures

There are many different types of mixtures. They cannot all be separated by the same method. Different mixtures are separated in different ways.

Filtration

Large particles can be separated from smaller particles by filtering the mixture. A mixture of stones and soil can be separated with a sieve, which is a kind of filter. Filters can also separate solids from a gas. Vacuum cleaners and breathing masks have filters inside.

In a mixture of a solid and a liquid, the solid is not always dissolved. This kind of mixture is called a **suspension** and could be separated by **filtration**. A liquid can pass through the tiny holes in a filter but the particles of a solid cannot. The solid part of a mixture that is trapped in a filter is called the **residue**. The liquid that passes through is called the **filtrate**.

filter paper

filter funnel

▲ **Fig 1** The small water particles can pass through the filter paper but the large sand particles are held back.

Decanting

Filtering is only one way to separate a solid from water. You could wait until the solid settles to the bottom of the container and then carefully pour off the liquid. This is called **decanting**.

Distillation

Liquids can be separated from mixtures by heating them. If a mixture of salt and water is boiled, the water will turn to steam. This rises out of the mixture and leaves the salt behind. If we want to save the liquid we need to cool it until it becomes a liquid again. One way to do this is shown in Fig 2.

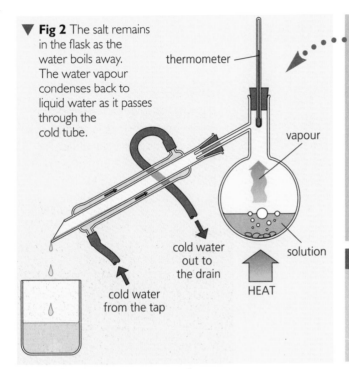

Fig 2 The salt remains in the flask as the water boils away. The water vapour condenses back to liquid water as it passes through the cold tube.

thermometer

vapour

cold water out to the drain

solution

cold water from the tap

HEAT

Fractional distillation

Vaporisation followed by condensation is called **distillation**. Different liquids turn to vapour at different temperatures. This means that liquids can also be separated from other liquids by heating them. Separating liquids by heating them is called **fractional distillation**.

Separating liquids by distillation depends on getting the temperature exactly right. Strong alcoholic drinks such as whisky are made this way.

ACTIVITY

With a partner.
- Discuss why a place where whisky is made is called a distillery.
- Why is heat needed in a distillery?
- Write your ideas down.

Chromatography

Chromatography is another way of separating mixtures. You can see how it works by using it to separate a mixture of coloured inks. First a spot of the mixture is placed near the bottom of a piece of filter paper and allowed to dry. When the bottom edge of the paper is dipped into a liquid that can dissolve ink, the liquid slowly rises up the paper and carries some of the ink with it. Because the different colours move at different speeds they will eventually be spaced out along the path of the solvent.

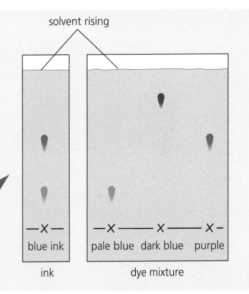

solvent rising

blue ink

pale blue dark blue purple

ink

dye mixture

▶ **Fig 3** The colours move apart as the solvent soaks upwards.

55

25 Energy resources

Uses of energy

Your body uses food as a source of energy. Modern towns and cities also need large amounts of energy. Transport, industry, heating, lighting and entertainment all use up energy.

▶ **Fig 1** Cities use up a lot of energy.

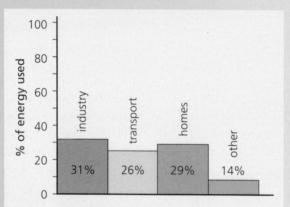

▲ **Fig 2** How energy in the UK is being used.

Our main energy resources:
- Coal
- Oil
- Gas
- Nuclear power
- Water power

Coal, gas and oil are called **fossil** fuels because they come from prehistoric animals and plants. Water power is mainly used to drive generators that make electricity. This is called **hydroelectric power**.

The way we manage our energy resources is changing all the time. We now use more gas and less coal but fossil fuels are still our main energy resource. Burning them causes pollution and environmental damage.

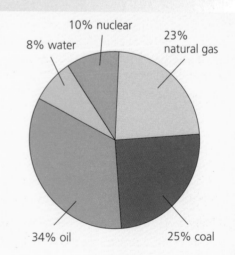

▶ **Fig 3** Sources of energy in the UK.

ACTIVITY

With a partner.
- Discuss some of the disadvantages of using the main energy resources listed on the previous page.

The Sun

The Sun supplies nearly all the natural energy on Earth. Plants use the Sun's energy to make food. This energy can be passed to animals that eat plants. Some dead plants and animals may be trapped under layers of rock. Over millions of years the plants can become coal and the animals can become oil. When we burn fossil fuels we are really getting energy that came from the Sun millions of years ago.

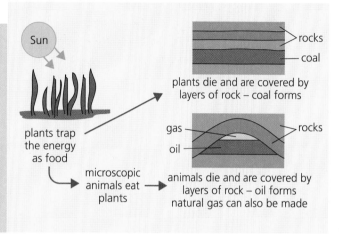

▲ **Fig 4** How coal and oil form.

Other energy resources

People have used wind power to move ships and turn windmills for hundreds of years. Running water has also turned water wheels to supply power for mills and other machines. Even the energy of tides has been used to drive mill-wheels. More recently, the Thames Barrier (see Fig 5) was built to protect London from dangerously high tides. It also makes use of the energy in normal tides. Wheels in the barrier are turned by the tide rushing past. The turning wheels are used to generate electricity.

▲ **Fig 5**

Batteries convert chemical energy into electrical energy. We use batteries to supply power for light bulbs and to start cars. A battery can also drive a car.

Wood and straw can also be burned to release energy. They are called **biomass**. Biomass can be changed into a more concentrated energy source such as alcohol. Alcohol made from plants can be burned to drive an engine. Other fast-growing plants, such as oilseed rape, make oil that can be used for fuel.

REVIEW

- In a group.
  o Discuss the importance of plants in the production of some energy resources.
  o Is it true that food is an energy resource?
  o Write your ideas down and prepare to discuss them with the rest of the class.

Make a list of all the electrical appliances that you switch on in a single day.
How could you reduce the amount of energy you use?

26 Fuels and energy

Energy from reactions

When methane gas burns we can see a number of changes. The gas flame is hot and blue. This means that when methane burns it gives out **heat** and light. We use the heat to cook food or keep us warm. The chemical reaction also changes methane gas into carbon dioxide and water. Chemicals that react with oxygen to give out heat are called **fuels**.

Energy in and energy out

The word equation for burning methane is:

methane + oxygen → carbon dioxide + water

There is a lot of energy stored in a methane molecule. When methane burns it combines with oxygen. This reaction releases a lot of heat. This is true for all fuels. Chemical reactions that give out heat are called **exothermic** reactions.

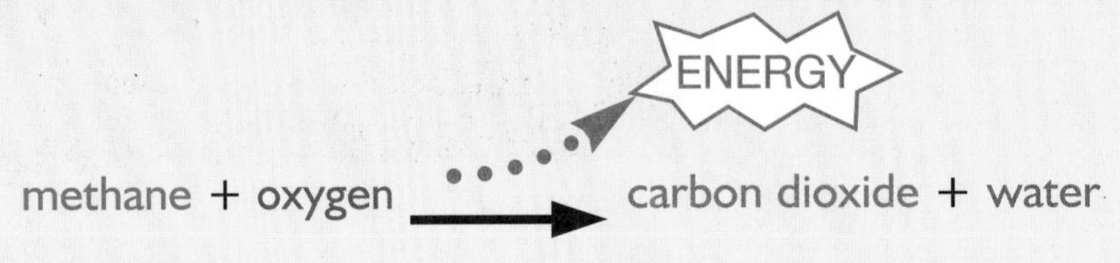

ENERGY

methane + oxygen ·····➤ carbon dioxide + water

ACTIVITY

With a partner.
- Write a word equation for another example of a fuel burning.
- What is the fuel used for?

Other fuels we use are coal, wood, butane, propane, paraffin, petrol and diesel. They provide energy for heating, transport and industry. Energy does not have to be heat or light. It can also be sound, movement and electricity. The chemical reactions in a battery produce electrical energy.

A sherbet sweet is fizzy because of a chemical reaction that begins when it mixes with moisture. Sherbet is a mixture of citric acid and sodium hydrogencarbonate. When water is added to this mixture, the two chemicals react to release carbon dioxide. You may also notice that fizzing sherbet

▲ **Fig 1** The massive release of energy from a forest fire can be uncontrollable.

makes your mouth feel cold. This is because the chemical reaction needs heat. It takes the heat from your mouth. Reactions that require heat are called **endothermic** reactions.

ENERGY

citric acid + sodium hydrogencarbonate ⟶ sodium citrate + carbon dioxide + water

Fuels and engines

If we want to use energy for any kind of work we need to be able to control the way it is released. Petrol burns in air very quickly. The energy is rapidly lost as heat, light and sound. If we trap some petrol and air in a cylinder and then add a spark, there will be an explosion. In a petrol engine, this explosion moves a piston. The moving piston turns a rod which eventually turns a wheel. In this way, the chemical energy in the petrol is changed to movement energy.

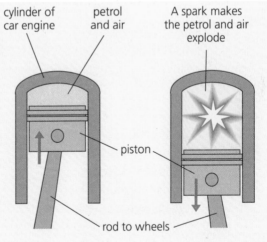

cylinder of car engine

petrol and air

A spark makes the petrol and air explode

piston

rod to wheels

▶ **Fig 2** Chemical energy harnessed in a car engine to drive the wheels.

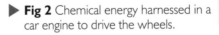

REVIEW

- In a group.
  - Make a list of all the different fuels mentioned above.
  - Give examples of how you have seen them used.
  - Describe why it is important that each fuel was one of the reactants in an exothermic reaction.
  - Write down your ideas and prepare to discuss them with the rest of the class.

27 Renewable energy resources

KEY IDEAS

In this section of the book you will have opportunities to:
- Explain that some energy resources can be used up
- Explain what the term 'renewable energy resource' means.

STARTER

In a group.
The Sun, water and wind can be used to provide energy. Discuss examples of this that you have seen.

Fossil fuels

Fossil fuels took millions of years to form. When we burn a fossil fuel it is destroyed. It cannot be used again. Fossil fuels are **non-renewable** energy resources.

People are still searching for new supplies of coal, gas and oil. Once they have been used we will need to find more. Our need for energy is also increasing. When all the fossil fuels have been used up there will be serious problems. This is why scientists are developing other energy resources.

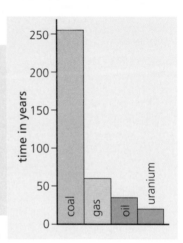

▶ **Fig 1** Estimated stocks of non-renewable fuels.

Renewable energy resources

Fossil fuels are burned to make steam. The steam is then used to drive a turbine. Some energy resources can drive turbines directly. No fuel has to be used up (see Fig 2).

Energy resources that are not used up are sometimes called **alternative energy**. Alternative energy resources do not run out when they are used. These energy resources are **renewable**.

Taking energy from wind, water and sunlight does not involve burning anything. It makes no smoke or steam or waste products. Some renewable energy resources are shown in Table 1 opposite.

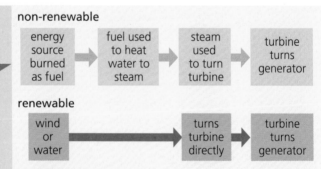

▲ **Fig 2**

ACTIVITY

With a partner.
- Discuss the difference between renewable and non-renewable energy.
- Write down an example of each.

Renewable energy resource	How is it used
Wind	Moves boats and turns wind generators
Tides and waves	Turns a turbine to generate electricity
Hydroelectricity	Water current turns turbines. When valves open, electricity is generated
Geothermal	Heat from underground rocks turns water to steam which can turn turbines or heat houses
Solar panels	Can heat water or generate electricity

▲ **Table 1**

Wind power

▼ **Fig 3** A wind farm.

Any turbine can turn a generator. The wind can turn a turbine. Wind generators make electricity in the same way as steam generators in power stations. Wind power is quiet and does not produce much pollution. Many small wind generators (Fig 3) are needed to make the same amount of electricity as a power station.

Solar power

Solar panels are used to recharge batteries in many small appliances such as calculators and wrist watches. Larger solar collectors can be built into the roof of a house. They use the energy in sunlight to heat water or to generate electricity.

In some parts of the USA there are large fields of solar panels making electricity for whole towns. The panels are turned by small motors so that they always face the Sun. Even in the UK, where the weather is often cloudy, solar panels on a roof can generate more electricity than one house needs.

Geothermal energy

In some parts of the world geothermal energy is taken from hot rocks underground. Water is pumped down into the rocks. The heat from the rocks turns the water into steam. The steam is pumped back to the surface. Here it can be used to heat homes or make electricity.

Hydroelectric power

Running water can turn turbines. The water can be stored in a reservoir until it is needed. When valves are opened the water flows downhill past the turbines and makes them turn. The reservoir can be refilled naturally by rainfall or by using spare electricity to pump water back up at night.

REVIEW

- In a group.
  - Design a poster to show some renewable energy resources and some non-renewable ones.
  - Include the advantages and disadvantages of each.

Why do we need to find ways of using alternative energy resources? Write down your ideas. Include some examples.

28 Energy transfers

KEY IDEAS

In this section of the book you will have opportunities to:
- Explain how energy moves from place to place
- Describe how energy can help us to do work and that energy can be stored.

STARTER

In a group.
Think back to your earlier work on food chains. Draw a picture showing how the energy from the Sun passes down a food chain to reach an eagle. What happens to the energy at each stage?

Work

▶ **Fig 1**

Work is done whenever a force makes something move. A cyclist has to work hard to make a bicycle go fast. The amount of work that the cyclist in Fig 1 is doing depends on:
- the distance she travels
- the mass of what she is moving, which is the bicycle and herself.

Expensive bicycles are made of light metal alloys. They also have many different gears. This helps the cyclist to use energy more efficiently.

Doing work requires energy. A cyclist gets chemical energy from food. Energy can be in many other different forms (see Table 1).

Energy	Description	Example
Wave	Waves carry energy. This can do work.	Radio, sound and light
Heat (thermal)	Molecules are made to move faster when heated. The molecules can do work.	Steam, hot air and hot coal warming a house
Electrical	Electric current is a flow of electrons. These can do work.	Torch and house circuits
Nuclear	Energy in the nucleus of an atom is released.	Nuclear power station
Chemical	Energy locked in chemicals is released.	Food and fuel
Gravitational potential energy	Objects lifted above the ground gain energy. Work can be done when these objects fall.	Water flowing from a reservoir
Kinetic energy	The energy in moving objects. If they hit other objects work is done.	A moving racing car or cyclist
Strain energy	Energy stored in a material that has been stretched or compressed.	The string of a bow; a coiled spring

▲ **Table 1**

Energy transfer

When a machine does work it often changes energy from one form to another. The change from one form of energy to another is called **energy transfer**. We can follow a series of energy transfers like a story (see Figs 2, 3 and 4). This is an energy transfer chain.

Wind power

▶ **Fig 2**

Sun warms the air	→	wind blows	→	wind turns a turbine	→	turbine turns a generator	→	generator makes electricity
thermal energy	→	kinetic energy	→	kinetic energy	→	kinetic energy	→	electrical energy

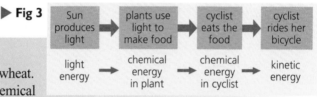

Energy comes from the Sun as **thermal energy** (heat). This becomes **kinetic energy** (movement) in the wind. The wind turns a turbine, which makes electricity.

Food for energy

▶ **Fig 3**

Sun produces light	→	plants use light to make food	→	cyclist eats the food	→	cyclist rides her bicycle
light energy	→	chemical energy in plant	→	chemical energy in cyclist	→	kinetic energy

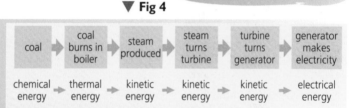

The Sun's light energy is changed into **chemical energy** by green plants such as wheat. When a cyclist eats some spaghetti the chemical energy it contains goes into his or her own body. It is then changed into many different forms of energy. Kinetic energy moves the cyclist around the track and thermal energy makes her hot.

ACTIVITY

With a partner.

- Write down an energy transfer chain that starts with some food you ate for breakfast.
- Discuss, then label the form of energy at each stage.

Connections

This unit builds on earlier work on plants, chemical changes, circuits and keeping warm, at Key Stage 2. It will lead on to further study of energy transfers and changes of state in Year 8.

A coal power station

▼ **Fig 4**

coal	→	coal burns in boiler	→	steam produced	→	steam turns turbine	→	turbine turns generator	→	generator makes electricity
chemical energy	→	thermal energy	→	kinetic energy	→	kinetic energy	→	kinetic energy	→	electrical energy

The chemical energy in coal changes into thermal energy when it burns. This changes into kinetic energy when water is heated until it expands into steam. Steam passes the kinetic energy on to the turbines. They pass the kinetic energy on to the generators. The generators change the kinetic energy into electrical energy.

Energy stores

Energy is stored in food and fuels. Energy can also be stored in other ways. Water in a high reservoir acts as a store of energy. It contains **potential energy**. When the water runs downhill, gravity converts the potential energy into kinetic energy. Energy can also be stored in a spring or stretched elastic. An archer uses the energy stored in a stretched string to shoot an arrow. Animals and plants also store energy.

REVIEW

- In a group.
  - Draw an energy transfer chain to show all the energy transfers involved in making hydroelectricity.

Carry out a survey at home to identify some energy transfers. Choose three and draw energy transfer chains for each.

29 Electric circuits

Conductors and insulators

Metals are **conductors**. They conduct electricity. Non-metals do not conduct electricity. They are **insulators**. This is why the wires that carry electric current are made of metal covered with plastic insulation (see Fig 1).

▶ **Fig I**

Testing materials

We can test a substance to find out whether it conducts electricity. The substance is placed across a gap in a circuit. If the substance is a conductor it will light up a bulb in the circuit.

Table 1 shows that:

- metals are conductors
- most non-metals are insulators.

Study tip

Water at home and in the laboratory is not pure. Impurities in water allow it to conduct electricity from a wire to your body.

▶ **Table I**

Substance	Conducts electricity
Silver	✔
Copper	✔
Aluminium	✔
Graphite	✔
Pure water	✘
Glass	✘
Rubber	✘
Plastics	✘

ACTIVITY

On your own.
- Write down the name of one non-metal that can conduct electricity.
- Is water an insulator or a conductor?

How metals conduct electricity

Electric **current** is caused by a flow of electrons. The atoms in a metal are packed closely together. Electrons often change places between atoms in a metal. If they are given energy they can be pushed along. Electrons are pushed away (repelled) from a negative charge and attracted towards a positive charge (see Fig 2).

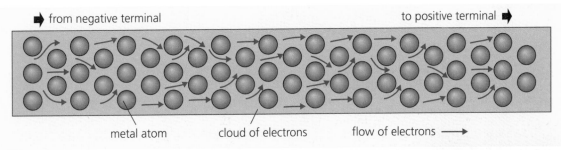

from negative terminal →   to positive terminal →

metal atom   cloud of electrons   flow of electrons ⟶

▲ **Fig 2**

▶ **Fig 3** The thin filament heats up when the electrons pass through it. This makes a light bulb glow.

Electrons can move easily through metal wires connected together. They pass between the atoms of the metal and rarely collide with them. When the electrons in a thick wire are pushed through a narrow section of wire they collide with the atoms more often. This can make the metal become hot. It may become hot enough to give out light. A light bulb contains a very thin filament of metal.

Electrons in insulating materials do not move freely. They are firmly held by their atoms. When an insulator is put into a circuit the current cannot pass through it. No current will flow.

Electric circuits

▶ **Fig 4**

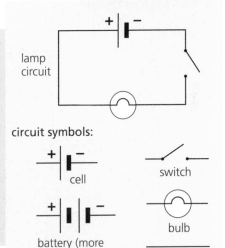

lamp circuit

circuit symbols:

+ |⊦−   cell

+ | | ⊦−   battery (more than one cell)

switch

bulb

wire

Bicycle lamps allow us to take electricity with us. Each lamp needs a cell, often called a battery, a bulb, wires and a switch. These components make up the electric circuit of the lamp. Electricity only flows if the wires are joined in a complete ring. This ring is called a **circuit**.

Fig 4 shows an electric circuit for a bicycle lamp. The battery pushes electric current through the circuit. Electrons flow from the negative terminal of the battery. The flow of electrons is the current. Wires link the battery to the bulb. If the circuit is broken the current will stop. The switch stops and starts the current.

REVIEW

- In a group.
  - Look back at your starter activity. How accurate were you with your circuit?
  - Now, design a safety poster that explains some of the dangers of electricity.
  - Include the words conductor, insulator and circuit.

Draw five examples of appliances at home that use electric circuits. Explain how these appliances use switches.

30 Electric current

KEY IDEAS

In this section of the book you will have opportunities to:
- Explain how to measure current in electric circuits
- Describe how the current in a circuit can be changed.

STARTER

In a group.
Discuss how metals conduct electricity. Draw and label a diagram to show how this happens.

Measuring current

The size of an electric current depends on the number of electrons flowing in the circuit. It is measured in amperes or **amps**. One amp (**A**) is about 1 million billion electrons per second flowing around the circuit. We use a meter called an **ammeter** to measure the size of the current. The circuit in Fig 1 has a current of 2 amps. This is written as 2 A.

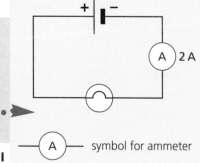

symbol for ammeter

▶ **Fig 1**

Series and parallel circuits

There are different ways of arranging electric circuits. A circuit with two bulbs can be arranged in two different ways (Fig 2). You could connect the bulbs up in a row, one after another. This is called a **series circuit**. You could connect the bulbs up side by side, with each one having its own part of the circuit. This is called a **parallel circuit**

The current in a series circuit has to pass through both bulbs. It does not matter where you place an ammeter in a series circuit. The current is the same everywhere on the circuit.

The current in a parallel circuit depends on the number of parallel lines it has. An ammeter shows a different reading depending on where it is placed in the circuit and how many lines are being used at the time.

In a series circuit the same current flows through the entire circuit.

In a parallel circuit each branch takes a separate share of the current.

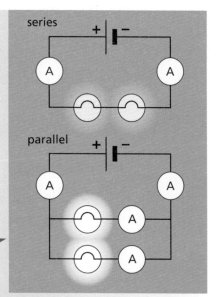

▲ **Fig 2** Parallel circuits have less resistance so more current flows.

With a partner.
- Look at Fig 2.
- Discuss what would happen if one of the bulbs in a series circuit failed.
- What would happen if the same thing happened in the parallel circuit?

Changing the current

A battery works by changing chemical energy into electrical energy. An arrangement of chemicals that generates electricity is called a cell. One battery may contain one or more cells.

chemical energy → electrical energy

The current carries energy from the battery to wherever it is needed. This energy can be used for lighting a bulb or turning a motor. Adding more energy increases the current. An ammeter reading will rise. A bulb in the circuit will glow more brightly.

Take care when building a circuit. Too many cells can make a bulb 'blow'. This happens when the **filament** becomes hot enough to melt or burn away.

Current and components

Electricity passes through all the components of a series circuit but the components are not all the same. Some of them allow the current to pass through easily. Others slow the current down. This is called **resistance**. The more a component resists the flow of electrons the lower the current in the circuit will be (see Table 1).

Components in a circuit do not 'use up' the current. Exactly the same number of electrons enter and leave each component. Some components resist the current by making it more difficult for the electrons to flow.

Device	Current in amps
lamp	0.2
motor	0.4
heater	0.6

▲ Table 1

- In a group.
  o Design a circuit that you could use to show that current is not used up by the components of a circuit.
  o Include a circuit diagram in your plan.

Study tip

You can remember the difference between a series circuit and a parallel circuit by thinking about a TV series. One programme follows another in a line just like the bulbs in a series circuit.

31 Voltage

KEY IDEAS

In this section of the book you will have opportunities to:
- Describe that cells and batteries are a source of electrical energy
- Explain that it is the voltage of a battery or cell which pushes the current around a circuit.

STARTER

In a group.
Produce a large poster showing a series and a parallel circuit each containing a battery, connecting wires, an ammeter and two bulbs. Explain what would happen to the bulbs and ammeter readings if an extra battery were added to each circuit.

How a battery works

A battery works by changing chemical energy into electrical energy. It is the electrical energy produced in the battery that is used to push the current around the circuit. When the current flows through a component the electrical energy is converted to another form of energy.

Remember, current is not used up in an appliance. The current carries the energy that is used.

Voltage

The electrical energy produced by a battery or other power source is called **electrical potential energy**. On its journey round the circuit this energy is used to power components such as bulbs or motors. The current returning to the battery or power source has less energy than when it began to travel around the circuit.

The difference in the energy at the start of the journey round the circuit and the energy at the end is called **potential difference**. This is often just called **voltage** and is measured in **volts V**. It is the voltage of a supply that pushes the current around a circuit. Voltage can be thought of as an 'electrical push'. The bigger the push, the more current flows around the circuit. Different batteries produce different voltages. As a general rule:

A battery of double the voltage may provide double the energy if all else is the same.

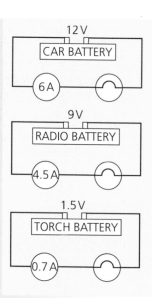

▲ **Fig 1** Different circuits with different batteries.

ACTIVITY

On your own.
- The voltage of a torch battery is 1.5 V.
- How could you use torch batteries to produce 6 V for an appliance.

Measuring voltage

A voltmeter is similar to an ammeter. However, how they are used is very different. A voltmeter is used to measure the difference between the energy entering a battery or other component and the energy leaving it. The circuit does not need to be broken when using a voltmeter as it is connected across the component.

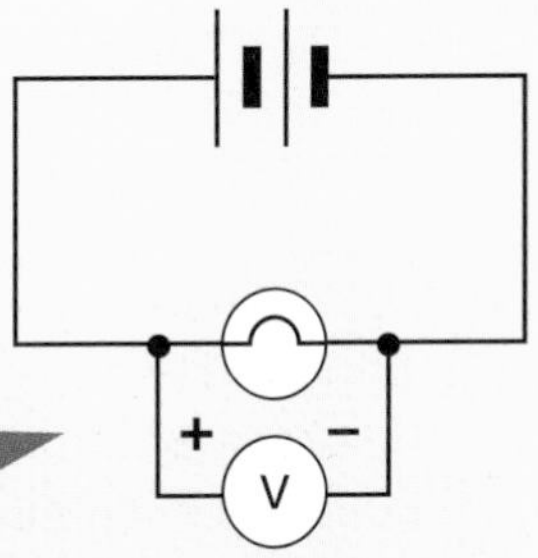

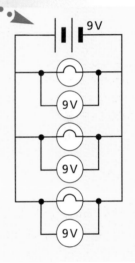

▲ **Fig 2** Voltmeter connected in parallel.

- In a series circuit the voltage across each individual component adds up to the supply voltage. Each component uses energy so there is a potential difference across each one.

- In a parallel circuit each meter shows the full supply voltage.

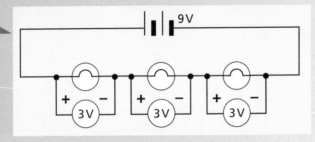

▲ **Fig 3** Measuring voltage in a series circuit.

▶ **Fig 4** Measuring voltage in a parallel circuit.

Connections

This work builds on earlier work on electricity and circuits at Key Stage 2. The ideas in this unit will be developed in later work on magnets and electromagnets in Year 8 and energy and electricity in Year 9.

Current and voltage

It is the voltage or 'electrical push' from a battery that pushes the current around a circuit. As voltage increases the current increases. There is not a simple mathematical link between the two because different components of the circuit can heat up and confuse the result.

REVIEW

- In a group.
  - Using three torch batteries it is possible to connect them up in a circuit in ways that give voltages of either 4.5 V or 1.5 V.
  - Draw circuit diagrams to show how this could be done.

- Design a poster that you can use to revise this topic on electricity. Include all of the main ideas such as conductors, insulators, current, voltage, series circuits and parallel circuits.

32 Speed

KEY IDEAS

In this section of the book you will have opportunities to:
- Describe how to work out the speed of a moving object
- Explain the relationship between speed, distance and time.

STARTER

In a group.
Discuss how you could calculate your average speed on your journey to school.

Units of speed

Some people run faster than others. The fastest person in a race will get to the end of the track before the rest. How quickly he/she gets there depends on his/her **speed**. You could just say that a person is a fast, medium fast or slow runner but this is not much help if you want to compare a person with a train.

The exact speed of any moving thing is the exact distance it travels in an exact length of time. You can work out your own speed by using a watch to check how far you walk or run in one minute.

The fastest person in the chart (see Table 1) managed to walk 60 metres in one minute. Another way of putting this is to say that her speed was 60 metres per minute. It is a good idea to pick units that are the right size for measuring speed. This is one reason why the speed of cars is normally measured in miles or kilometres per hour. The most common unit for measuring speed is metres per second. This is written as m/s.

Pupil	Distance in 60 seconds (metres)
Anita	35
Brenda	40
Colin	38
Diana	60
Vikram	51
Fiona	42
Guy	55

▲ **Table 1**

Calculating speed

Before we can work out the speed of anything we need to know exactly how far it moved and exactly how long it took. There are different ways of finding these out.

A car can easily be timed between fixed start and finish lines with a stop clock. The clock is started when the car crosses the start line. It is stopped when the car crosses the finish line. Calculating the speed then involves one easy equation:

Average speed = distance travelled ÷ time taken

▲ **Fig 1** The speed of this attempt to break the world land speed record was calculated by timing the car over a set distance.

We can make it shorter by using d for distance, t for time, and v for speed (velocity). The shorthand equation is:

$$v = \frac{d}{t}$$

This equation only gives us the average speed of the object. It does not tell us exactly how fast the car was going at every single moment along the way.

So if an object takes 10 seconds to travel a distance of 100 metres:

$$v = \frac{d}{t}$$

v = 100 metres ÷ 10 seconds

v = 10 metres per second or 10 m/s

ACTIVITY

With a partner.
- If an object takes 30 seconds to travel a distance of 90 metres, calculate its average speed.
- Why is it useful to be able to calculate speeds in this way?
- Write your ideas down.

Average speeds can be measured very accurately using a computer. In Fig 2, instead of a person with a stop clock, a light beam across the track is broken when a car goes past. The computer can measure the exact length of time that the beam is broken. If we know the exact length of the car we can calculate its exact speed at that spot.

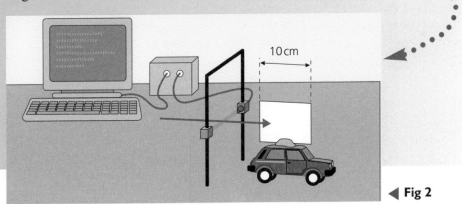

10 cm

◀ Fig 2

REVIEW

- In a group.
  - Look back at the starter activity.
  - Discuss how the average speed of your journey to school may not be a true picture of the journey.
  - Write your ideas down and prepare to share them with others.

  Try to collect pictures of animals and machines that can travel at different speeds. Place them into an order that groups together the fastest and the slowest.

33 Identifying forces

KEY IDEAS

In this section of the book you will have opportunities to:
- Explain that balanced forces do not change the movement of an object
- Explain that a force can change the speed, shape and direction of an object.

STARTER

In a group.
Think back to your earlier work on forces. Write down some examples of forces that you have seen on your way to school. Choose one example and try to draw a diagram showing the direction of the forces.

Forces

▶ **Fig 1** Contact forces.

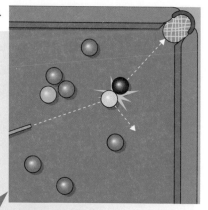

A force is a push or a pull. Pushing or pulling forces can be caused by different things.

Gravitational force pulls everything down towards the Earth. A climber must work very hard to overcome the force of **gravity**. Gravity pulls most things together, but this is hard to measure with small things. It is easier to see how gravity works on massive things like planets in Space (see Unit 106).

Contact force comes when two objects collide. This can happen when one snooker ball hits another (see Fig 1) or when two cars crash.

Frictional force can slow down or stop a thing that is moving. A floor can be made safer to walk on by covering it with a substance such as rubber that adds to the **friction**. Friction can also help something to move. Car tyres use friction to grip the road so that they can move the car forward when they spin (see Unit 34).

Electric forces and magnetic forces are described in Units 31 and 68.

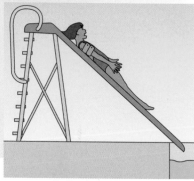

▶ **Fig 2** Gravity and friction are two forces acting on this person.

Force and movement

Contact force can change the shape of an object. If you squeeze a lump of modelling clay it changes shape. Metal needs a much larger force to make it change shape. A crushing machine at a scrap yard is strong enough to force a whole car to change shape (see Fig 3).

Forces therefore vary in size.

▶ **Fig 3**

On your own.
- Make a list of some other examples of contact forces altering the shape of an object.

Measurement of force

We need a way to measure forces accurately. The unit of measurement we use for measuring force is called a newton (N). Your mass plus gravity makes a force of about 500 newtons. If you stood on a car bonnet you would hardly dent it. A car crushing machine can make a force of many thousands of newtons.

Changing the balance

Forces can change the direction and speed of an object. A shopping trolley standing on a level surface (see Fig 4) does not move by itself. It has equal forces all around it. The forces are balanced. When you push the trolley you add extra force in one direction. The other forces are not as strong. You make the trolley move.

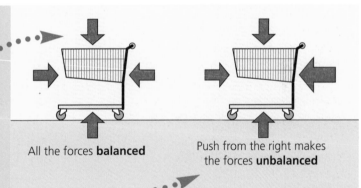

All the forces **balanced**

Push from the right makes the forces **unbalanced**

▲ Fig 4

Weight and mass

The words **weight** and **mass** are often used wrongly. The mass of an object is a measure of how much matter there is in it. This depends on what the object is made of and its size. Mass is measured in kilograms.

Weight is the force of gravity pulling the object down towards the Earth or other body. A big body has a greater gravitational pull on an object than a small body. Weight is measured in newtons. On Earth a mass of 1 kg has a weight of 10 N.

- In a group.
  - Try rolling a ball in as many different places as you can. Roll it downhill and uphill, down the stairs and up the stairs. Try to roll it around a corner.
  - Write down how far the ball went each time, and how far it travelled.
  - What were the forces involved?

Research the forces involved in floating, sinking and stretching.

34 Friction

KEY IDEAS

In this section of the book you will have opportunities to:
- Describe how friction affects the movement of an object
- Explain how the force of friction can be helpful or unhelpful.

STARTER

In a group.
Imagine a world where everything slides around as if it was on ice. Make a list of some of the problems this would cause.

What causes friction?

You can warm your hands up on a cold day by rubbing them together. The heat is real. It is made by friction.

When surfaces get very close together their molecules touch. Even if the surfaces are smooth, rubbing their molecules together produces heat. If the surfaces are rough it is very difficult for them to slide past one another.

Friction has three effects:

1   it produces heat when two surfaces rub against each other

2   it prevents objects from sliding or slows them down

3   it wears surfaces down as they rub together.

▼ **Fig 1** Friction produces heat, slows down movement and causes wear and tear.

brakes become hot as they wear out

the force of friction in this arrangement helps a climber to control the speed of sliding down a rope

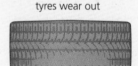
tyres wear out

Using friction to go and to stop

Car tyres grip best on a dry road. It is more difficult to steer on a wet or icy road and very hard to stop. Grooves and ridges, or tread, on the tyre can help to push water away when the tyre touches the ground. This improves friction and makes the tyres safer in wet weather. The same name is used for the ridges on the soles of trainers or walking boots. They help your feet to grip more firmly, especially on wet or muddy ground.

Brakes also work by friction. Brakes get hot when they are used. Some of the rough surface also rubs off. Brakes and tyres gradually wear out as they are used. This is why they need to be checked regularly.

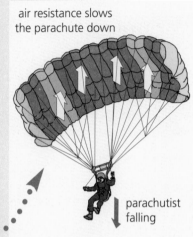

air resistance slows the parachute down

parachutist falling

▲ **Fig 2** Using air friction.

> ### ACTIVITY
>
> With a partner.
> - List three examples where friction between objects is useful.
> - List three examples where friction between two objects can cause problems.

Even air causes friction. When you move through the air you have to push past millions of gas molecules. This is why it is hard to walk into the wind, when all the gas molecules are rushing towards you. It is even harder if you are wearing loose clothes. This is how a parachute works. The wind is caused by a person rushing through the air towards the ground. The parachute's large surface hits many more air molecules than a person's body. This **air resistance** makes the parachutist fall very slowly.

Overcoming friction

One way to reduce friction is to **lubricate** smooth surfaces with oil. This helps them to slide past each other more easily. It also reduces heat and wear.

Air resistance can be reduced by changing the shape of a vehicle or a building. Cars are designed to cut into the air in front and help it to flow smoothly past as they go along. A vehicle designed to reduce air resistance is said to be **streamlined**. Water is even more difficult to cut through than air. Machines such as boats and animals such as fish that can move quickly through water are also streamlined.

▼ **Fig 3** ▶

Which car is streamlined?

> #### REVIEW
> - In a group.
>   - Discuss some of the ways in which friction has been useful or a problem for you recently.
>   - Write down your ideas for increasing or decreasing friction to overcome these problems.
>
> Plan an investigation to find out which shapes are the most streamlined through water. Remember to make the test a fair test. Draw a diagram to show the apparatus.

> ### Connections
>
> This work builds on earlier work on friction and forces at Key Stage 2. The work leads on to further work on gravity and space, speeding up, and pressure and moments in Year 9.

35 The Sun and other stars

KEY IDEAS

In this section of the book you will have opportunities to:
- Explain what stars and galaxies are
- Describe how the Sun produces light and heat and that planets are visible because they reflect sunlight.

STARTER

In a group.
Make a list of the constellations you have heard of. Discuss what these constellations are and write your ideas down.

Constellations

The stars have fascinated people since very early times. Patterns of stars – or **constellations** – are given names, and legends have been made up about them. Over 1800 years ago 48 constellations were known and more have been added since then. The stars are not arranged in these groups. They are very far apart and only appear to form a shape when seen from Earth (see Fig 1).

▲ **Fig 1**

▼ **Fig 2** Orion is supposed to look like a hunter and Leo a lion.

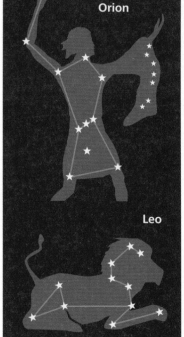

Orion

Leo

Stars and galaxies

Stars shine by their own light. Our own Sun is a star. Nuclear reactions taking place inside the Sun and other stars also produce a great deal of heat and other forms of energy.

Clusters of stars form **galaxies**. There are billions of galaxies in the **Universe**. Our Sun is part of a galaxy called the Milky Way. The Milky Way contains approximately 100 000 million stars and the Sun is just one of these. Our Earth is just one tiny planet circling a single star in the Universe.

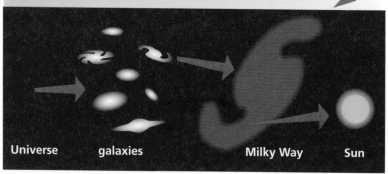

Universe   galaxies   Milky Way   Sun

▲ **Fig 3**

The Sun

The Sun supplies the Earth with energy. Without the Sun, there would be no life on Earth. Plants use sunlight to make food (see Unit 85) and during the day we use sunlight to see. The Sun also warms our world. The Sun's hot core reaches temperatures of 15 million degrees Celsius but its surface is much cooler – only about six thousand degrees.

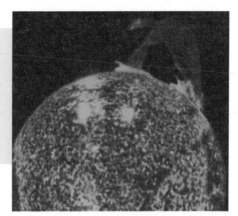

▶ **Fig 4** Flaming gases leap from the Sun's surface. At the same time invisible radiation also escapes.
⚠ **Never look at the Sun directly.**

ACTIVITY

With a partner.
- Discuss how the Sun produces light, heat and other forms of energy.
- Why is this important to life on Earth?
- Write down your ideas.

Seeing objects in space

The light from distant stars and galaxies takes years to reach the Earth. Distances in space are too great to be measured in kilometres. Figures as large as this are even hard to imagine. Scientists measure these distances in **light years**.

One light year is the distance light travels in a year. Light travels at 300 000 kilometres a second and it would only take one eighth of a second for a flash of light to circle the Earth. There are more than 30 million seconds in a year and the second nearest star to Earth is 4.2 light years – 40 billion kilometres – away. Light from the far side of the Milky Way takes over 100 000 years to reach us.

Other objects in the Solar System are visible because they reflect the Sun's light. When you see the Moon it is reflecting light from the Sun to Earth.

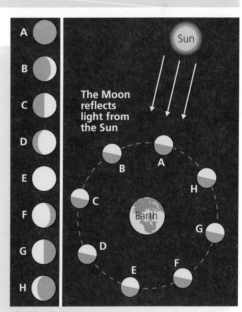

The Moon reflects light from the Sun

▲ **Fig 5** The Moon appears to change shape as its shadow moves (not drawn to scale).

REVIEW

- In a group.
  - Find out your star signs and look up the pattern of stars that form its constellation.
  - Copy the stars and add your own version of the whole picture, like the ones in Fig 2.

🏠 Explain why the Moon appears to have a different shape at different times of the month. Fig 5 may be useful.

36 The Solar System

▲ **Fig 1** Mars is one of nine planets in the Solar System.

▶ **Fig 2** The nearest star on the same scale as this would be a kilometre away.

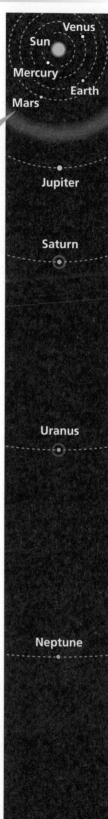

The Solar System

The **Solar System** contains nine planets. Each planet moves in an **orbit** around the Sun. The four planets closest to the Sun are called the inner planets. The other five, called the outer planets, are a very long way away.

Planets are not the only objects in our Solar System. There are thousands of minor planets and debris known as asteroids. Most of them orbit the Sun between Mars and Jupiter. The largest asteroid is only 700 kilometres in diameter. Some planets also have their own moons.

Mercury is not much bigger than our Moon. It is only 50 million kilometres from the Sun and its surface temperature can reach 350°C. Venus is twice as far away but its surface is even hotter. This is because Venus has an atmosphere containing carbon dioxide, which traps heat (see Unit 98).

The Earth is 150 million kilometres from the Sun. The surface temperature on our own planet varies between 40°C and –40°C.

ACTIVITY

On your own.
- Write down why Earth's position in the Solar System is so important for life on Earth.

Pluto and Neptune are the planets furthest from the Sun. Neptune orbits the Sun once in 165 years. Pluto's orbit takes 247 years. These outermost planets are very cold and it is probably very dark there. From the surface of Neptune your view of the Sun would be 30 times smaller than it is from Earth – and a thousand times less bright.

 Remember that planets do not give out light. We can only see them because they reflect light from the Sun. Planets near to the Sun look brighter than the outermost planets. Venus is the third brightest object in our sky. Pluto is so dim that it was not seen until 1930.

Mercury, Venus, Mars, Pluto and Earth are small planets. Jupiter and Saturn are giant planets. Jupiter is more massive than all the other planets added together.

Planet	Relative size	Distance from Sun/ millions of km	Temperature of surface/ °C	Planet	Relative size	Distance from Sun/ millions of km	Temperature of surface/ °C
Mercury		58	450	Saturn		1427	−160
Venus		108	500				
Earth		150	20				
Mars		228	−40				
Jupiter		778	−150	Uranus		2870	−220
				Neptune		4497	−230
				Pluto		5900	−230

- In a group.
  - Make a model of the Solar System. Take two metres of string, nine pieces of card and nine paper clips.
  - Write the name of a planet on each piece of card and clip the planets onto the string the following distances from one end:
    Mercury 1 cm; Venus 2 cm; Earth 3 cm; Mars 4 cm; Jupiter 20 cm; Saturn 35 cm; Uranus 70 cm; Neptune 110 cm; Pluto 145 cm.

37 Days and seasons

KEY IDEAS

In this section of the book you will have opportunities to:

- Explain that nights and days are due to the Earth's rotation
- Explain how seasons are caused by the Earth's movement around the Sun.

STARTER

In a group.
Discuss why we have night and day and seasons. Produce a diagram that explains your ideas. Prepare to share your ideas with others.

Day and night

Every day, the Sun appears to move across the sky. People once believed that the Sun was orbiting the Earth. Now we know that this is not so. The Earth is simply spinning round on its own **axis**, like a top. It makes a complete turn every 24 hours.

One half of the Earth is always in **shadow** and the other half is lit by the Sun. We have our daytime when the place where we live is turned towards the Sun. Night comes when our region moves out of the light and into the shadow.

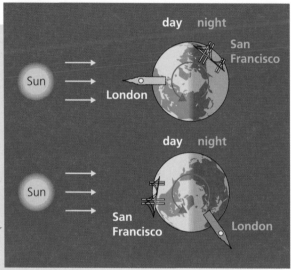

▲ **Fig 1** Daytime for Britain is night-time for the USA.

During the night, the stars appear to move around the sky. Our Earth is not the centre of the Universe. Remember that it is the Earth's rotation that makes the stars look as if they are moving.

The seasons

As the Earth orbits the Sun (Unit 36) the seasons on the Earth's surface gradually change. This happens because the Earth is not perfectly vertical. Its axis is tilted at an angle of 23.5° (see Fig 3).

When the Northern **hemisphere** tilts towards the Sun it gets more light and heat. The days are longer and the Sun is higher overhead.

▲ **Fig 2** The North Star is almost directly over the North Pole. It seems to stay still while other stars revolve around it.

The weather becomes warmer. At the same time, the Southern hemisphere tilts away from the Sun. When it is summer in the Northern hemisphere, it is winter in the Southern hemisphere.

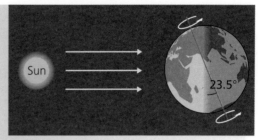

▲ **Fig 3** The Earth is tilted at an angle of 23.5°.

ACTIVITY

With a partner.
- Discuss why Europe has summer while Australia has winter.
- Write your ideas down and prepare to discuss them with others.

At the **equator** there is little difference between summer and winter. As you go towards the **Poles** the seasons become more important. The North Pole gets no sunshine at all in winter but during the summer the Sun never really sets. Study Fig 4 carefully to see how this works.

▼ **Fig 4**

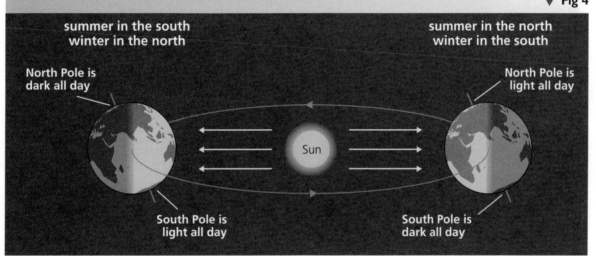

Leap years

The Earth takes 365.25 days to make a complete orbit of the Sun. We simply save up the extra quarters until we have enough to make one whole day. This is why we have three years of 365 days followed by a leap year with 366.

Connections

This work builds on earlier work on Earth, Sun and Moon at Key Stage 2. The unit links with work on gravity and on light in Year 9.

REVIEW

- In a group.
  - Look back at your starter activity.
  - Discuss how accurate your explanations of night and day and the seasons were.
  - What would you add to your answers to improve them?

🏠 Carefully push a knitting needle through a ball of wool and add a twist of cotton to mark a special spot. Spin it in front of a lamp to show night and day. Try to make a model of the seasons by tilting the ball and orbiting the lamp with it.

Summary of Year 7 topics

Biology (pages 8–31)

After studying the first part of the Year 7 topics you should have learned about life processes and living things.

Cells

1. What are the basic functions necessary for life?
2. List two differences between plant and animal cells.
3. How are red blood cells and nerve cells adapted to do their job?

Reproduction

4. Why do sperm and egg cells need to meet inside the female?
5. Why does the uterus need a thick lining?
6. How does oxygen and food pass from the mother to the embryo?

Environment and feeding relationships

7. List five examples of habitats in your area.
8. How are sharks adapted to their habitat?
9. What is meant by the term 'consumers'?

Variation and classification

10. What is meant by 'normal distribution'?
11. Name the five kingdoms of living things.
12. Explain why keys are so useful.

Chemistry (pages 32–55)

The second part of the Year 7 topics should have helped you to learn a great deal about materials and their properties. You will know about some important chemicals and be able to describe some chemical reactions.

Acids and alkalis

13. What is the pH of a neutral solution?
14. Name the salt made when hydrochloric acid reacts with copper oxide.
15. Why are indicators so useful?

Simple chemical reactions

16. Give an example of a chemical change.
17. Which gas is produced when metals react with acids?
18. How would you test for the gas carbon dioxide?

Particle model of solids, liquids and gases

19. Describe how particles are arranged in a solid and a gas.
20. Write down three differences between solids and liquids.
21. Write down three examples of diffusion.

Solutions

22. What is the difference between a solvent and a solute?
23. How does temperature affect solubility?
24. How would you show that the mass of water is conserved when it freezes?

Physics (pages 56–81)

The third part of the Year 7 topics should have helped you to understand more about energy, electricity, forces and the Solar System.

Energy resources

25. Where does most of the Earth's energy originally come from?
26. Name the substances produced when methane burns in air.
27. What are fossil fuels? Write down three examples.
28. Sketch a diagram that shows how electricity is generated from coal.

Electric circuits

29. Draw the circuit symbols for a bulb and an ammeter.
30. Design a circuit that has three bulbs in parallel.
31. Explain how voltage is measured.

Forces and their effects

32. If an object takes 30 seconds to travel 90 metres, what is its average speed?
33. Gravity is one type of force, name two others.
34. Describe two ways of reducing friction between two objects.

The Solar System and beyond

35. Mars does not give out light. How are we able to see it from Earth?
36. Name the inner planets of the Solar System.
37. Sketch a diagram that shows why we have night and day.

Introduction to Year 8 topics

Biology (pages 86–113)

The first part of the Year 8 topics is designed to help you to understand life processes and living things in greater detail. It is divided into four sections. Each section covers a unit from the Scheme of Work for Science.

Food and digestion

In this section you will study some common nutrients and understand that these, with water and fibre, form part of a balanced diet. You will be encouraged to identify foods containing these nutrients and explain the role of these nutrients in your body. The unit goes on to help you to understand that large molecules are broken down during digestion so that they can enter the body. Finally, you will study how nutrients enter the blood.

Respiration

This section covers how blood transports carbon dioxide from, and oxygen to, the lungs. You will study why tissues need a good blood supply and learn that aerobic respiration is a reaction involving oxygen. The work goes on to help you to understand the effects of an inadequate oxygen supply and the differences between inhaled air and exhaled air.

Microbes and disease

In this section you will learn that bacteria, fungi and viruses are classified as microorganisms. You will be able to name some diseases caused by microorganisms and how these can be transmitted. You will study the body's defence mechanisms and how these can be helped by immunisations. You will also learn how antibiotics can be effective against bacteria but not viruses.

Ecological relationships

This section will give you opportunities to classify some plants and animals and recognise how they are adapted to the environmental conditions in their habitat. You will study how the abundance of organisms is related to the resources available within a habitat and learn how to show this by using pyramids of numbers. Finally, you will study how pyramids of numbers represent feeding relationships within a habitat.

Chemistry (pages 114–137)

The second part of the Year 8 topics is designed to help you to gain a greater understanding of materials and their properties. It is divided into four sections. Each section covers a unit from the Scheme of Work for science.

Atoms and elements

In this section you will build on your earlier work on particles and learn that elements are made up of atoms. You will also learn that compounds are made when atoms of different elements join together. The unit also helps you to understand that elements can be represented by symbols and that chemical reactions can be represented by word equations.

Compounds and elements

This section will give you opportunities to learn the differences between elements, mixtures and compounds. You will learn that this is linked to the particles they contain. You will also learn some examples of mixtures and how to separate them. Finally, the unit will cover melting and boiling points and how these can be explained by using the particle model.

Rocks and weathering

This unit of work encourages you to describe rock specimens by using properties such as texture, porosity and particle size. You will learn about the processes involved in weathering rocks and in transporting the particles that are eroded from them. Finally, you will study how these particles are deposited as sediments. Throughout the unit you will be expected to link the weathering of rocks to the landscape around you.

The rock cycle

In this section you will study how sediments become sedimentary rocks. You will be introduced to various examples of sedimentary rocks. You will also study igneous and metamorphic rocks and learn how they form. The unit encourages you to understand the formation of rocks as a continuous cycle that takes millions of years. Finally, you will have opportunities to describe some of the features of different rocks and use these features to classify rocks as igneous, metamorphic or sedimentary.

Physics (pages 138–165)

The third part of the Year 8 topics builds on your earlier work on physical processes. It is divided into four sections. Each section covers a unit from the Scheme of Work for Science.

Heating and cooling

In this section you will learn to distinguish between temperature and heat, and give examples of common temperatures using the Celsius scale. The idea that energy flow is the result of temperature difference is introduced. You will learn that expansion and contraction can be explained by using the particle model. The unit moves on to describe conduction, convection and radiation, and to give some examples.

Magnets and electromagnets

This unit of work will allow you to develop your earlier ideas about magnets and magnetism. You will have opportunities to distinguish between magnetic and non-magnetic materials and learn about the Earth's magnetic field. This will lead on to study of the use of magnets for navigation and how to show the shape and strength of a magnetic field. You will also be introduced to some examples of the use of magnets and electromagnets.

Light

This section helps you to build on your earlier work on light and shadows. You will go on to learn that light travels in straight lines at very high speed and can be reflected and refracted at plane surfaces. The unit goes on to explain the origin of colour and to describe the effects of coloured filters. You will also study the effects of coloured lights on the appearance of coloured objects.

Sound and hearing

This section will help you to develop your understanding of sound and how we hear. You will study how changes in pitch and loudness can be related to vibrations, for example in musical instruments. The unit also explains how these vibrations create sound waves that can be shown using an oscilloscope. You will also learn that sound needs a medium to travel through and that sound travels at different speeds through different media. The unit will also provide opportunities for you to study hearing ranges and how hearing can be damaged.

38 A balanced diet

KEY IDEAS

In this section of the book you will have opportunities to:
- Describe the role of the main nutrients in the body
- Describe how your body gets these substances.

STARTER

In a group.
Make a list of the foods you have eaten in the past 24 hours. Next to each, write whether you think the food is healthy or not. Give your reasons.

What is in your food?

The food that you eat is broken down in your body to give you energy and the materials you need to grow strong and stay healthy.

Food contains six main groups of essential chemicals or nutrients:

carbohydrates   proteins   minerals   fats   vitamins   water

Different foods contain different amounts of these nutrients so we need to eat a variety of foods (see Fig 1). This is called a **balanced diet**. What you need to eat will not be exactly the same as what someone else needs. You must decide what is a healthy diet for you.

▶ **Fig 1**

Why do we need different nutrients?

Carbohydrates such as sugars and starches give your body energy.

Fats form a vital part of cell membranes. Fat is also stored in your body as an energy reserve. Eating too much fat can sometimes cause health problems. This is why doctors advise us to keep the total fat content of our diet low, but it would be dangerous to stop eating fats altogether. Most fats found in plant oils cause fewer health problems than fats from animal sources.

Proteins are used for growth and repair of body tissues. You need protein to grow, and to replace damaged cells after you stop growing. Muscles are mostly protein. Enzymes (see Unit 40) are also proteins.

Foods that are rich in protein include meat, eggs, fish, cheese, wholemeal bread, lentils and beans. There are also processed protein foods, such as tofu (made from soybeans) and Quorn (made from a fungus).

Vitamins and minerals are also essential. Vitamins help your cells to work properly. Minerals are needed to build some of the molecules in your cells. Eating a varied diet (lots of different foods) helps you to get all the vitamins and minerals you may need.

The minerals and vitamins in Table 1 are only a few of the ones essential for good health.

▶ Table 1

Vitamin	deficiency problems	some sources
Vitamin A	dry skin, night blindness	carrots, liver, eggs, green vegetables
Vitamin C	scurvy (bleeding gums, bruising, tender skin)	citrus fruit, potatoes, tomatoes
Vitamin D	rickets (soft bones)	milk, butter, cheese, sunlight on skin

Mineral	deficiency problems	some sources
Calcium	weak teeth and bones	milk, cheese, green vegetables
Iron	anaemia (blood deficiency)	nuts, meat, eggs
Iodine	thyroid problems (cold, tired, overweight)	shellfish, green vegetables

ACTIVITY

With a partner.
- Discuss what might happen to a person who did not eat enough green vegetables.
- Make notes of your ideas.

About 70% of your body weight is **water**. Every chemical reaction in your body needs water. It is also the main part of blood. You use water to dilute poisonous waste and excrete it as urine. You lose water when you breathe and when you sweat. The water that leaves your body through excretion, sweating and breathing must be replaced. You could survive for up to a month without food, but would die in a few days without water. We get most of our water by drinking liquids and a little from our food.

REVIEW

- In a group.
  - Design a poster that encourages people to eat a balanced diet.
  - Make sure you present the scientific ideas clearly.
- Information about the nutritional contents of foods can be found on labels. Check the labels on 10 food substances at home and decide which ones would be good sources of protein, carbohydrate and fats. Which ones contain the most vitamins?

39 Energy for life

KEY IDEAS

In this section of the book you will have opportunities to:
- Describe that cells use food to give them energy
- Explain that different activities and life-styles demand different amounts of energy.

STARTER

With a partner.
When people get tired they often say they have run out of energy. Discuss any examples that you can remember when you have felt like this. When was it and what did you do about it?

What do we need energy for?

All living things must have energy to survive. Approximately 70% of the energy you use every day keeps your body working. This includes your heartbeat and all the chemical reactions that take place in your cells. The remaining 30% is used for extra work and activities. So the total amount of energy used in a day depends on how active you are.

It may be influenced by:

age – growing children need more energy than older people

size – larger people may need more energy

gender – men generally need more energy than women

occupation – people with active jobs need more energy

activity – people who take part in active sports need more energy

motherhood – pregnant women and women who are breast feeding need more energy.

Activity	Kilojoules per day	Kilocalories per day
Mountain climber	23 000	5400
Building worker	21 000	5000
Athlete	19 000	4500
Footballer	16 000	3800
Teenage boy	12 500	3000
Secretary	11 000	2600
Teenage girl	9 500	2300

▲ **Table 1** Energy needed by some

ACTIVITY

With a partner.
- Discuss where you would place the following people in Table 1
  a a retired man who watched television a lot
  b a female athlete.
- Record your reasons.

Energy is measured in kilojoules (kJ). Heat energy was once measured in calories (c or cal) or kilocalories (C, Cal or kcal), which you sometimes see on food labels.

Food	Energy in 100 grams (kJ)
Celery	35
Sugar	1600
Lard	2700
Breakfast cereal	1500
Toast	1000
Mashed potatoes	400

◀ **Table 2** Amounts of energy in some different foods.

Some very big carbohydrates called **dietary fibre** cannot easily be broken down by your body. Dietary fibre helps food to pass through your digestive system (see Unit 40). Cellulose from plant cell walls is an important source of dietary fibre.

Food	fibre	starches	sugars
Wholemeal bread	✔✔✔	✔✔✔	–
Cereals	✔✔✔	✔✔	–
Vegetables	✔✔✔	–	–
White rice	✔	✔✔✔	–
Potatoes	✔	✔✔✔	–
Jam	–	–	✔✔✔
Grapes	✔	✔	✔✔✔
Chocolate	–	–	✔✔✔
Honey	–	–	✔✔✔

◀ **Table 3** Carbohydrate in some different foods.

REVIEW

- In a group.
  - Make a list of the foods you eat during a full day.
  - Use food labels to try to work out how many kilojoules of energy the food contained.
  - Discuss why eating too much fatty food would not be healthy.

🏠 Look at some food labels at home. Write down the energy content of each food and draw a chart showing your findings. Remember to do a fair comparison by comparing an equal number of grams for each food.

40 Digestion

KEY IDEAS

In this section of the book you will have opportunities to:
● Explain that food is broken down into smaller molecules by a process called digestion
● Explain how digestion occurs in the digestive system.

STARTER

With a partner.
Try to recall your knowledge of particle theory. Using this, discuss your ideas about how food can be broken down into smaller pieces. Write down your ideas.

Digestion

Nutrients are often large and complicated molecules. Before they can be used by your body they must first be broken down into smaller ones. This process is called **digestion**.

Food molecules and enzymes

A protein molecule (see Fig 1) is made up of a long chain of much smaller molecules joined together. The smaller molecules are called **amino acids**. The bonds between amino acids can be broken by **enzymes**. An enzyme that breaks down a protein will have no effect on starch. Each type of enzyme only works on one type of food.

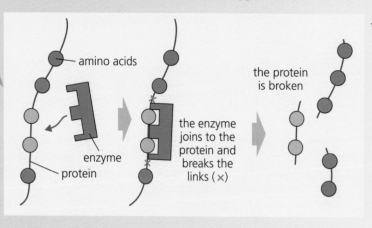

amino acids

enzyme

protein

the enzyme joins to the protein and breaks the links (×)

the protein is broken

◀ **Fig I** The enzyme is breaking the protein down into amino acids. An enzyme that breaks down proteins is called a **protease**.

The digestive system

The food you eat passes from your mouth to your anus through a long tube called the gut. As the food makes this journey it is broken down by two processes:

physical action + chemical attack

Breakdown of food begins in your mouth. Your teeth grind food up while enzymes in your saliva begin to digest it. Teeth are shaped to do different jobs. Sharp chisel-shaped teeth (incisors) can bite a piece from a big chunk of food. Flat teeth (molars) can grind it up so that is easy to swallow.

Food is moved down by squeezing movements, not by gravity. Mucus made by the gut also helps the food to slide down.

In your stomach the food is churned and mixed into a paste with water, acids and enzymes.

More enzymes are added as the food moves around the first bend in your gut.

When it reaches the small intestine it is a well digested watery fluid. Here, the digested nutrients pass through the gut wall into the blood (see Units 41 and 42).

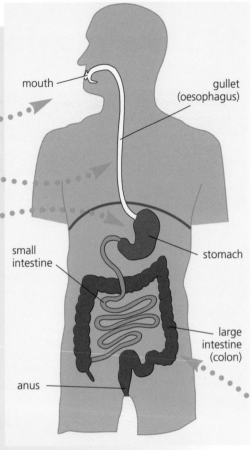

▲ **Fig 2** The human digestive system.

(see Units 41 and 42)

ACTIVITY

With a partner.
- Design a set of five questions about digestion.
- Once you have done this, take it in turns with another pair to ask each other your questions.
- Keep a score of how well you do.

After the nutrients have been taken out, the gut contains waste material (e.g. fibre) and water. The colon's main job is to reclaim water. Some diseases, such as cholera, force food to 'run' through your gut too quickly for the water to be recovered. This is dangerous because it makes a person's body lose water.

Finally, the nearly-solid unwanted material is **egested** from the gut through the anus. It is now called faeces. When flushed down the toilet, faeces become part of the **sewage**. Faeces can be a source of disease because they contain billions of bacteria. This is why we wash our hands after using the toilet.

REVIEW

- In a group.
  - Produce a large diagram of the digestive system.
  - Make separate labels for each part.
  - Now label your diagram and, without looking at your notes, try to write down the role each part has in digesting your food.

- Research some other animals to find out what type of teeth they have. How does the type of teeth the animal has relate to the food they eat?

41 How nutrients enter the blood

KEY IDEAS

In this section of the book you will have opportunities to:
- Explain that food is absorbed into the blood as it passes through the small intestine
- Describe how the wall of the small intestine is specially adapted to help this process.

STARTER

In a group.
Nutrients are transported around the body in the blood. Discuss how the blood moves around the body and then produce a simple diagram to show your ideas.

The small intestine

After your food is broken down it passes through the gut walls into your blood. The blood will take the food to all the cells of your body. The passage of vital nutrients from the gut to the blood is called **absorption**.

The small intestine is specially adapted to do this job.

1. The small intestine is very long and narrow. Food can only squeeze through slowly. This gives the nutrients time to be absorbed into the blood.
2. The walls of the small intestine are lined with thousands of fingers and folds which increase its surface area.

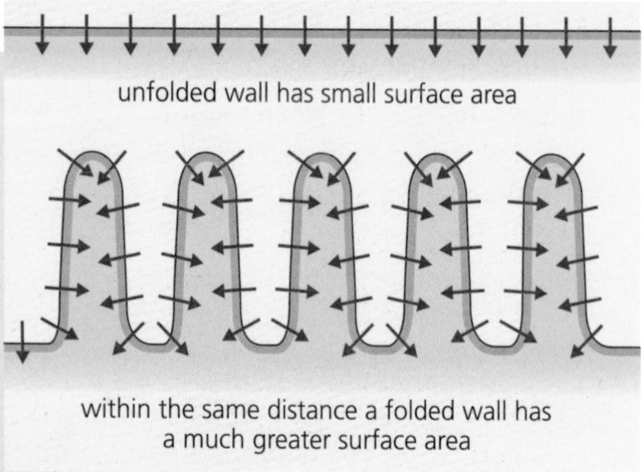

unfolded wall has small surface area
within the same distance a folded wall has a much greater surface area

▲ **Fig 1** Use a piece of string to measure the surface.

The small intestine of an adult person is between six and seven metres long. The walls are lined with finger-shaped folds called **villi**. By increasing the surface area on the inside of the small intestine, villi greatly increase the amount of food that can be absorbed as it goes along. The small intestine is very narrow so that as much food as possible is pressed against the walls. This also helps absorption.

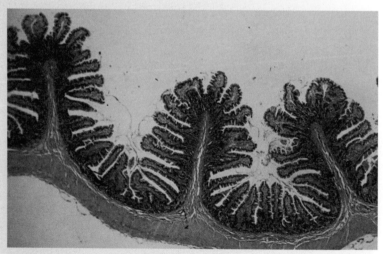

▲ **Fig 2** Villi.

With a partner.
- Discuss how villi can help to increase absorption of nutrients from the small intestine.
- Why is it important that the small intestine is narrow?
- Write your ideas down.

The small intestine has a very good blood supply. This also helps nutrients to go into the blood. Tiny thin-walled blood vessels called **capillaries** run inside the villi.

Connections

This work builds on earlier work on food and digestion and is closely linked to work on health and simple chemical reactions. It leads on to further study of respiration, health and fitness.

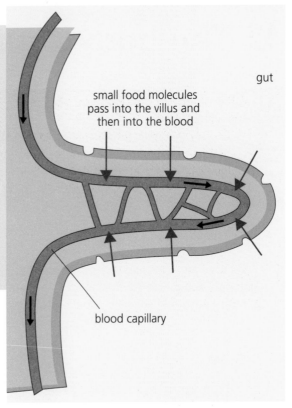

gut

small food molecules pass into the villus and then into the blood

blood capillary

▲ **Fig 3** Villus.

Moving on

Blood leaving the villi of the small intestine is full of simple sugars, amino acids and nutrients from broken-down fats. Some of the food goes to be stored. Fat is stored under your skin and around some body organs. Some sugar is stored as glycogen in your **liver** and muscles. Fat stores help your body to survive without food for a while. Glycogen stores are a fast energy reserve for extra activity.

Most of the food is pumped around your body in your bloodstream. This is how it reaches the tips of your fingers and toes, your brain and your heart. This is also how it reaches places where fat is stored.

REVIEW
- In a group.
  o Discuss the journey taken by a single molecule of sugar between your mouth and a muscle cell in your finger.
  o Now show the journey as a colourful diagram for display.

42 The body's transport system

KEY IDEAS

In this section of the book you will have opportunities to:
- Explain that your blood carries essential gases and nutrients to all parts of your body
- Describe that your heart is a muscular pump that pumps blood around your body.

STARTER

In a group.
Design an experiment to determine the pulse rate for each of the people in the group. Plan a fair test and then carry it out. How does exercise alter the pulse rate? Why?

The circulatory system

Cells need nutrients and oxygen in order to survive and grow. They also produce waste materials that must be taken away. The circulatory system brings food and oxygen to every cell of your body and takes away waste products. It also carries other things your body needs.

What is blood?

Blood is made up of a mixture of substances. A liquid called **plasma** carries dissolved gases, foods and waste materials. Plasma flows easily because it is mainly water. This enables blood to flow along the narrow tubes called capillaries.

The plasma contains **red blood cells**, **white blood cells**, and some tiny granules called **platelets**.

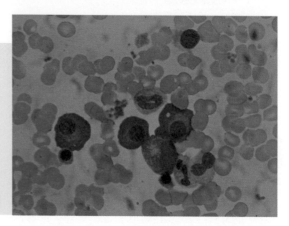

▶ Fig I

Red blood cells

Red blood cells are flattened and have no nucleus. They are filled with a red substance called **haemoglobin** that can catch oxygen. This is how the red blood cells carry oxygen around the body.

White blood cells

White blood cells protect the body from diseases caused by bacteria that enter the blood. One type of white blood cell can wrap itself around bacteria and digest them. Another type helps your body to make defensive chemicals called antibodies, which protect you from future attacks from the same bacteria (see Unit 46).

Platelets

These tiny granules pack themselves together whenever a blood vessel is damaged. They help to seal cuts and make the blood clot into a scab. Messages from white blood cells send out the alarm which tells the platelets where to go.

Pumping the blood

The heart is a pump made of powerful muscle. Each time it beats, it sends a spurt of blood around the body. You can feel this as a pulse. Blood travels out of the heart in blood vessels called **arteries** with strong, thick, elastic walls. Arteries become narrower and narrower as they go away from the heart.

ACTIVITY

On your own.
- Study Fig 2.
- Write down in your own words the route that blood takes from entering the heart at the right atrium to leaving the heart from the left ventricle.
- Why is this route taken?

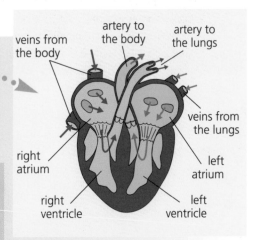

▲ **Fig 2** Vertical section of the human heart.

Very narrow blood vessels are called **capillaries**. The walls of capillaries are very thin so that nutrients and oxygen from the blood can leak out into the cells around them. At the same time, waste materials pass in the opposite direction.

Blood returns to the heart in **veins**. Veins do not need thick walls because the blood in them is not being forced hard by the heart. There is even a danger that the blood could stop flowing altogether. Veins therefore have **valves** to keep the blood moving and prevent it from going backwards.

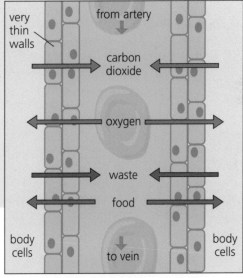

▶ **Fig 3** Capillary in tissue.

- In a group.
  - Design and make a board game that shows how blood moves around the body.
  - Players move by throwing dice and the blood cells (counters) must go through all four chambers of the heart and to the lungs, as well as flow around the body.

43 How we get our oxygen

KEY IDEAS

In this section of the book you will have opportunities to:
- Learn that the oxygen we need to stay alive comes from the air
- Describe how our lungs are adapted to allow gases to pass into and out of the blood.

STARTER

In a group.
Think back to the work you have done on burning. Produce a labelled diagram showing what is needed for fuels to burn. Also, show the products of burning.

Breathing

Your body cells need oxygen to obtain energy from sugars (see Unit 39). Oxygen is transported by the blood (see Unit 42). This oxygen enters the blood in your lungs.

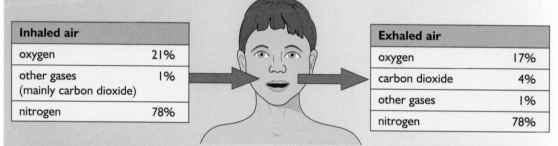

Inhaled air	
oxygen	21%
other gases (mainly carbon dioxide)	1%
nitrogen	78%

Exhaled air	
oxygen	17%
carbon dioxide	4%
other gases	1%
nitrogen	78%

▲ **Fig 1** Your body has changed the composition of the air between breathing in and breathing out.

Taking air into the lungs is called **breathing**. Breathing in is called **inhalation**. Breathing out is called **exhalation**. Every breath you inhale contains a mixture of gases. Every breath you exhale also contains a mixture of gases but the proportions have changed.

ACTIVITY

With a partner.
- Discuss the composition of inhaled and exhaled air.
- How has the air changed between inhaling and exhaling?
- Write down why you think this is so.

How do we breathe?

Every time you inhale, the muscles between your ribs tighten. This lifts your ribs upwards and outwards. At the same time, your diaphragm tightens and moves downwards. This increases the space inside your chest, which pulls air in to fill up the extra space inside your lungs.

Every time you exhale, the muscles between your ribs relax and allow your ribcage to collapse. At the same time, your diaphragm relaxes and moves upwards. This reduces the space inside your chest and pushes air out of your lungs.

Connections

This work builds on your earlier work on food, digestion and health. It leads on to further work on fitness and health at Key Stage 3 and finally to blood and circulation at Key Stage 4.

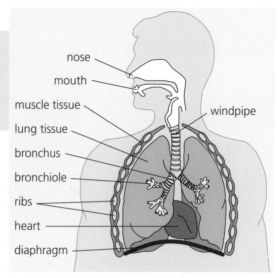

▲ **Fig 2** Inside your chest.

The structure of your lungs

When you inhale, air flows from your nose or mouth into your windpipe. This divides into two smaller tubes called **bronchi**. One bronchus goes to each lung. There they divide into smaller tubes called **bronchioles**. The bronchioles carry on branching until they finally end in tiny air sacs called **alveoli**. Alveoli make the lung tissue spongy (see Fig 3).

The alveoli increase the surface area of the lungs many times. Each alveolus contains a net of blood capillaries. The walls of the alveoli are very thin and the walls of the capillaries are very thin so it is easy for gases to pass between them. It is here that oxygen from the air enters the blood and unwanted carbon dioxide leaves the blood.

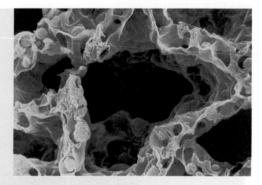

▲ **Fig 3**

This is called **gas exchange**. Oxygen in the blood is sent from the lungs to the heart and then pumped around the body. Carbon dioxide in the alveoli is exhaled.

REVIEW

● In a group.
  ○ Take it in turns to count how many times you breathe every minute. This is your breathing rate.
  ○ Take some gentle exercise and then count your breathing rate again. What happens?
  ○ Discuss why do you think it happens?
  ○ Write down your ideas so you can discuss them with other groups.

🏠 Many scientists have studied breathing and circulation. Carry out research on two of them, listed below. Find out what they studied and how it has helped our understanding of the human body.

Galen   Vesalius   Harvey   Withering   Ibn-al-Nafis

44 Respiration

KEY IDEAS

In this section of the book you will have opportunities to:
- Explain how oxygen is used to break down food in your cells and release energy
- Describe how glucose is broken down to carbon dioxide and water during aerobic respiration.

STARTER

With a partner.
Discuss why it would be impossible for living things to get energy from food by just burning them. Write your ideas down and prepare to discuss them with other groups.

Energy from sugars

A glucose molecule can dissolve in blood and is small enough to pass into cells. It also releases energy very easily. If glucose catches fire, a flash of heat is released.

Cells do not burn glucose by setting fire to it but the end result is the same. Cells release energy from glucose gradually, in stages. At each stage the energy is either used to stay alive or stored to be used later. To do this the cell must:

1. use enzymes to break down the glucose slowly

2. store the energy that is released in a large molecule that works a little like a battery storing electricity.

▲ **Fig 1** Glucose burns in air to give **carbon dioxide** and **water**. The energy is released in one step.

The energy storage molecule can stay in a cell until it is needed. Cells that need large amounts of energy in a hurry, e.g. muscle cells, contain many of these molecules. It is important to realise that animal **and** plants cells obtain their energy from breaking down glucose in this way.

Respiration

Glucose is broken down in stages (see Fig 2 opposite). First the molecule is broken in half to make two smaller molecules. This gives out a small amount of energy.

Before it can break down the glucose any further the cell must have oxygen.

Oxygen allows the cell to break the glucose down completely. This process is called **aerobic respiration** because it uses oxygen. In aerobic respiration, all the **hydrogen** from the glucose joins up with the **oxygen** to make **water**. This is already a normal part of your

▶ Fig 2

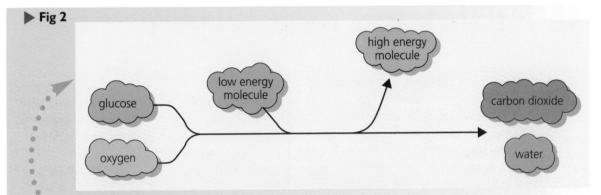

body. All the **carbon** joins up with **oxygen** to make **carbon dioxide**. Carbon dioxide dissolves in the blood and goes to the lungs to be breathed out. A word equation for respiration is given below.

glucose + oxygen → carbon dioxide + water + energy

ACTIVITY

With a partner.
- Study Fig 2.
- Make a list of the reactants and the products.
- Discuss how these compare to the products and reactants when glucose burns.
- What is the difference between respiration and burning?

Energy without oxygen

If you run very fast your muscles use up a lot of energy. Your blood tries to carry as much oxygen to your muscles as it can but sometimes it cannot work fast enough to keep up. When this happens, the sugar in your muscle cells cannot break down completely. This is known as **anaerobic respiration**. The cells turn the half-broken-down glucose into an acid called lactic acid that can give you cramp. Some living things, such as yeast and bacteria, produce enough energy using anaerobic respiration to live with little or no oxygen. These organisms produce acids and alcohols that are useful to us. The biotechnology industry uses this fact to produce many useful products, including alcoholic drinks.

REVIEW

- In a group.
  - Design a leaflet that explains to somebody who knows nothing about Science why your arms will get cramps if you hold a heavy weight for a long time.

 Connections

This work builds on your earlier work on food, digestion and health. It leads on to further work on fitness and health at Key Stage 3 and finally to blood and circulation at Key Stage 4.

45 Health and microorganisms

KEY IDEAS

In this section of the book you will have opportunities to:
- Explain how we catch some diseases
- Explain how bacteria and viruses can affect health.

STARTER

In a group.
Some microorganisms are very useful; others are harmful. Make a list of some of the useful and harmful things that microorganisms can do.

Microorganisms

Microorganisms are so small you need a microscope to see them. Two main types of microorganisms that can cause disease are **bacteria** and **viruses**.

Bacteria

There are millions of bacteria everywhere you go. Your skin is covered in them and they are present in air, water and soil. Most are harmless and many are useful. Yoghurt is one good thing made by bacteria.

Some bacteria can cause diseases. If these bacteria enter our bodies and start to multiply we say we have an **infection**. Bacteria can enter your body in different ways.

from the air you breathe

from the food you eat

from contact with infected people

from the water you drink

through cuts in your skin

from contact with some animals

▼ Fig 1

A person with a chest infection may cough and sneeze. This sprays tiny drops of water into the air (see Fig 1). The water can contain the bacteria that caused the infection. Breathing in the bacteria can give the infection to somebody else.

Bacteria can also get into drinking water. This may happen if sewage goes into rivers without being cleaned. Drinking infected water can make you ill. A disease called cholera is spread in this way.

Bacteria can get into our mouth from our fingers. It is very important to wash our hands after visiting the toilet. This is especially true if we are going to handle food, because bacteria from a person's hands can infect other people who eat the food.

Cooking food kills many bacteria because they cannot survive high temperatures. But it is important to cook food thoroughly. Each year there are thousands of cases of food poisoning caused by undercooked food. It is important to know that bacteria like to grow in warm, moist places.

ACTIVITY

With a partner.
- Use your knowledge of how bacteria can be spread to write down some rules that people working in restaurants should follow.

Your skin helps to keep bacteria out of your body. If bacteria enter through a cut they may cause an infection. One serious infection that comes from soil is called tetanus. Washing cuts thoroughly and keeping them clean while they heal helps to prevent infections.

Some animals such as flies and rats can carry bacteria that cause diseases in humans. These animals may pass the bacteria on by biting or by infecting food or water. An animal that passes on bacteria in this way is called a **vector**. Plague bacteria are carried from rats to humans by rat fleas.

Some diseases are caught by touching a person who is ill. These are called contagious diseases. Some diseases are passed on during sexual intercourse. These are called **sexually transmitted diseases** (STDs).

▲ **Fig 2** Flies can carry bacteria from faeces to uncovered food.

Viruses

Viruses are much smaller than bacteria but can be spread in the same ways. Viruses multiply inside a living cell. Viruses are only genetic material inside a protein coat. They must use the cytoplasm of other cells in order to multiply. The virus takes over the cell and more viruses are produced. The cell bursts open and the viruses escape and infect other cells. Colds, influenza, chicken pox and smallpox are caused by viruses.

REVIEW

- In a group.
  - Look up the examples of diseases mentioned in these pages.
  - Make a table that shows which diseases are caused by bacteria and which are caused by viruses.
  - For each disease write down one way that the spread of the disease could have been halted.

46 Your body's defence system

KEY IDEAS

In this section of the book you will have opportunities to:
- Explain that the body has natural defences against disease
- Explain the role of skin, white blood cells and the immune system in fighting disease.

STARTER

In a group.
Make a group list of any illnesses you have had in the past year. Discuss how you felt, how long you felt ill and how you recovered.

Defence

Your body's three main natural lines of defence are your skin, white blood cells and **immune system**.

Skin

Skin is a natural barrier against infection. Every normal opening in your body has special defences. Your nose contains hairs and mucus which help to trap microorganisms. Your ears have hairs and wax and your eyes have eyelids and tears. Tears help to wash dust away and contain chemicals that kill bacteria. Your body has other lines of defence against bacteria and viruses that get past the skin.

White blood cells

When bacteria enter a cut in your skin, platelets (see Unit 42) help to seal up the cut while white blood cells move to the site of the damage. Some white blood cells directly attack bacteria and destroy them (see Fig 1). This may also kill the white blood cells. Dead white blood cells are part of the pus in an infected cut.

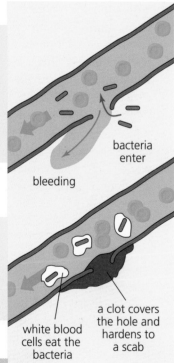

bacteria enter

bleeding

white blood cells eat the bacteria

a clot covers the hole and hardens to a scab

▲ Fig 1

ACTIVITY

With a partner.
- Discuss why white blood cells are an important defence against infection.
- Produce a series of drawings to explain how your body defends itself against bacteria entering a cut.

The immune system

Your body can recognise that bacteria and viruses are invaders. It produces special proteins called **antibodies** to fight them. Antibodies stick to bacteria or viruses and make it easier for your body to destroy them (see Fig 2). Your body makes a special antibody for every bacterium and virus it meets.

The first time you are infected with a new microorganism a new antibody has to be made. During this time you may feel unwell.

If you are ever infected again with the same microorganism the antibodies are made much quicker. This is why it is unusual to catch some diseases twice. Your body already has some immunity.

Some diseases attack the immune system and make it less effective. HIV is a virus that does this. The virus destroys the white blood cells and this makes the person more open to other infections. Some people have to have their immune system deliberately closed down by medicines. This can reduce the risk of transplant patients rejecting their new organs. However, it does mean they can more easily catch diseases.

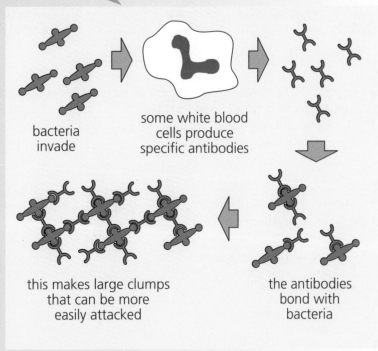

bacteria invade

some white blood cells produce specific antibodies

the antibodies bond with bacteria

this makes large clumps that can be more easily attacked

▲ Fig 2

An important way to protect your body from disease is to have a healthy diet and a healthy lifestyle. People who do not eat a balanced diet, take drugs or have stressful lives are more open to becoming ill. Being run down in this way can allow bacteria to invade. Also, the normal bacteria in our bodies that do us no harm often protect us from invaders. If we lose these normal bacteria we are more open to infection.

REVIEW

- In a group.
  - Design five questions about how our body protects us from infection.
  - Swap questions with a nearby group.
  - How many of their questions can you answer without checking the book?

47 Helping your body's defences

KEY IDEAS

In this section of the book you will have opportunities to:
- Explain that immunisation can help the natural defences of your body
- Explain that medicines can help the natural defences of your body.

STARTER

In a group.
Make a list of any injections or jabs you have had to protect you from diseases. Discuss these and see if the group members have had similar or different experiences.

Helping your body's defences

Your immune system cannot protect you from a really dangerous disease that could kill you before you have time to make antibodies. Luckily, doctors and scientists have found a way of safely starting up your immune system before you catch a serious disease. This is called immunisation or vaccination.

▶ **Fig I**

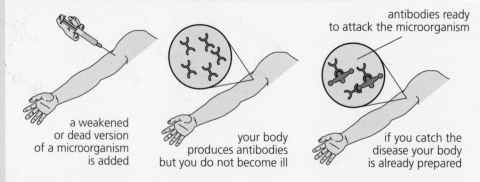

antibodies ready to attack the microorganism

a weakened or dead version of a microorganism is added

your body produces antibodies but you do not become ill

if you catch the disease your body is already prepared

A weak or dead microorganism can work on your immune system as well as a strong one can. Your body will make antibodies even if the microorganism is too feeble to hurt you. Weakened or dead organisms can be used to make a vaccine which can be injected into your body (see Fig 1) to protect you in the future. If you catch a serious disease after being vaccinated against it, your body will be able to beat the disease. You may not even know that you caught it.

Vaccinations for children

An important way of improving health in a large population is to carry out vaccinations on a large scale. This can be started from a very young age. Babies as young as two months old are vaccinated to protect them from a range of diseases. Vaccination continues as part of a set programme until people are fifteen years old (see Table 1 for some examples). Not all people agree with vaccinations and there are some risks attached to some vaccines.

Vaccination	Age
Diptheria, Tetanus, Whooping cough, Polio	2 months
Measles, Mumps, Rubella	15–18 months
Rubella	11–13 years (girls)
Tuberculosis (TB)	13 years

ACTIVITY

On your own.
- Find your age range in Table 1.
- Which vaccinations are you likely to have had?
- How does this compare with the list you made during the starter activity?

▶ **Table 1** Some vaccinations given to children.

Medicines

When we cannot prevent a disease we may need to use medicines to treat it. One group of medicines that have been very useful in treating diseases are the **antibiotics**. These chemicals kill bacteria but do not cause much damage to the cells of your body. They can work very quickly. Antibiotics are produced naturally by bacteria and fungi and this is used by the biotechnology industry. Antibiotics in very small doses will kill or prevent the growth of harmful bacteria.

Some bacteria are developing resistance against antibiotics because in the past they have been used too readily. These resistant bacteria can cause serious problems in hospitals and are sometimes known as 'superbugs'. Antibiotics do not work against viruses and so cannot be used to treat colds, flu and many other diseases.

Antibiotic	How it works
Penicillin	Prevents bacteria making a cell wall
Streptomycin	Prevents bacteria making proteins
Rifampicin	Prevents bacteria making genetic material
Sulphonamides	Interfere with the chemical reactions in the cytoplasm of bacteria
Polymyxin B	Breaks down the cell membrane of bacteria

▲ **Table 2** Some common antibiotics.

Connections

This work builds on earlier work on health and microorganisms. It is closely linked to work on fitness and health and leads on to further work on diseases.

REVIEW

- In a group.
  - Design an information sheet that explains the advantages of having children vaccinated. Remember to explain the background science but also remember that some people may disagree with vaccinations for a number of reasons.
- Ask for permission to collect some leaflets about vaccination from your doctor's surgery. Using the leaflets, make a list of the diseases that can be prevented by vaccination.

48 Investigating habitats

KEY IDEAS

In this section of the book you will have opportunities to:
- Review your knowledge of habitats
- Explain how sampling techniques are used to study habitats.

STARTER

In a group.
Make a list of five different habitats from around the world. Now pass your list to another group. When you receive a list try to write down one animal and one plant you might find in each habitat.

Surviving in a habitat

In order to survive in a habitat an organism must be able to obtain the essentials for life. Animals must have oxygen, food, water and shelter. Plants need sunlight, carbon dioxide, water and essential elements such as iron and magnesium. Living things also need space in which to move or grow.

▲ **Fig 1** The plants and animals in a habitat need the essentials for life.

Investigating habitats

Habitats may contain many different animals and plants. The animals and plants are the **biotic factors** in a habitat. It is also important to study the environmental factors in a habitat. These are called **abiotic factors** and these include temperature, moisture content, pH, light intensity and oxygen content. It is usually impossible to study every part of a habitat as it would take too long. It is essential to study parts of a habitat in a way that gives an accurate picture of the whole habitat. This is called **sampling**. It is important to sample in ways that make the investigation fair. This involves random sampling, so that areas are selected at random rather than the investigator choosing a place.

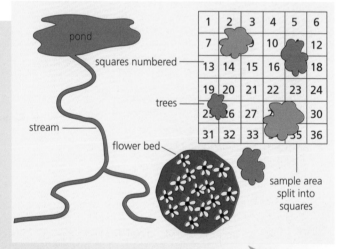

▲ **Fig 2**

Covering a map of the sample area with numbered squares (Fig 2) is a common way of obtaining random samples. Numbers can be selected at random using a computer program, throwing dice or drawing lots from a hat if necessary.

The methods used to study a habitat depend on the question being investigated. Commonly, scientists are trying to find out which organisms live in a habitat and how abundant they are.

Quadrats

A common way of studying the animals or plants in a habitat is to use **quadrats**. These are usually square metal frames that come in different sizes. The quadrat is set down at a place randomly selected and the animals or plants found in the quadrat are counted. Abiotic factors are also measured. This is done several times and the organisms recorded. The most abundant organisms are likely to be quadrat samples more often than less abundant organisms. This gives a good idea of the range of organisms throughout the habitat without having to study every part.

Number of quadrats used	Number of species found
1	10
4	8
8	30
16	32

▲ **Table 1** Types of quadrats used depends on the type of investigation.

With a partner.
- Discuss the advantages of using quadrats to study a habitat. Make a list.
- Now think about potential problems.
- Write down some examples of when quadrats would not be a good way of studying habitats.

Transects

A transect is a line placed across an area in order to study the living things found there. There are different ways of using transects (see Fig 3) but they are very useful for studying changes or trends across an area. For example, near the edge of a wood or across the seashore from low water to high water.

 sun   line transect   quadrat    shade

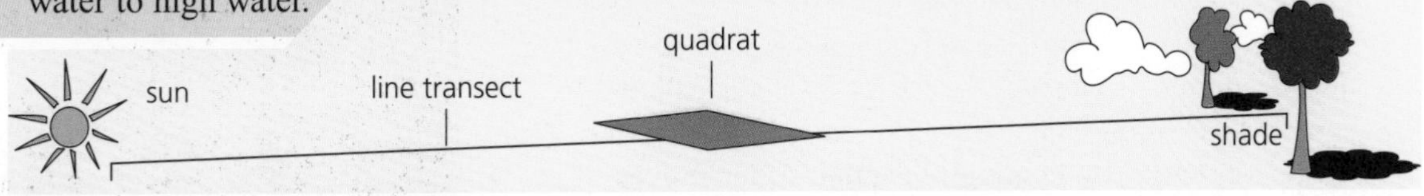

▲ **Fig 3** Belt and line transects are useful for looking at trends such as sun and shade.

REVIEW

- In a group.
  ○ Imagine you are about to undertake a field trip to a rocky shore at the coast.
  ○ Plan an investigation to measure the types and abundance of different seaweeds as you move from low water to high water.
  ○ Include the techniques you would use and the abiotic factors you would measure.

Draw a plan of your garden or a local park. Design a number grid for your plan so that the site is split into 20 equal-sized squares. Now select eight sample sites at random. Describe how you did this. Why is random sampling so important when studying habitats?

49 Adaptation and survival

KEY IDEAS

In this section of the book you will have opportunities to:
- Explain that some organisms can compete better than others
- Describe how these organisms contribute more offspring to the next generation.

STARTER

In a group.
Discuss some of the ways that giraffes are well adapted to survive in their African habitat. Include ways they can feed and avoid being eaten by predators. Make a list of your ideas.

Variation and survival

Every organism is slightly different from others of its species (see Units 10 and 79). Variation plays an important part in survival. A big, strong piglet will get more milk than a small, weak one. The biggest piglet will grow but the smallest one might not survive.

▶ **Fig 1** Some piglets are already stronger. They will be more successful in the struggle for milk than the weaker ones.

Other useful variations

Antelopes escape from predators by running fast. Natural variation will mean that some antelopes run faster than others. Even a small difference in speed might mean that another antelope is eaten instead.

Some animals hide instead of running away. They may be disguised to look like leaves or sticks. This is called **camouflage**. Many butterflies have wing markings that startle a predator by looking like a pair of large eyes. If some of the offspring of these animals look even more like a stick or have slightly better wing markings they will have a better chance of surviving.

There are two different varieties of a species of moth that normally sit on the bark of trees during the day. One variety is very dark and the other is very pale (see Fig 2). Both varieties occur in polluted and unpolluted areas, but the dark variety is more common in polluted areas and the light one is more common in unpolluted areas. The dark variety has better camouflage on sooty, polluted bark

▲ **Fig 2** Peppered moths.

where a pale moth is easy to spot. In unpolluted areas the opposite happens. Dark moths are easier to see on clean bark and more of them are eaten by birds. Keeping both varieties going means that some moths always survive, even when the level of pollution changes.

ACTIVITY

With a partner.
- Discuss what you think would happen to a brightly coloured stick insect.
- Write down your ideas and reasons.

Plants also vary. A plant that grows slightly taller than the rest can get more light. This will help it to grow even taller and collect even more light. The variation in height that gives the plant an advantage over other plants may be a disadvantage in a windy place, so plants also benefit from staying variable.

Natural selection

Characteristics that help a living thing to survive also help it to reproduce. The most successful organisms have most offspring. Their genetic material will be passed on to the next generation, which will also contain some individuals that are more successful than others. In this way a species becomes better adapted to its habitat. Living things that fail to adapt become **extinct**. Instead of selective breeding (see Unit 80) nature selects the survivors. This is called **natural selection**. Natural selection is sometimes known as the 'survival of the fittest' (see Fig 3).

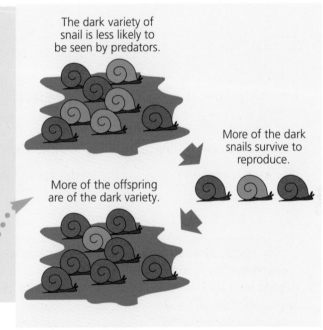

The dark variety of snail is less likely to be seen by predators.

More of the dark snails survive to reproduce.

More of the offspring are of the dark variety.

▲ **Fig 3** Organisms better adapted to their habitat will reproduce and have more offspring than less well-adapted individuals.

REVIEW
- In a group.
  - Study this list of plants and animals.

        polar bear   fir tree   mole   pike   whale   coconut palm   person
  - Name three characteristics of each that help it to survive in its environment.

50 Abundance and distribution

KEY IDEAS

In this section of the book you will have opportunities to:
- Describe what affects the size of a population
- Describe how competition and predation can limit the size of a population.

STARTER

In a group.
When rabbits were first introduced to Australia they reproduced very quickly and soon became a major problem. Discuss why you think the rabbit population increased so quickly.

Populations

A **population** is the number of organisms of the same species living in the same area at the same time. The total number of dandelions in a field is the dandelion population at the time they are counted. Populations change with time. One year later there may be a different number of dandelions in the same field.

Changes in population

Whether a population grows, shrinks or stays the same depends on the rate of arrival and the rate of departure. If more organisms arrive than leave the population will increase.

Rate of arrival = organisms being born + those moving into the area

Rate of leaving = organisms dying + those moving out of the area

The most important factors are the **birth rate** and **death rate**.

Disease and population growth

When a population increases, the organisms become more crowded. They may meet more frequently. This makes it easier for diseases to spread. A disease spreading through a population may kill some of the organisms and make the population smaller. As the space between organisms increases the disease spreads more slowly. If the disease does not kill too many organisms at once the population may remain fairly constant. If the disease is serious, the population may swing from one extreme to the other.

Competition and population growth

When a population increases each organism has a smaller share of space and food. There is more **competition**. About 100 years ago a few moose walked across a frozen lake to an island in Lake Superior. At first they had plenty of space and plenty of food. After 30 years the population had grown to 3000.

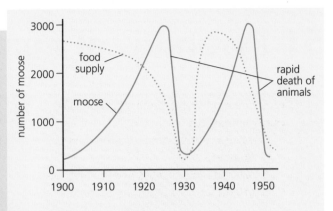

Soon after this 90% of the moose died of starvation. Then the plants grew back and the moose population started to grow again. Within 20 years the population had grown back to 3000 again, and again most of the moose starved.

Competition for food is one reason why larger animals normally defend a territory. The size of the territory will depend on how much food they need and how much is available. If there is plenty of food the territory can be small. If there is very little food they need a larger territory to supply enough to eat.

▲ **Fig 1** The moose population falls when competition for food increases.

ACTIVITY

With a partner.
- List some of the resources that animals in a habitat may be competing for.
- Use this information to explain why there are larger populations of animals and plants in rainforests than deserts.

Predation and population growth

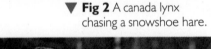

▼ **Fig 2** A canada lynx chasing a snowshoe hare.

A major cause of death for many animals is being eaten by other animals. A population of small animals such as mice, in an area with no predators will increase dramatically. Soon there will be thousands of mice. A predator such as a cat can help to control the population. There is a complex relationship between predators and **prey**. If a predator eats all the prey it will eventually die of starvation itself. Prey and predator populations are linked.

▶ **Fig 3** As the population of hares falls, so does the population of lynx. This is a typical example of a prey/predator relationship.

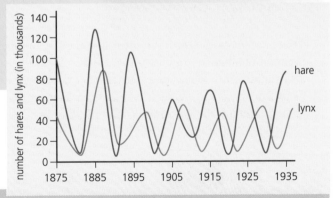

REVIEW

- In a group.
  - Fox populations are supposed to be higher in some cities than in the countryside.
  - Can you think of some reasons why this might be true?
  - Write your ideas down.

51 Pyramids of numbers

In this section of the book you will have opportunities to:
- Describe some examples of pyramids of numbers
- Explain the importance of pyramids of biomass.

In a group.
Discuss why a shark must eat many small fish in order to obtain enough energy to survive. Write down your ideas and prepare to discuss them with other groups.

Pyramids of numbers

Counting the numbers of organisms at each stage in a food chain gives us a **pyramid of numbers**.

The pyramid of numbers for the pond (see Fig 1) is what you would expect. As energy is lost at each stage, the secondary and tertiary consumers must always eat larger amounts of food than the stage below. Each stage is called a **trophic level**.

However, the pyramid for the tree looks different (see Fig 2). This is because one tree can produce lots of leaves for the caterpillars and other animals that eat them.

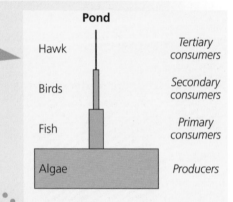

▲ Fig 1

▼ Fig 2

ACTIVITY

With a partner.
- Look back at the marine food web.
- Try to show one of the food chains as a pyramid of numbers.

There are many different types of pyramids of number. It isn't the number of organisms at a trophic level that is the important factor. What really matters is the amount of usable material and energy that can be passed to the next level. If **mass** was measured instead of numbers, the

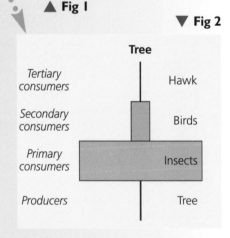

pyramid would always be the right way up. This would be a **pyramid of biomass**. This would make the tree pyramid of numbers look more like a real pyramid.

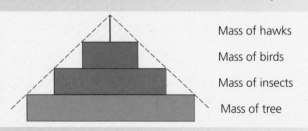

▲ **Fig 3** Pyramid of biomass.

Trophic levels and energy loss

Pyramid of biomass

A trophic level is the level at which a living thing is positioned within a food chain. A sheep is at a trophic level higher than grass. When a sheep eats grass, half the energy contained in the grass is used by the sheep just to keep it alive. Very little of the energy is trapped in the body of the sheep. An animal eating the sheep will gain very little of the energy that was in the grass. At each trophic level much of the energy is lost. This is why there are fewer animals at the higher trophic levels. They must eat large amounts of food to gain enough energy.

Connections

This unit builds on work on environment and feeding relationships and variation and classification. It links with work on disease, plants and the environment. It provides an important basis for your further work on plants for food.

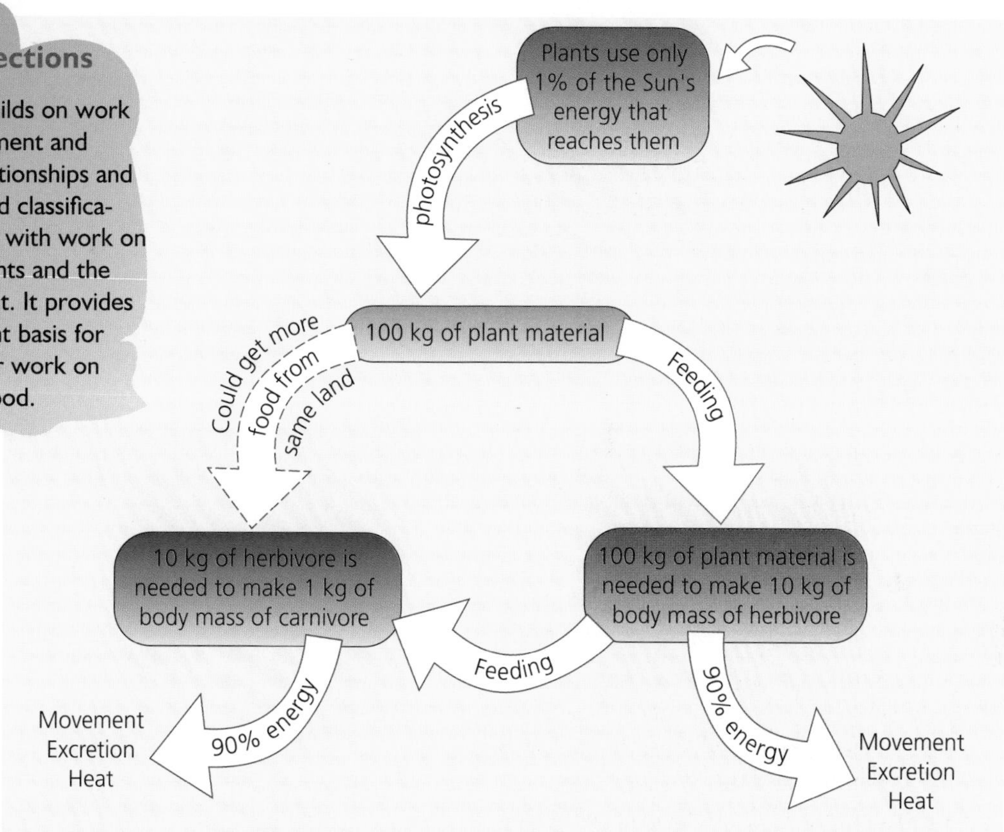

Plants use only 1% of the Sun's energy that reaches them

photosynthesis

100 kg of plant material

Could get more food from same land

Feeding

100 kg of plant material is needed to make 10 kg of body mass of herbivore

10 kg of herbivore is needed to make 1 kg of body mass of carnivore

Feeding

90% energy

Movement Excretion Heat

90% energy

Movement Excretion Heat

▶ **Fig 4**

- In a group.
  - Choose a vegetable, a fruit and an animal product you have eaten recently.
  - Place each food and yourselves into a food chain that shows how the energy in the food reached you and where it came from.
  - Which trophic level are you at for each food?

Try to find and cut out some pictures of plants and animals that form part of the same food chain. Arrange the animals and plants into a pyramid of numbers, showing each trophic level. Make the pictures into a clearly labelled display.

52 Atoms

A model of an atom

An atom is the smallest unit of an element. Each atom is made up of even smaller components called **sub-atomic particles**. These particles cannot be separated by chemical reactions.

We now believe that each atom contains a dense **nucleus** surrounded by **electrons**. The electrons are very small and fly around the nucleus at high speed. Most of the atom is empty space.

Electrons carry a negative electrical charge. The nucleus consists of two different types of particles called **protons** and **neutrons**. Protons carry a positive electrical charge. Neutrons carry no charge; they are neutral.

A single proton has the same mass as a single neutron. Electrons are much smaller than protons and neutrons. It takes 1850 electrons to make up the mass of one proton or neutron. Most of the mass of an atom is therefore in the nucleus where the protons and neutrons are clustered together.

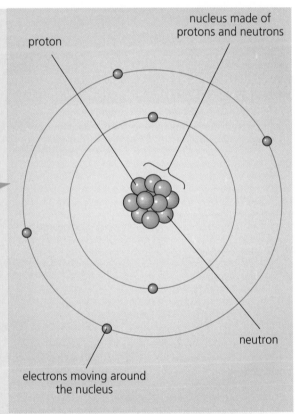

▲ **Fig 1** A simplified drawing of a single carbon atom. electrons were discovered in the early 20th century. The protons and neutrons in the atom's nucleus were discovered later. None of them can be seen: scientists worked out atomic structure by deduction.

Sub-atomic particle	Relative mass	Electrical charge
Proton	1	+1
Neutron	1	neutral
Electron	$\frac{1}{1850}$	−1

◀ **Table 1** The charges and masses of sub-atomic particles.

Atomic number

The electrical charge on a proton is exactly opposite to the electrical charge on an electron. Each atom of an element contains the same number of electrons as protons. The whole atom therefore has no electrical charge even though it contains positive protons and negative electrons. The number of protons or electrons in an atom is called its **atomic number**. Each element has its own unique atomic number.

ACTIVITY

With a partner.
● Discuss how we know that the number of protons and electrons in an atom are the same.
● Write your ideas down.

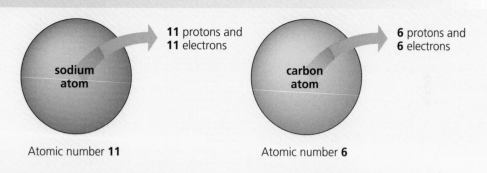

▲ **Fig 2** The atomic number for sodium is 11. This means that it has 11 protons and 11 electrons. The 11 positive charges cancel out the 11 negative charges.

The atomic number for carbon is 6. This means that it has 6 protons and 6 electrons. The 6 positive charges cancel out the 6 negative charges.

 Study tip

Explaining your ideas to a partner is a very good way of learning. Try to explain the structure of carbon and sodium atoms to another person.

● In a group.
 ○ Think back to the starter activity.
 ○ Using your knowledge of atomic structure explain and discuss any changes or improvements you wish to make to your ideas.

How many protons and electrons are in one atom of each of the following elements?
 Lead (atomic number = 82); magnesium (atomic number = 12); chlorine (atomic number = 17); iodine (atomic number = 53).
Which do you think has the heaviest atoms?
Which has the lightest ones?

53 Elements

KEY IDEAS

In this section of the book you will have opportunities to:
- Explain that elements consist of specific atoms
- Describe how the elements can be listed in order according to their atomic numbers.

STARTER

In a group.
Gold, hydrogen and carbon are very different substances. Discuss why you think this is the case. Write down your ideas and prepare to discuss them with other groups.

Elements

A substance that is made up of only one type of atom is called an **element**. There are over 100 different atoms, which means there are over 100 different types of element. Aluminium is an element. It is made up of nothing but aluminium atoms. They are different from the atoms in other elements. For example, lead atoms are heavier and larger than aluminium atoms. This is why lead is a heavier metal than aluminium.

Element	Type	Uses
Oxygen	gas	respiration; burning
Silicon	non-metal	electronic components; glass
Iron	metal	in steel for buildings and cars
Aluminium	metal	aircraft; cooking foil; cans
Sulphur	non-metal	fertilisers; dyes; paper-making
Carbon	non-metal	may be diamond (very hard) or graphite (very soft) in pencil 'lead'
Hydrogen	gas	fertilisers; margarine; plastics

▲ **Table 1** Some elements and a few of their uses.

Molecules

The atoms of most elements are normally linked together. Oxygen atoms in the air are normally linked in pairs. Each pair is called an oxygen **molecule**. Hydrogen and nitrogen also join up into pairs. Molecules do not have to be pure elements. Any group of atoms chemically linked together (e.g. water) is called a molecule.

A molecule is a single particle of a compound.

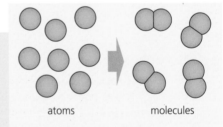

atoms   molecules

▲ **Fig 1** Oxygen atoms in the air join up into pairs to form oxygen molecules.

ACTIVITY

With a partner.
- Discuss which of the following substances you think are mixtures, which are chemical compounds, and which are elements:

    air   iron   lemonade   sugar   soil
- How could you test your answers to see if they are correct?

The symbols for elements

There are more than 100 different elements. Scientists often have to write their names down many times. To make this easier, each of the elements is given a short **symbol**. The symbol for an element usually comes from the first one or two letters of its full name. The symbol for carbon is C, which is easy to understand. Some elements have symbols that are more difficult to work out. This is because ancient scientists preferred to use Latin words. The Latin word for lead is *plumbum*, which is why the symbol for lead is still Pb.

Some simple rules for chemical symbols.

1. The symbol is usually the first one or two letters of the name.

2. Sometimes the old name is used.

3. The first letter of a symbol is always a capital letter.

4. The second letter of a symbol is always a small letter.

5. Every element has a different symbol.

The symbols for some common elements are shown in the table opposite. Notice how calcium, carbon, copper and chlorine have been given different symbols because they all begin with the same letter of the alphabet.

▼ **Table 2** Some common elements with their symbols.

Element	Symbol	Element	Symbol
Aluminium	Al	Magnesium	Mg
Bromine	Br	Nitrogen	N
Calcium	Ca	Oxygen	O
Carbon	C	Phosphorus	P
Chlorine	Cl	Potassium	K
Copper	Cu	Silicon	Si
Gold	Au	Silver	Ag
Hydrogen	H	Sodium	Na
Iodine	I	Sulphur	S
Iron	Fe	Tin	Sn
Lead	Pb	Zinc	Zn

The Periodic Table

It is not especially helpful to list elements alphabetically. The atomic number of an element is much more important than its name. Scientists normally set out the elements in order of atomic number. They are also arranged according to the natural groups that they fall into. This arrangement is called the **Periodic Table**. A Periodic Table is shown on page 247.

The Periodic Table groups similar elements together in vertical rows. The Periodic Table is especially useful when we need to understand an element that we know very little about. Looking at where they come in the Table can also help us to predict how two elements may react together when they meet.

REVIEW

- In a group.
  - Produce a short radio script where a scientist is being asked questions about elements and the Periodic Table. Include the words:
    atom   symbol   atomic number   group

54 Word equations

Equations

The names of elements and compounds can be written in a shorthand way (see Units 53 and 92). This is also true for chemical reactions. The shorthand way of writing down a chemical reaction is called an **equation**. We shall begin by using the full names of the chemicals. This is called a word equation.

Word equations

A word equation is like a short sentence that summarises a chemical reaction. Some of the words from the sentence are changed into symbols to save space. Fig 1 shows the main symbols used and what they mean.

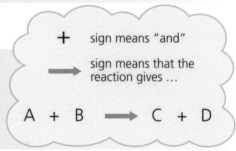

+ sign means "and"

→ sign means that the reaction gives …

A + B → C + D

▲ **Fig 1** Chemicals A and B were added together and a reaction happened. The reaction gave two new chemicals, C and D.

Some real reactions

Marble is made of calcium carbonate. This reacts with hydrochloric acid to give off carbon dioxide. Carbon dioxide makes the reaction fizzy. The reaction also produces calcium chloride and water. The word equation for this is:

calcium carbonate + hydrochloric acid → calcium chloride + water + carbon dioxide

The decomposition of limestone also occurs when it is heated. The word equation for this reaction would be:

calcium carbonate → calcium oxide + carbon dioxide

This tells us about the reactant and the two products. It does not tell us that the limestone was heated. We can add this information above the arrow. This is where we write information about the conditions that are needed to make a reaction happen.

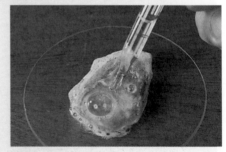

▲ **Fig 2** Acid fizzing on marble.

calcium carbonate $\xrightarrow{\text{HEAT}}$ calcium oxide + carbon dioxide

The word equation for photosynthesis is given in Unit 86. However, we can now look at it and understand what it means.

carbon dioxide + water $\xrightarrow[\text{CHLOROPHYLL}]{\text{LIGHT}}$ glucose + oxygen

Ammonia is manufactured by combining nitrogen and hydrogen. High temperature, high pressure and a catalyst are needed to make this happen.

ACTIVITY

On your own.
- Write down a word equation that shows how ammonia is made from nitrogen and hydrogen.

Reversible

You may see a double arrow in a chemical equation. It looks like this: $\rightleftharpoons$
The double arrow means that a reaction can go either way depending on the conditions. The reaction is **reversible**. In the right conditions the products can react together and change back into the reactants. When ammonium chloride is heated it breaks up into ammonia gas and hydrogen chloride gas. If the mixture of ammonia and hydrogen chloride cool together they combine to make ammonium chloride again.

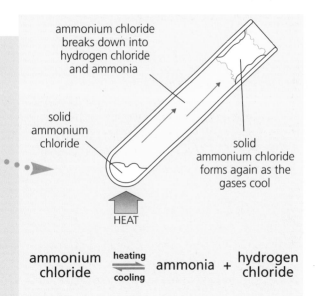

ammonium chloride breaks down into hydrogen chloride and ammonia

solid ammonium chloride

solid ammonium chloride forms again as the gases cool

HEAT

$$\text{ammonium chloride} \underset{\text{cooling}}{\overset{\text{heating}}{\rightleftharpoons}} \text{ammonia} + \text{hydrogen chloride}$$

▶ **Fig 3** Ammonium chloride can be made to split into ammonia and hydrogen chloride. This reaction can also go backwards if the mixture cools before the gases fly away.

REVIEW
- In a group.
  - Look back at your descriptions of the chemical reactions.
  - Try to write word equations for each one.
- 🏠 Try to write down a word equation for iron rusting in oxygen to give iron oxide. Use your experience to work out what the necessary conditions might be.

Connections

This unit is closely linked to work on the particle model studied in Year 7. The work will help you with further work on compounds and mixtures at Year 8 and chemical reactions in Year 9.

55 Elements, mixtures, compounds

KEY IDEAS

In this section of the book you will have opportunities to:
- Explain that substances can be mixtures, compounds or elements
- Explain that compounds are made when elements join together.

STARTER

In a group.
Think back to earlier work you have done on mixtures. Make a list of five different mixtures. For each one try to write down the chemicals that are mixed together.

Mixtures

A **mixture** is a collection of different substances that are not connected in any special way. A cup of tea is a mixture of hot water and chemicals from the tea leaves, perhaps with milk and sugar added.

Compounds

The water in your tea is not a mixture. Water is a **compound**. It cannot be 'unmixed'. The only way to divide water into its separate parts is by a chemical reaction. When water is divided chemically it breaks up into hydrogen gas and oxygen gas.

Atoms

If we could look at the hydrogen gas from the water, we would find that it is made up of many tiny particles. All the particles are exactly the same. They are called **atoms**. It is almost impossible to see atoms because they are so small. You would need to line up at least 2 billion atoms to span one metre. Each atom is made up of an exact number of even smaller parts (see Unit 52).

Making compounds

A compound is made when two or more elements join together. Not all elements will combine easily with others. Some, such as neon and argon, will not combine at all. They are **inert**. Elements such as sodium and chlorine combine very easily. They are highly reactive. When elements do combine they follow certain rules.

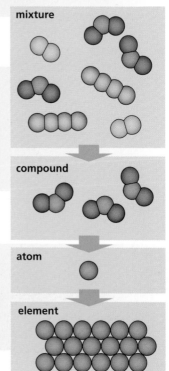

▶ **Fig 1** Particles in different substances.

Metals and non-metals

Elements can be divided into metals and non-metals (see Fig 2). Metals never combine with other metals to make chemical compounds. Compounds can only be formed between:

1. metals and non-metals
2. non-metals and other non-metals.

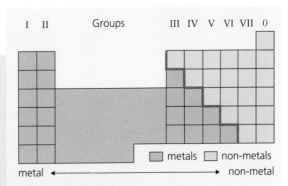

▲ **Fig 2** The Periodic Table divided into metals and non-metals.

ACTIVITY

With a partner.
● Discuss why there is no such compound as sodium magnesium.
● Write down the names of two compounds that do contain sodium.

A compound gets its name from the elements in it. If one of the elements is a metal then this comes first in the name. The names of the other elements in the compound are changed slightly so that we know the substance is a compound and not a mixture. Oxygen in a compound often becomes oxide. Chlorine often becomes chloride.

Chemical reactions

When carbon is burned in air it joins with the oxygen and makes carbon dioxide. This is a chemical reaction. Carbon and oxygen are elements but carbon dioxide is a compound. Carbon dioxide is a totally new substance. It does not behave like carbon or like oxygen. It does not behave like a mixture of carbon and oxygen. It has its own unique properties.

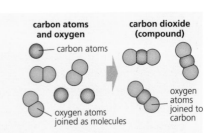

▲ **Fig 3** One carbon atom combines with two oxygen atoms to make one molecule of carbon dioxide.

sodium is a reactive metal

chlorine is a poisonous gas

sodium chloride is the salt we add to our food

A dramatic change between the elements and the compound they form is seen in sodium chloride (Fig 4).

◀ **Fig 4**

REVIEW

● In a group.
  ○ Identify the elements contained in each of the following compounds:
     iron oxide lead sulphide magnesium chloride
  ○ Which of the elements are metals?

🏠 Carry out a survey of food labels. List any compounds that are named. What do the names tell you about the elements that make up the compound?

56 Mixtures and separation

KEY IDEAS

In this section of the book you will have opportunities to:
- Review your understanding that mixtures contain substances that are not chemically combined
- Explain how some mixtures can be separated into their component parts.

STARTER

In a group.
Discuss how you would separate salt from a mixture of salt and sand. Write down your ideas as a plan.

Mixtures

Mixtures contain more than one substance. A mixture can contain solids, liquids or gases but these substances are not chemically joined.

This means that the materials in a mixture can be separated without using chemical reactions.

Types of mixtures

Mixtures can be made of substances in the same state or in different states. Solids can be mixed with other solids, or can be mixed with liquids and gases. Table 1 shows some examples of mixtures.

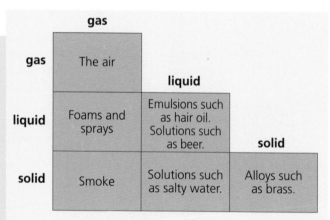

	gas	liquid	solid
gas	The air		
liquid	Foams and sprays	Emulsions such as hair oil. Solutions such as beer.	
solid	Smoke	Solutions such as salty water.	Alloys such as brass.

▶ **Table 1** Some different kinds of mixtures.

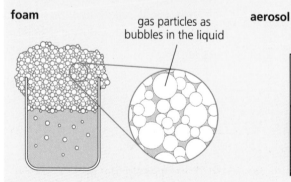

foam

gas particles as bubbles in the liquid

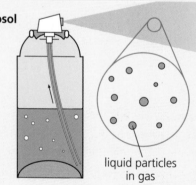

aerosol

liquid particles in gas

◀ **Fig 1** Deodorant sprays and shaving foams are mixtures of gases and liquids.

Gases can be mixed with gases. The air is a mixture of gases. Air contains oxygen, carbon dioxide and nitrogen and some other gases (see Unit 43). We know that the gases in air are not combined because we can easily remove oxygen from the air we breathe.

▶ **Fig 2** Foam is a mixture of air and water. Sea water is also a mixture. It has solids and gases dissolved in it.

Separating mixtures

As you have seen in earlier work there are many different types of mixtures. They each require their own special methods for separating. Different mixtures are separated in different ways.

Filtration

When working in a dusty environment it is essential to wear a breathing mask with a filter inside. This will trap the dust and prevent it from entering your lungs. Molecules of gases will be too small to be trapped by the filter in the breathing mask. This means that air can pass through. It also means that any toxic gases will also pass through so the mask can only be used to protect you from dust and large particles.

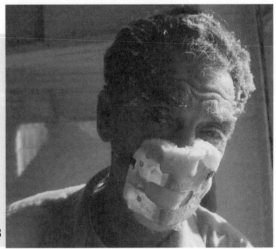

▶ **Fig 3**

ACTIVITY

With a partner.
- Discuss why it is not possible to separate salt from sea water by filtration.
- Write down your ideas.

REVIEW

- In a group.
  - Look back at the starter activity.
  - Now discuss how you would separate a mixture of sand, salt, water and alcohol into its constituents.
  - Write down your plan. Hint: you may need to use more than one method.

- Make a list of some of the mixtures you can find at home. Try to classify them into groups, e.g. gas in gas, gas in liquid, solid in liquid.

57 Melting and boiling points

KEY IDEAS

In this section of the book you will have opportunities to:
- Explain that different substances have specific melting and boiling points.

STARTER

In a group.
Discuss examples of melting and boiling that you have seen. Make a list. What happens to the particles in substances when they melt or boil?

Melting and freezing points

Materials can exist as solids, liquids or gases. When materials change between these states their particles either get closer together or move further apart. This usually happens when the substance is heated or cooled.

When a solid is heated it will eventually turn into a liquid. In other words, it will melt. The temperature at which this happens is called the **melting point**. When a liquid is cooled it will eventually turn into a solid. The temperature at which this happens is called the **freezing point**. Melting and freezing points are the same. Each substance has its own melting and freezing point. This is why melting points or freezing points can be used to identify chemicals.

The freezing point of pure water is 0°C. Adding a substance such as sodium chloride (table salt) changes the freezing point. Salty water freezes at a much lower temperature. This is why salt is sometimes spread on roads in winter.

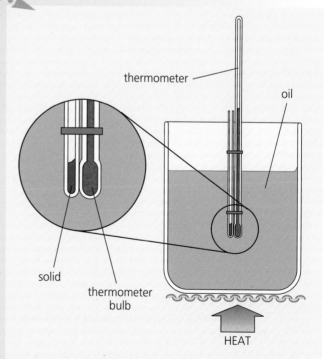

▶ **Fig I** Every pure substance has its own special melting point, which is the same as its freezing point. This is one way to test how pure a solid substance is.

Boiling point

When a liquid is heated it changes state from liquid to gas. As the temperature rises, bubbles of gas begin to form in the liquid. This happens at the **boiling point** of the substance. Every pure substance has its own unique boiling point, just as every pure substance has its own unique melting/freezing point.

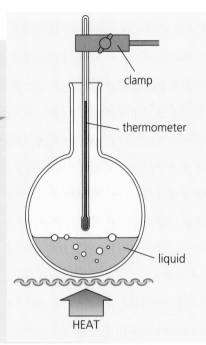

ACTIVITY

With a partner.
● Discuss why the water in an aluminium pan will boil but the pan will not melt.

The boiling point of a liquid can be changed by adding another substance. It is also affected by air pressure. As you go up a mountain the air gets thinner and the air pressure falls. At sea level, water boils at 100°C; up a mountain it may boil at 80°C.

▲ **Fig 2** Every pure substance has its own special boiling point. This is one way to test how pure a liquid substance is.

Room temperature and state

We usually think of water as a liquid, iron as a solid and oxygen as a gas. This is the state they are in at room temperature, which is about 25°C. It only seems normal to us because this is our normal temperature. Room temperature on Mars and Venus would be totally different. Water, oxygen and iron would be in different states there.

Temperature	−218°C	25°C	200°C	2000°C
Oxygen state	solid	gas	gas	gas
Water state	solid	liquid	gas	gas
Iron state	solid	solid	solid	liquid

▲ **Table I**

↻ Connections

This work builds on earlier work on the particle model of substances. It is closely linked to ideas about atoms and elements and the ideas will be useful when studying rocks. The work is an important basis for work in Year 9 when you will be studying chemical reactions in more detail.

REVIEW

● In a group.
  ○ Decide which of the following would be a liquid, a solid or a gas at 500°C and at −200°C:
  a nitrogen **b** lead **c** iodine.

⌂ Research the melting and boiling points of some common substances. Select two that are solid, two that are liquid and two that are gases at room temperature (25 °C).

58 Rocks and landscape

KEY IDEAS

In this section of the book you will have opportunities to:
- Explain what rocks are made up of
- Describe how the type of rock in an area affects the landscape.

STARTER

In a group.
List some examples of rocks you have studied during earlier work. For each rock, write a description. Now discuss which rock would be best for making the steps outside a building.

Rocks

Rocks are found everywhere beneath the surface of the Earth. The rocks may be hidden by soil, roads or buildings but they are still there. These rocks form many of the features of our **landscape**.

The rock of Devil's Tower (Fig 1) is very hard. Softer rock around it has been worn away. This has left the tower standing on its own.

▲ **Fig 1**

What are rocks?

You may think that rocks are hard and solid. Many of them are but it may surprise you to find out that sand and mud are rocks. Rocks are made up of smaller particles called **minerals**. Minerals are pure substances but most rocks are a mixture of different minerals. In hard, solid rocks such as granite and sandstone the mineral particles are held tightly together. In sand, mud and peat the particles are not held tightly together. They are loose.

▲ **Fig 2** In granite the minerals are held tightly together. In sand the minerals are loose.

ACTIVITY

With a partner.
- Draw a diagram that explains the difference between the arrangement of particles in granite and in sand. Which would be washed away by rain most easily?

Rocks and landscape

There are many different types of rock and each is made in a different way (see Units 61–63). Each type of rock has its own characteristic **properties**. Properties are split into physical and chemical properties. Hardness is an example of a physical property. An example of a chemical property is whether a rock reacts with acids or not.

Rocks are used for many things. Sandstone is used for making buildings. Marble is used for statues and for decorating buildings. Slate is useful as a roofing material. These uses are linked to the property of the rock. A very soft rock could not be used for buildings. A **porous** rock could not be used for roofing tiles.

In nature the properties of rocks influence the landscape. Soft rocks can easily be worn away. This can form valleys and bays (see Fig 3). Harder, more resistant rock is not easily worn away. These rocks can form cliffs, headlands, hills and mountains.

The cave in Fig 4 has formed because acidic water has reacted with the limestone. Granite does not react with acids easily and no caves are found in granite. The chemical properties of limestone have helped to shape the landscape.

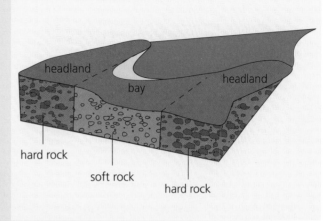

▲ **Fig 3**

▲ **Fig 4**

- In a group.
  - Discuss how the physical and chemical properties of rocks can shape the landscape.
  - Draw a large poster to show some examples.

Research the following landscape features:
   canyon   tor   glaciated valley   stack
For each one write down how the type of rock has helped to form the feature.

59 Weathering and erosion

KEY IDEAS

In this section of the book you will have opportunities to:
- Explain that the rocks of the Earth are constantly breaking down
- Describe how the forces of expansion and contraction can break rocks down.

STARTER

In a group.
Think about your journey to school. Try to list some examples of rocks that have been naturally damaged over time. Write down some possible causes of this damage.

Changing rocks

You only need to look at old gravestones to see that rock does not last forever. Many old gravestones are difficult to read. Their surfaces may be broken and peeling. Our world is constantly being changed by the weather.

▶ **Fig 1**

Weathering of rocks

When a rock is changed by natural forces we say that it is weathered. This process is called **weathering**. It may happen in one or more ways. The acid in rain can start to attack the rock. This can be seen in Fig 1. The statues have also been exposed to the wind, rain and sun for centuries. Even plants can help to break down rocks. When they push their roots into tiny cracks in the rock, this makes the cracks a little bigger.

The heat of the day and the cool of the night

Rocks are a mixture of different substances. Rock expands when it is heated by the Sun. The different substances in the rock expand in different ways. This creates forces inside the rock. When the rock cools again, it will contract. Again, the different substances inside the rock will contract in different ways and at different speeds. After months and years of heating and cooling, the forces in the rock may eventually break it down. Heating and cooling can be very extreme in deserts or high up in the mountains. The days may be very hot and the nights can be very cold. The rock expands and contracts most at the surface, where the weather and sun can easily reach it. Sometimes the whole surface can peel away.

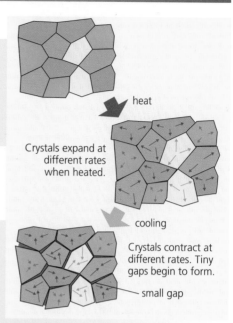

▶ **Fig 2** The substances in rock expand and contract according to the temperature.

Crystals expand at different rates when heated.

heat

cooling

Crystals contract at different rates. Tiny gaps begin to form.

small gap

Ice power

Many rocks contain tiny cracks. These cracks can fill with water every time it rains. Water can slowly wear away a rock or dissolve some of the substances in it but it will not damage the rock very quickly. Freezing water can damage rocks very quickly (see Fig 3). Unlike other liquids, water expands when it freezes. This can create pressure inside tiny cracks. When water in the cracks freezes and thaws over and over again, the cracks become wider and wider until the rock breaks down. This freeze-thaw action is very common in mountains. It is the reason why so many mountains are covered with sharp, broken rocks. A mass of ice-broken rock is called **scree**.

ACTIVITY

With a partner.
- Discuss why sharp, broken rocks are found on mountains but rounded rocks are found on beaches.
- Write down your answers.

Pieces of broken rock may be moved away by ice or rivers. They can be transported many kilometres. This is all part of a larger cycle called the rock cycle. You can find out more about the rock cycle in Unit 63.

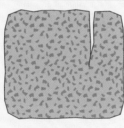
A rock with a small crack.

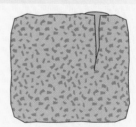
The crack fills with water.

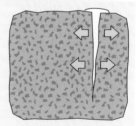
The water freezes and expands. This widens the crack.

▲ **Fig 3**

- In a group.
  - Think about how the rocks you discussed in the starter activity could have been weathered.
  - Write down your ideas.

60 Transport and sedimentation

KEY IDEAS

In this section of the book you will have opportunities to:
- Explain that eroded pieces of rock can be transported to other areas.

STARTER

In a group.
Discuss where the sand on a beach could have come from. Write your ideas down.

Weathering and transport

The rocks at the surface of the Earth are attacked by heat and cold, expanding ice, wind, rain and living things. They break down into smaller particles.

? What happens to these particles?

Fragments broken away from large masses of rock can either remain where they are or be moved somewhere else.

Soil and scree are usually formed from rock fragments that have not moved very far. It is easy to see that scree is the same as the bigger rocks. You may need a hand lens to find the rock fragments in soil.

Weathered rock can be carried away by:

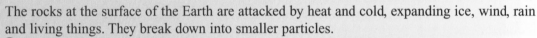

water   ice and snow   wind   gravity

Removal of material from the landscape is called **erosion**.

Water transport

Rivers can carry rock fragments away. As they bounce along in a fast flowing river the fragments rub against each other and the sides of the river. They become rounder and smaller as they go along.

Tiny particles worn away from rocks in a river are called **sediment**. When the flow of the river slows down the sediment settles to the bottom.

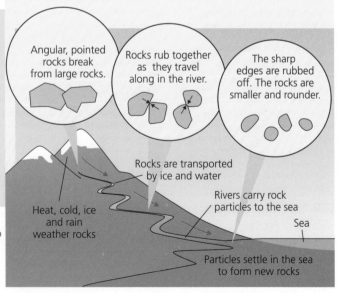

Angular, pointed rocks break from large rocks.

Rocks rub together as they travel along in the river.

The sharp edges are rubbed off. The rocks are smaller and rounder.

Rocks are transported by ice and water

Rivers carry rock particles to the sea

Heat, cold, ice and rain weather rocks

Sea

Particles settle in the sea to form new rocks

▶ **Fig 1** In their journey down a river to the sea, large sharp rocks gradually become small smooth pebbles.

With a partner.
- Explain why rocks become rounded as they are transported by rivers.
- Write down your ideas.

Glaciers

Glaciers are like giant frozen rivers. As the ice in the glaciers slowly flows down from mountains they cut deep valleys. The bottom of a glacier contains many broken pieces of rock. These rocks act like giant pieces of sandpaper. Rock in the path of the glacier is eroded and the fragments are transported. Deposits of these rocks can be seen along the edge and at the front of glaciers. They are called **moraines**. When the glaciers melt they leave behind deep U-shaped valleys and deposits of the eroded rock fragments.

▲ **Fig 2** Rocky moraines may be many kilometres long.

Desert deposits

Particles that are eroded from rocks in the desert become desert sands. These sands are easily blown by the wind. Large sand dunes are formed. When the wind is very strong it is possible to have sand storms. These storms can move a great deal of sand and cause roads and railway lines to be blocked. When the wind stops, the particles of sand are deposited in a new area.

Connections

This work builds on your earlier work on rocks and soil, acids and alkalis, and solutions. It is linked to work on mixtures and changes of state and forms the basis for following work on the rock cycle.

▲ **Fig 3** Desert sand dunes are blown into these shapes by the wind.

REVIEW

- In a group.
  - Design and make a large poster that shows the ways that fragments of rock can be eroded and then transported.
  - On the poster explain the difference between weathering and erosion.

Research some examples of how some deposited rock fragments are used commercially in industry and road building.

61 Rocks from fire

KEY IDEAS

In this section of the book you will have opportunities to:
- Explain how igneous rocks are formed.

STARTER

In a group.
Write down the names of as many different rocks as you can. Underline the rocks you think are the hardest and most resistant to weathering. Discuss why this might be the case.

Granite

Granite is a very hard type of rock. It does not weather easily. This is why it is often used for building. The reason why granite is so hard is that it is made up of **crystals** that are locked tightly together. The way a rock appears and feels is called its **texture**. The texture of granite tells us a lot about how it was made.

▶ **Fig 1** Granite is a tough rock that resists weathering.

Molten rocks

The crystals in granite were made when hot liquid rock called **magma** cooled down, millions of years ago. Magma comes from deep inside the Earth where it is very hot. Great pressures inside the Earth can force liquid magma upwards through weak parts of the Earth's crust (see Figs 2 and 3).

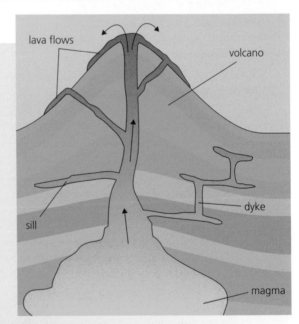

lava flows
volcano
dyke
sill
magma

▲ **Fig 2** Magma can reach the surface when a volcano erupts. It cools and forms solid rock.

◀ **Fig 3**

When magma reaches the surface it cools down and becomes a solid. Rocks formed in this way are called **igneous** – from *ignis*, an ancient word for fire.

Magma that reaches the surface cools very quickly and becomes lava. Magma that does not reach the surface cools more slowly. Deep underground, a pool of magma can remain hot for a long time. Small vertical **dykes** and horizontal **sills** may make and fill cracks in the surrounding rock. These cool down more slowly than lava but more quickly than big pools of magma.

When magma cools slowly there is a lot of time for crystals to grow. Slow forming crystals grow close together and interlock. This makes a hard and strong rock. Rocks that cool very slowly deep underground form very large crystals. Some of the crystals in granite are more than three centimetres long. The rocks in sills and dykes have smaller crystals but you can still see them quite easily. Magma that cools quickly at the surface forms very small crystals. You would need a hand lens to see them clearly.

ACTIVITY

With a partner.
- Describe how the size of the crystals in an igneous rock can give us clues about how it formed.

Interlocking crystals make many igneous rocks very strong and resistant to weathering. Igneous rocks with large crystals have cooled more slowly and were formed deep underground. The smaller the crystals are in an igneous rock the more likely it is that the rock was at or near the surface of the Earth when it cooled.

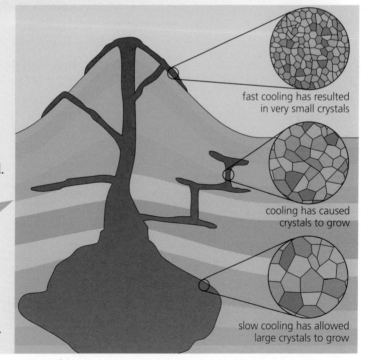

fast cooling has resulted in very small crystals

cooling has caused crystals to grow

slow cooling has allowed large crystals to grow

▶ **Fig 4** The largest crystals grow where magma cools most slowly.

REVIEW
- In a group.
  - Describe how a rock with large interlocking crystals could have formed.
  - Look for some examples on buildings. Hint: they are often polished to show the crystals.

62 Sedimentary rocks

KEY IDEAS

In this section of the book you will have opportunities to:
- Explain how sedimentary rocks are made.

STARTER

In a group.
Make a list of the different ways that particles of rock can be transported. Discuss what happens when the particles are deposited. Write down your ideas.

Formation of sedimentary rocks

The fragments of rock broken away from large masses of rock cannot be transported forever. Rock fragments being transported by rivers will eventually be deposited. This happens when the water arrives at a slow part of the river – or a lake or the sea. The sediment sinks to the bottom. Sediment can build up for millions of years until the weight of all the layers on top squashes the bottom layers into solid rock. Rock formed in this way is called **sedimentary rock**. Sedimentary rock often contains rounded particles. Rounded particles do not lock together as crystals do. They are held together by a weak cement made of smaller rounded particles mixed with chemicals. Because of the way they form, sedimentary rocks are usually found in layers.

As the particles enter the sea the biggest and heaviest ones sink first. Smaller particles move further away from the shore. The very smallest may be washed far out to sea and eventually sink to the bottom of the deepest oceans. This means that the size of the particles or grains in a sedimentary rock can give us a clue as to where they were formed. Marine sandstones are made from small grains of sand. They usually form near the coast. Mudstones are made from tiny particles of mud. They usually form in deep water far away from shore.

▼ **Fig 1** Sedimentary rock has rounded grains. Igneous rock has interlocking crystals.

sedimentary rock
(such as sandstone)

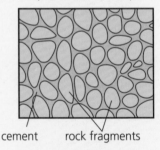

cement   rock fragments

igneous rock
(such as granite)

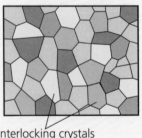

interlocking crystals

◄ **Fig 2** Diagram showing particle size and distance from shore.

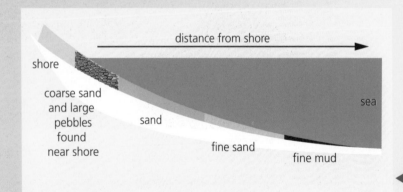

distance from shore

shore

coarse sand and large pebbles found near shore

sand

fine sand

fine mud

sea

Rock fragments that have not been transported very far will not be rounded. The pieces will be angular. If these angular pieces of rock eventually form a solid rock then it is called a **breccia**.

▶ **Table 1** Sedimentary rocks, grain size and shape.

Name	Grain size	Grain shape
Breccia	large	angular
Conglomerate	large	round
Sandstone	medium	round
Shale	medium and small	round
Mudstone	very small	flat plates or rounded

ACTIVITY

With a partner.
● Describe the differences between a breccia and a conglomerate.
● How does the appearance of the rocks give you clues about how they were formed?
● Write your ideas down.

Connections

This unit builds on your earlier work on rocks and weathering, and brings together ideas about particle theory, heating and cooling, and chemical reactions. The work leads on to further study of rocks at Key Stage 4.

Shells and rocks

Chalk and limestone are also sedimentary rocks. They are not made of rock grains but from the skeletons of long-dead water animals. When the animals died, their skeletons sank to the sea-bed. Over a period of millions of years they turned into rock in the same way as other sediments do. These rocks are made from the chemicals that the animals used to make their skeletons. They are easily attacked by acids and are often weathered by water to form tunnels and caves. The shells can be seen as **fossils** and these fossils tell us a lot about conditions in the past.

▲ **Fig 3** Fossil trilobites in a sedimentary rock.

REVIEW

● In a group.
  ○ Discuss the sedimentary rocks you have just studied.
  ○ Design an identification key to help other people find out which rock is which.

🏠 Shake up some soil and sand with water in a jam jar. Leave it to settle until the water clears. Which particles settle first? Why do layers form?

63 New rocks from old

Changing rock types

When magma erupts through the Earth's crust it comes into contact with rocks that are already formed. It makes these rocks very hot and may also create tremendous pressure. The heat and pressure can change the rocks. It may change them so much that they become a different type of rock.

▶ **Fig 1** The powerful forces that folded these rocks also changed their properties.

Metamorphic rocks

Rocks that have been altered by heat and pressure are called **metamorphic** rocks. 'Meta' means change and 'morph' means shape.

Limestone becomes marble when it is heated and squeezed by magma. Marble is a white rock with interlocking crystals. It is chemically the same and fizzes with acid like limestone does but it has a new structure. Marble is used to make statues and decorative buildings.

ACTIVITY

On your own.
- Explain how marble is different from limestone.
- Present your ideas as a table.

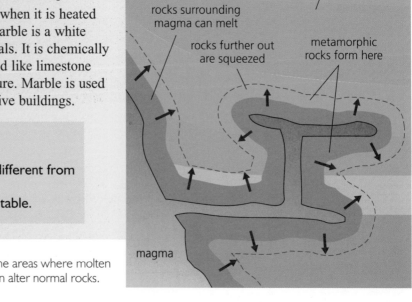

▶ **Fig 2** Some areas where molten magma can alter normal rocks.

Sandstone contains a lot of the **mineral** called quartz. When heated and squeezed by magma, its grains melt and turn into crystals called quartzite. Quartzite is a very hard rock.

Rocks that are a long way away from the magma may be only slightly changed by the heat. They may not look very different from the way they were before. A layer of coal might become a little harder and change to coke. This is something we can also do to coal, so it does not involve great heat or force.

High pressure alone can create metamorphic rocks. Mudstone becomes slate when it is compressed. This involves tremendous pressure, such as when the surface of the Earth is folded to make new mountains. Slate is still made of layers, as the mudstone was, but they are thin and hard. This is why slate is good for making roof tiles.

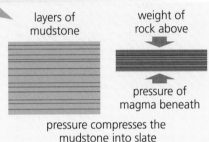

layers of mudstone   weight of rock above

pressure of magma beneath

pressure compresses the mudstone into slate

▶ **Fig 3** Layers of mudstone in a great upheaval like Fig 1 may be compressed into slate.

The rock cycle

▼ **Fig 4** The rock cycle.

Igneous, sedimentary and metamorphic rocks are all connected together in the **rock cycle**. Sedimentary rocks may take millions of years to form. Igneous rocks can form quickly, especially if they erupt out of a volcano. Metamorphic rocks are made wherever and whenever igneous rocks are forming. The whole cycle takes millions of years. The solid rocks that miners cut through to get our coal were fragments floating in a shallow sea more than 300 million years ago.

weathering and erosion

transport

metamorphic rocks

sedimentary rocks

melting

igneous rocks

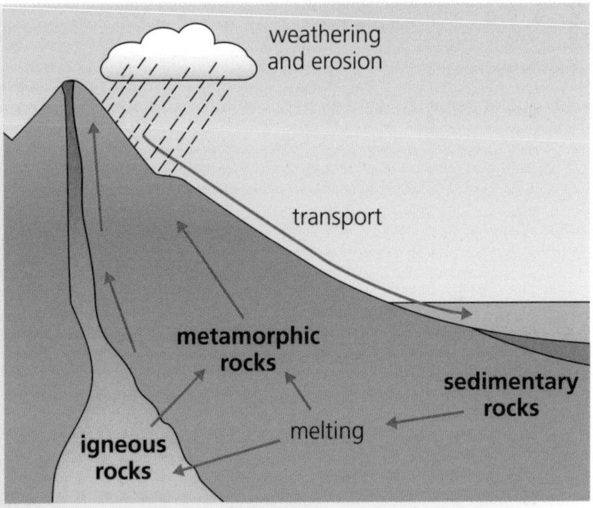

? Why is it called a cycle?

Igneous, metamorphic and sedimentary rocks are forming and being weathered all the time. New mountains are made and then eroded, sending new sediments into the sea. These sediments are hardening into rock that may be pushed up to create new mountain chains. Sea shells are often found in desert rocks, which isn't very surprising, but they are also found in the rocks at the top of Mount Everest. All these rocks were once beneath the sea.

REVIEW

● In a group.
  ○ Work together to write a short story to describe how a particle of granite from a mountain becomes a grain of sand in the sea and then a quartzite slab in a quarry.

🏠 Write a short newspaper article that describes how rocks on Earth are constantly being formed and re-formed. Include some diagrams to help you to explain your ideas.

137

64 Temperature and energy

In this section of the book you will have opportunities to:
- Explain the differences between heat, energy, and temperature
- Describe some different ways of measuring temperature.

In a group.
Discuss why people arriving in this country from hot countries might think the weather is cold, and people arriving from cold countries might think the weather is hot. Why are the terms hot and cold not always useful in science? Write down your ideas.

Heat and temperature

The word **heat** is used to describe a form of energy. The word **temperature** is used to describe how hot or cold an object is. These words are connected but they are not the same.

Measuring temperature

▶ **Fig 1**

A thermometer can be used to find out how hot a person is or how cold a refrigerator is. You may have used a thermometer at home or in a laboratory.

The thermometer in Fig 1 is measuring the temperature of the water. The temperature of the water can tell us how much energy is in the water molecules. We cannot measure the energy directly. We have to find out what effect the energy has on other substances.

Heating a substance makes it expand (see Unit 65). Liquids expand more then solids. Thermometers contain a small amount of liquid. Heat energy makes the liquid expand. As it expands, the liquid moves up the thin tube of the thermometer. We can see how far it moves by reading the scale.

▼ **Fig 2** Setting the scale on a thermometer.

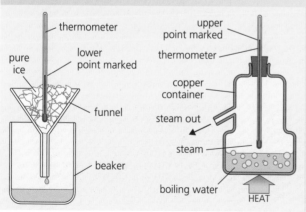

The scale on a thermometer is set by using two fixed points:

1. the boiling point of pure water
2. the freezing point of pure water.

The freezing point is fixed by putting the thermometer in ice and marking the top of the liquid. The boiling point is fixed by putting the thermometer in steam and making another mark. The gap between the upper and lower marks is divided into 100 equal parts. Each part represents one degree Celsius (°C).

Different thermometers

Scientific thermometers often contain mercury. Some thermometers contain alcohol. Alcohol is cheaper than mercury. A bimetal strip can also be used to measure temperature (see Unit 65). It is less accurate than a liquid-filled thermometer. Thermometers can also be made in other ways. Very accurate thermometers work electronically. Some thin plastic strips or discs contain dyes that change colour at different temperatures.

Mercury	Alcohol
expands easily, is accurate	sticks to glass, may not be accurate
high boiling point (360°C) and high freezing point (−37°C)	low boiling point (78°C) and low freezing point (−110°C)
warms up quickly	takes time to warm up
expensive	cheap
easy to see	needs added colour

▲ **Table 1** Mercury versus alcohol.

Energy and heat

A substance can contain a lot of energy without being hot. Sugar and coal are fuels. They contain energy all the time but this energy is only released when they burn. Burning fuels release heat energy that can raise the temperature of objects around them. Heat energy is measured in **joules** (J).

> Temperature is a way of describing how hot or cold a substance is compared with freezing and boiling water. We use a thermometer to measure temperature.
> The unit of temperature is the Celsius degree.

> Energy may be contained in a substance without giving it a high temperature.
> Energy is measured in units called joules.

65 Expansion and contraction

In this section of the book you will have opportunities to:
- Explain that materials expand and contract when they are heated
- Describe that expansion and contraction can create powerful forces.

In a group.
On hot days plastic windows open and close easily but aluminium windows may stick. Discuss why this might be the case.

What causes expansion and contraction?

When particles are heated they move faster and further apart. A substance therefore grows bigger when it is heated. This is called **expansion**. When the substance cools down the particles slow down and move closer together. The substance becomes smaller. This is called **contraction**.

▼ **Fig 1** Expansion can create enough force to damage a road or a bridge.

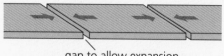
concrete road

gap to allow expansion

if no gap …

… the road can buckle

Expansion in different substances

Different states affect the way substances expand.

Particles in solids are held tightly together. Solids do not expand very far.

Particles in liquids are loosely arranged. Liquids expand more than solids.

Gas particles move very freely. Gases expand most of all.

With a partner.
- Discuss how the particle model helps us to understand how solids, liquids and gases expand at different rates.
- Write your ideas down and include some diagrams to help your explanation.

Some solids expand more than others. It is important to know how much a solid will expand when choosing materials for a special job. Fig 2 shows how much different solids expand when heated.

The fact that steel and concrete expand the same amount means that steel can be safely combined with concrete. Steel rods are used to make concrete beams stronger. If the steel and concrete expanded differently they would damage each other.

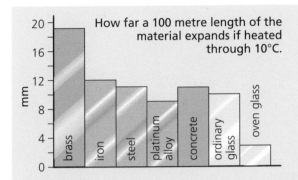

◀ **Fig 2**

How far a 100 metre length of the material expands if heated through 10°C.

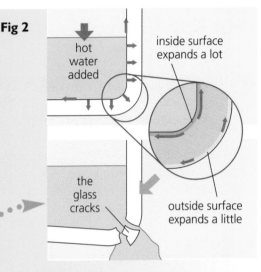

inside surface expands a lot

outside surface expands a little

When you pour hot water into a glass container, the inside of the container heats up a moment before the outside. While the hot inside is pushing against the cold outside, the glass can crack. Thick glass cracks more easily this way than thin glass.

▲ **Fig 3** The forces created by pouring hot water into a thick glass container can break it.

Uses of expansion

Expansion and contraction are not always bad. They are also used for many everyday jobs.

When a steel tyre is fitted onto a train wheel, it is first heated until it expands. The expanded tyre slips easily onto the wheel. After it cools and contracts it grips the wheel very tightly.

Expansion of metals is also used very cleverly in the **bimetal strip** (see Fig 4). This is made from a strip of brass and a strip of iron joined together. When it is heated, the brass expands more than the iron. This makes the strip bend. Some thermometers contain a coiled bimetal strip which turns a needle as it expands or contracts. Bimetal strips are most commonly found in heat alarms and **thermostats**.

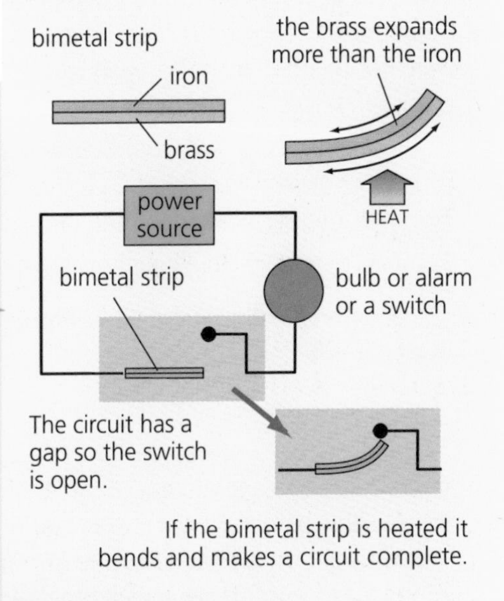

The expansion of liquids also makes thermometers work. A measured amount of alcohol or mercury expands and moves up a narrow tube marked with the corresponding temperature.

bimetal strip
iron
brass

the brass expands more than the iron

HEAT

power source

bimetal strip

bulb or alarm or a switch

The circuit has a gap so the switch is open.

If the bimetal strip is heated it bends and makes a circuit complete.

▲ **Fig 4** If the bimetal strip is heated it bends and makes a circuit complete.

REVIEW

- In a group.
  ○ Make a list of advantages and disadvantages of expansion and contraction.
- Describe how you could safely use expansion to loosen the metal lid from a glass jam jar.

66 Conduction

KEY IDEAS

In this section of the book you will have opportunities to:
- Explain that heat energy can flow from one place to another
- Describe how heat transfer occurs through conduction.

STARTER

In a group.
Discuss why the handle of a spoon becomes hot when the spoon is placed into hot water. Write your ideas down.

Heat transfer

The scientist in the photograph (see Fig 1) understands that heat (**thermal**) energy moves from one place to another. Without his protective clothes he would die very quickly. The molten rock from the volcano is over 1000 °C! The thermal energy is being transferred to him in different ways. His clothes are **thermal insulators** and protect him from the heat.

▲ **Fig 1**

Sometimes we want to prevent heat from leaving our body. In cold water we would quickly die, so divers and cavers must wear special clothes. These insulate them from the cold water. The materials used to make the clothes are insulators.

The two examples above show an important fact about heat transfer.

Heat energy will move from a hotter to a cooler place.

Conduction

If you have ever stirred hot tea with a metal spoon you will know that heat can travel through metals. The handle of the spoon can be too hot to touch after a few minutes. This movement of heat through metals is called **conduction**. Metals conduct heat this way because of the way their atoms (see Unit 52) are packed together. One atom will start to vibrate because of the heat energy, and this causes the atoms near to it to vibrate also. In this way the heat energy passes along the metal.

▼ **Fig 2** Metallic structure.

Heat energy

Heat energy

Materials that do not have this structure will not conduct heat. Plastics, rubber and wood will not conduct heat. They are insulators.

Uses of conductors

There are many times when it is important that heat passes through an object. When we heat food or liquids in a saucepan we need the heat to pass from the cooker to the food (see Fig 3). The heat must pass through the pan. This is why pans are made of metals such as copper, steel or aluminium. Radiators in rooms are made of metals. This is so the heat from the hot water inside the radiator can pass into the room. The metal of the radiator conducts the heat energy from the water to the room.

▲ Fig 3

Uses of insulators

Insulating materials have many uses. Plastic handles on kettles and saucepans can protect us from hot metal. Oven gloves carry out the same job. Tables can be protected from heat by using table mats. These are made of insulating materials such as wood or cork.

Trapped air can act as an insulator. This is why layers of clothes can be used to keep us warm. The same idea is used in sleeping bags and duvets. Many animals keep warm by trapping air in feathers, wool or fur.

Houses are insulated to reduce the amount of heat lost (see Fig 4). The insulating materials are placed in the loft and within the walls. Double glazed windows also help to reduce heat loss because they have a layer of air trapped between the two panes of glass.

▶ Fig 4

67 Convection and radiation

KEY IDEAS

In this section of the book you will have opportunities to:
● Explain that heat transfer occurs through convection and radiation.

STARTER

In a group.
List five examples of heat energy moving through metals without the need for conduction.

Convection

Heat energy does not only travel through metals. It can also travel through liquids and gases. If this was not possible you could not heat water or warm up a room. The molecules of the liquid or gas move, and take heat energy with them. This is called **convection**. As the substance is heated it expands (see Unit 65) and becomes less dense. This makes it rise. As it does so it starts to cool. This makes it fall. This rising and falling sets up **convection currents**.

 more particles per cm^3
greater density

 fewer particles per cm^3
lower density

 Fig I The density of air before and after heating.

particles of air before heating   particles of air after heating

Convection in liquids is very important. Domestic hot water systems use convection. The water is heated in the boiler and rises by convection to the top of a storage tank. Cold water sinks back down to the boiler to be heated. Any hot water used in the house is taken from the top of the boiler.

Convection in air

Convection in air occurs because warm air rises and cold air sinks. Convection is important in warming rooms. Warm air from a heater or radiator near the floor rises to the top of the room. Cooler air sinks and is warmed by the heater. Convection also occurs in refrigerators. The freezer compartment is placed at the top so that cold air will sink away from it. This cold air will chill the food. Warm air rises up to the freezer compartment to be cooled.

ACTIVITY

With a partner.
● Draw a diagram of a refrigerator showing how air is circulated by convection.

Convection can occur on a large scale in nature. Convection currents are important in the generation of weather and are used by birds and glider pilots.

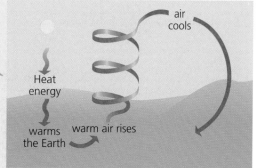

air cools

Heat energy

warms the Earth

warm air rises

▶ **Fig 2** These currents are important in the generation of weather and are used by birds and glider pilots.

Radiation

When you place toast on a grill it is underneath the heating element. The bread is not being heated by conduction. The bread cannot be heated by convection because the hot air will rise upwards and away from the bread. Some heat is being transferred directly down from the element. This is called **radiation**. The heat is transferred by waves of heat energy.

The Sun (see Fig 3) heats the Earth from 150 million kilometres away. This shows that heat can be radiated without needing any particles or materials. Unlike conduction and convection, radiation needs no help in moving heat energy from place to place.

▲ **Fig 3**

Connections

This work builds on your earlier work on keeping warm and changing state at Key Stage 2. It also develops work you have done on energy resources and particles. The work will help you in your later studies of energy in Year 9.

Study tip

Remember:
- Conduction – heat energy travels through metals.
- Convection – takes place through the movement of gases and liquids.
- Radiation – involves waves of heat energy.

REVIEW

- In a group.
  - Examine a vacuum flask closely.
  - Make a list of the ways that heat transfer from the hot liquid is reduced.
  - Which design features are there to reduce: **a** conduction **b** convection **c** radiation?

  Draw or collect pictures of kitchen appliances. Stick the pictures onto plain paper and then label them to show any examples of heat transfer by conduction, convection or radiation.

68 Magnets

Uses of magnets

We often use small magnets to attach notes to the refrigerator. They may also help to keep cupboard doors closed. Magnets have many more important uses in industry and other activities.

Navigation and magnets

One of the oldest uses for magnetism is the compass needle (see Fig 1). If you dangle a small magnetic bar on the end of a thread it will turn until it lines up in a north–south direction.

▶ **Fig 1**

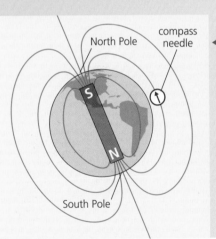

◀ **Fig 2**

One end of the magnet points north. It is called the **north-seeking pole** or north pole. The other end of the magnet points south. This called the **south-seeking pole** or south pole.

The compass needle points north–south because the Earth is also a giant magnet. The compass lines up with the Earth's **magnetic field** (see Fig 2). Knowing that the north pole of the compass needle always points to the Earth's North Pole can help us to move in a straight line in any direction we wish.

Magnetic substances

Most substances are not magnetic. Non-metals are not magnetic. Iron and steel are the most important magnetic metals. Nickel and cobalt are also magnetic.

We can use a compass to find out whether a substance is magnetic. One end of the compass needle normally points to the north. If a magnetic substance comes close to the needle, it will make the needle turn

Some electrical equipment is magnetic (see Unit 70) and some rocks also contain magnetic minerals. In parts of Scotland, a compass could lead you round in circles.

On your own.
- Explain how magnetic objects such as some rocks and electrical equipment can make a compass unreliable.

Magnetic fields

When you slowly bring a metal object towards a magnet you will notice the pull of the magnet before the object touches the magnet. Magnetism must be reaching out into the air around the magnet. We can use iron filings to make a pattern around a magnet.

The lines in Fig 3 show how iron filings fall into place around a bar magnet. Each filing behaves like a tiny compass needle. The lines show the magnetic field around the magnet. Tightly packed lines show where the magnetic field is strongest. Widely spaced lines show where it is weakest.

The north pole of one magnet will repel the north pole of another magnet. The magnets will push apart. If the north pole of one magnet is pointed towards the south pole of another magnet they will be pulled together (see Fig 4).

Similar poles repel.
Opposite poles attract.

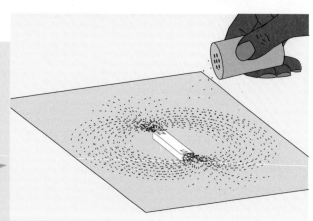

▲ **Fig 3** Compare this pattern with Fig 2. (Wear goggles if you do this experiment yourself.)

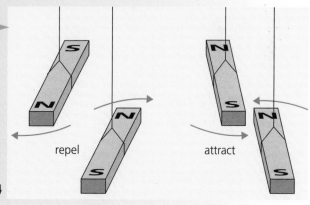

repel   attract

▶ Fig 4

- On your own.
  ○ Plan a short newspaper article describing what magnets are and how useful they are.
  Use a small compass to find out how many articles in your home are magnetic. Can you see any difference in the strength of the magnetic fields?

REVIEW

69 Electricity and magnetism

KEY IDEAS

In this section of the book you will have opportunities to:
- Explain that there is a link between electricity and magnetism
- Describe some uses of electromagnets and how to make them stronger.

STARTER

In a group.
Discuss and then draw the magnetic field pattern you would expect to see around a bar magnet. How is this similar to the Earth's magnetic field?

Electricity and magnetism are linked

When the current in Fig 1 is switched on we find that the compass needle moves. This shows that there is a magnetic field. When the current is switched off the compass needle returns to its normal north–south position. The magnetic field was only there while the electric current was flowing. This must mean that electricity and magnetism are linked in some way.

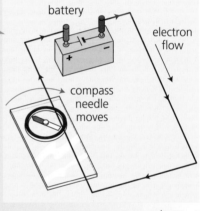

▲ **Fig I**

When a current flows through a wire, the wire has a magnetic field around it.

The magnetic field around an ordinary electric wire is not very strong. We can draw the field around a thick wire carrying a large current by setting up the arrangement in Fig 2. The field is too weak to move iron filings so we need to use sensitive plotting compasses instead.

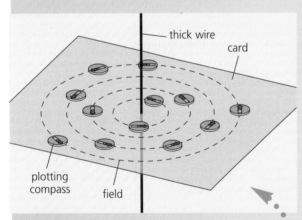

▲ **Fig 2** Finding the magnetic field around a straight wire.

Electromagnets

A coiled wire (see Fig 3) makes a much stronger magnetic field. If the wire is coiled around a rod of iron the field becomes even stronger. The iron inside the coil is called the **core**. The coil and the core together make an **electromagnet**. The field pattern is like the pattern for a bar magnet.

If the core is made of soft iron the magnetic field will disappear when the current is switched off. This means we have a magnet that can be turned on and off. If the core is made of steel it remains magnetic after the electricity is switched off. This is one way of making magnets.

With a partner.
- Discuss why it is useful to have a magnet that you can turn on and off. Write down your ideas.

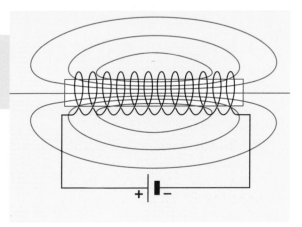

▲ Fig 3

Making the field stronger

A stronger electromagnet can attract more magnetic material. One way to make an electromagnet stronger is to pass a larger current through the coil. Another way to make an electromagnet stronger is to increase the number of coils around the core.

The substance used to make the core can also affect the strength of the field. Fig 4 shows how many paperclips could be attracted by three electromagnets with different cores. The magnets have the same number of coils and are carrying the same current. Only the core materials are different.

All three of these methods are used to make different kinds of electromagnets for use in medicine and industry. Some of these uses are described in Unit 70.

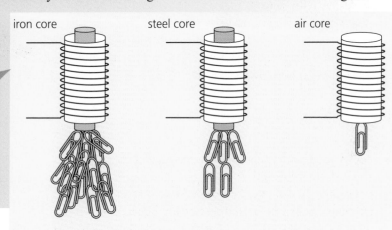

▲ **Fig 4** Different cores can change the strength of an electromagnet.

- In a group.
  - Design an investigation to show that the number of coils increases the strength of the magnetic field around an electromagnet.

70 Using electromagnets

Why electromagnets are so useful

Electromagnets have many uses. One reason for this is that they can be made more powerful than ordinary magnets. Another important reason is that an electromagnet can be switched on and off. This means that it can be used to pick up a metal object from one place and drop it somewhere else, just by turning the electricity on and off.

Electromagnets are used in scrapyards to move heavy cars around. They are also used to separate magnetic substances from non-magnetic substances. This is a good way of sorting out metals for recycling.

▲ **Fig 1** Electromagnets can pick up heavy metal objects and drop them again.

Electric bells

▶ **Fig 2**

An electric bell contains an electromagnet. Fig 2 shows how the circuit is arranged. The circuit is closed by pressing the bell push. When the current starts to flow, it turns on the electromagnet. The electromagnet immediately attracts a metal arm called an **armature** which hits a gong and makes the bell ring once. As the arm is pulled towards the electromagnet the circuit is broken.

As soon as the circuit is broken the electromagnet stops working. This allows the armature to spring away from the gong. When the armature swings back to its original position it closes the circuit again, the electromagnet is switched back on and the armature is pulled towards it again. This goes on happening for as long as you press the bell-push. The bell is struck many times in a few seconds.

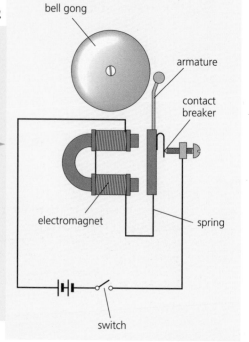

bell gong

armature

contact breaker

electromagnet

spring

switch

ACTIVITY

With a partner.
- The electric bell arrangement is often called a 'make and break' circuit.
- Discuss how it gets this name.

Transport and medicine

Some modern trams and trains use electromagnets. The Maglev train at Birmingham airport rides just above the surface of the track. It is held there by electromagnets. The ride is very smooth and quiet because the train stays 15 mm away from the track and does not touch it. As well as being quiet, this saves wear and tear on the wheels and the track.

Electromagnets are also used in medicine. Metal splinters can be eased out of a wound with a small electromagnet. This causes much less damage than probing around with a pair of tweezers. If you did not wear goggles when using iron filings, you might need to have some sharp pieces of iron removed from your eye in this way.

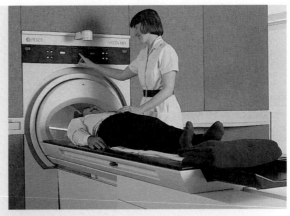

▲ **Fig 3** A lot of modern medical equipment, like this Magnetic Resonance Imaging (MRI) scanner, uses electromagnetism.

Entertainment

Loudspeakers and television tubes contain electromagnets. The way they work is much more complicated than an electric bell. It is important to know that there are electromagnets in many household articles because strong magnetic fields can spoil computer discs and audio and video tapes.

Connections

This work builds on work done on magnets at Key Stage 2 and electrical circuits in Year 7. This work leads on to further study of electricity in Year 9.

REVIEW
- In a group.
  - Design and produce a leaflet advertising the importance of electromagnets. Include how electromagnets work and what they are used for.

  Draw a circuit that uses an electromagnet to ring an alarm bell whenever a door is opened.

71 Light

KEY IDEAS

In this section of the book you will have opportunities to:
- Explain that light is a form of energy
- Describe how we can see objects.

STARTER

In a group.
Discuss where the light in your classroom comes from. What happens when there is no light? Write down your ideas and prepare to discuss them with other groups.

How light behaves

The caver in Fig 1 would not be able to see anything at all without a lamp. The photograph gives us several clues about the way light behaves.

1. A light beam is straight.

2. Light bounces off the walls of the cave.

3. Light from outside cannot get in by following bends in the tunnel.

4. The region outside the light beam is dark.

5. There are dark shadows behind lit-up rocks.

▶ **Fig 1** Natural light never shines into this cave.

What is light?

Light is a form of energy. The caver's lamp contains a battery which produces electrical energy and a light bulb that changes the electrical energy into light energy. Burning gases also give out light energy. The Sun gives out light energy. Light travels out from these light sources.

Straight lines

We cannot see round corners. Our vision depends on light travelling from an object to our eyes. The reason why we cannot see round a corner is because light cannot bend around a corner.

▶ **Fig 2** Sometimes it would be useful to be able to see around corners.

ACTIVITY

With a partner.
- Describe how you could use three pieces of card and a light source to show that light travels in straight lines.
- Draw a diagram to show your ideas.

Text

The speed of light

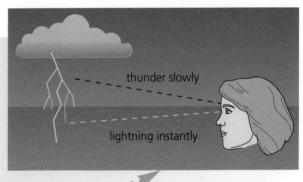

Light travels very fast. The light from the Sun only takes eight minutes to travel 150 million kilometres to the Earth's surface. This means that the speed of light in space is approximately 300 million metres per second. Most of the light we see arrives so quickly that it seems to take no time at all. Compared with light, sound is slow. The speed of sound in air is about 340 metres per second.

▲ Fig 3

When a thunderstorm is 2 kilometres away you see the lightning almost six seconds before you hear the thunder (see Fig 3).

Luminous and non-luminous

If you place a coat on a table in a dark room you will not be able to see it. The coat does not give out light. If you switch on a lamp you will be able to see the lamp and the coat. The lamp gives out light. It is **luminous**. The coat does not give out light. It is not luminous. The coat becomes visible because it **reflects** light given out by the lamp.

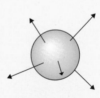

light sources produce light

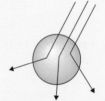

non-luminous objects scatter light

▲ **Fig 4** Luminous objects emit light. Non-luminous objects reflect light.

REVIEW

- In a group.
  - Make a list of objects in the room that emit light.
  - Make a list of 10 objects that you can see because of reflection from these light sources.
  - Why is the ability to detect light important to animals?

  Research what a pinhole camera is. Make your own pinhole camera from a small box. Point it towards some light sources. Draw the images that appear on the screen.

72 Reflection and refraction

In this section of the book you will have opportunities to:
● Explain reflection and refraction of light.

In a group.
Discuss why you can see yourself by looking in a mirror, but not by looking at a wall. Write your ideas down.

Reflecting light

Most objects have a rough surface that scatters light. Objects can therefore be seen from many directions. A mirror is an object. It can be seen from many directions, but the image reflected from its surface changes when you move or when the mirror moves. This is because the glass of a mirror is perfectly flat and very smooth. It is called a **plane** surface. A plane surface does not scatter light.

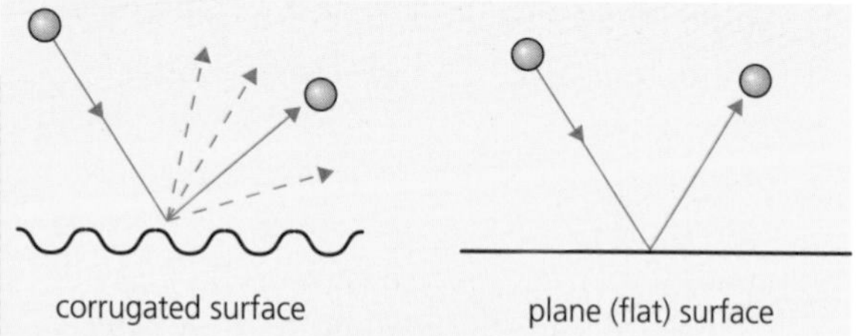

corrugated surface   plane (flat) surface

▲ **Fig 1** A ball bounces off a corrugated surface at different angles. It bounces off a flat surface at a regular angle.

When light hits the plane surface of a mirror it bounces off at a regular angle. This is called regular reflection. We show this by shining a beam of light onto a mirror and marking where its reflection lands.

The light hitting the mirror is called the **incident ray**. A line drawn at right angles to the mirror is called a **normal**. The angles of rays hitting and leaving the mirror are usually measured from the normal. The angle at which it hits the mirror is called the **angle of incidence**. The light leaving the mirror is called the **reflected ray**. The angle at which it leaves is called the **angle of reflection**. These two angles are the same.

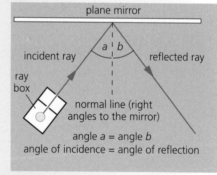

plane mirror

incident ray   reflected ray

ray box

normal line (right angles to the mirror)

angle *a* = angle *b*
angle of incidence = angle of reflection

▲ **Fig 2** Angle **a** is always the same as angle **b**.

> angle of incidence = angle of reflection

With a partner.
● Use the rules about reflection of light to design a periscope so that you can see over objects.

Refraction of light

The straw in Fig 3 is perfectly straight. The straw only looks bent because the light we see it by was bent when it came out of the water. When light passes from air into a different substance, such as water or glass, it changes direction. This is called **refraction**.

The rays of light entering a clear substance are called **incident** rays. The rays of light leaving a clear substance are called **refracted** rays. Rays hitting the surface at right angles are called **normal** rays.

Any light ray passing at an angle from air into water or glass bends towards the normal. This is because water and glass are denser than air.

▲ **Fig 3**

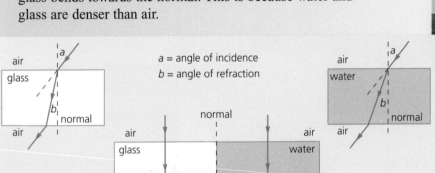

a = angle of incidence
b = angle of refraction

◄ **Fig 4** A single ray going through a block of glass or a fishtank is bent twice, first when it enters and again when it leaves.

When the light rays leave the glass or water they bend away from the normal. This is because air is less dense.

> Light rays passing into a dense material bend towards the normal.
> Light rays passing into a less dense material bend away from the normal.

You can try the coin trick (see Fig 5) at home. Simply drop a coin into an empty cup and find a position where you can see about halfway into the cup without seeing the coin. Now sit someone else in the same place and tell them that you can make the coin appear without touching it or the cup. All you need to do is add some water. Not magic, only refraction.

▶ **Fig 5**

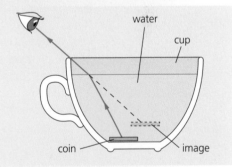

- In a group.
  - Use your knowledge of light to explain how mirrors and magnifying glasses work.
  - Write down your ideas and prepare to discuss them with other groups.

Think of some examples of the uses of mirrors. Choose one and build a model of it. Design and make a small leaflet to explain to a younger person how they can see around corners using a mirror.

73 Light and colour

In this section of the book you will have opportunities to:
- Explain that white light can be split to give a range of colours
- Describe the effect of different coloured light on coloured objects.

STARTER

In a group.
Review what you know about light by discussing why it is only possible to see objects in the room when there is light.

Sunlight

▲ Fig 1

Light from the Sun is white. White light is really a mixture of colours. The range of colours that make up white light is called the **spectrum**. When light from the Sun hits a dewdrop it may sparkle with all the colours of the rainbow (see Fig 1).

The colours of a rainbow are:

red orange yellow green blue indigo violet

The light from the Sun is refracted or bent when it passes from the air into water (see Unit 72). Different colours bend at slightly different angles. Violet light bends through a bigger angle than red light. Each of the colours in between has its own angle. In the 17th century Sir Isaac Newton created a spectrum in his laboratory. He used a triangular prism made of glass (see Fig 2). The angle of the glass faces in a prism is perfect for splitting white light into bands of colour.

Study tip

You can remember the correct order by learning this phrase:
Richard **O**f **Y**ork **G**ave **B**attle **I**n **V**ain

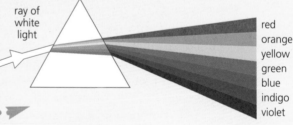

ray of white light

red
orange
yellow
green
blue
indigo
violet

▲ Fig 2

ACTIVITY

With a partner.
- Discuss how the colours of the rainbow appear. Write down your ideas.

Mixing colours

Red, blue and green are called **primary colours**. All other colours can be made by mixing together combinations of these three primary colours. We can make white light by adding different coloured lights together. We do not need a whole rainbow. Mixing the primary colours – red, green and blue – will give us white light.

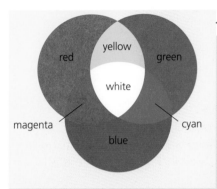

◀ **Fig 3** The primary colours of light and how they mix.

Light colours work differently from the colours in a paintbox. Paint colours reflect light. Light colours are light.

Some substances give out coloured light when they burn. Sodium burns with a yellow flame. Orange-yellow street lights are often called sodium lights. Coloured light can also be obtained from white light by passing it through a transparent **filter**. The colour of the filter is the same as the colour of the light that comes through it.

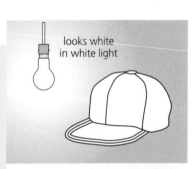

▶ **Fig 4** A red filter absorbs all the colours of the spectrum except red.

Coloured objects

Most substances do not let light through them. They are **opaque**. Opaque objects absorb some colours of light and reflect others. Their colour depends on the colour of the light they reflect. White objects reflect all the light landing on them. Black objects absorb all the light landing on them.

Water absorbs some of the light passing through it. Pure water absorbs a lot of red, some yellow and some green light. This is why deep clear water looks blue. Objects underwater also look blue because the water filters out other colours they reflect.

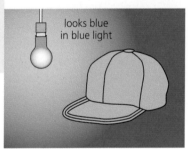

▶ **Fig 5**

↺ **Connections**

This work builds on earlier work on light, shadows and seeing at Key Stage 2. Light and sound will be compared in the work on sound and hearing.

REVIEW

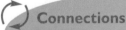

- In a group.
  - Decide how you would create stage lighting effects for a ghost story.
  - Write down the scientific explanations of what you decide to do.

Using coloured sweet wrappers as filters, look at different colours through different coloured filters. Make a chart to show your results.

74 Your hearing

KEY IDEAS

In this section of the book you will have opportunities to:
- Explain that sound travels by vibrations
- Describe how we hear sounds.

STARTER

In a group.
Discuss how banging a drum makes a sound. How would you make the sound louder?

Sound

Sound is important to us. We use our voices to speak to one another. Alarms and warning cries protect us from harm. Hearing tells us what is going on around us. Listening to music gives us pleasure.

? But what is sound?

▶ **Fig 1** Sound is so important that old silent movies were accompanied by a piano-player paid to supply a live 'sound track'.

Vibrations

Sound is made by something vibrating. When you press a piano key it makes a hammer strike a string inside. This makes the string vibrate. The vibrating string makes the air around it vibrate. Each time the string moves in one direction it pushes air molecules together. When it moves back in the other direction the air molecules spread out again. Sections of air are alternately compressed and expanded. As these sections move away from the string they become sound waves.

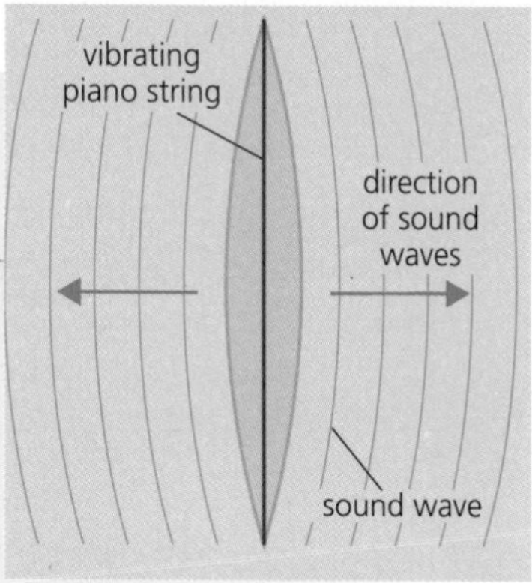

Many instruments do not have strings. A wind instrument, like a recorder, is designed to make the air inside vibrate when somebody blows into it. Your voice works like a combination of a wind instrument and a stringed instrument. Air from your windpipe passes through your voice-box on the way out. Your voice-box contains vocal cords. These tiny strings vibrate when air passes across them. They make sound waves come out of your mouth.

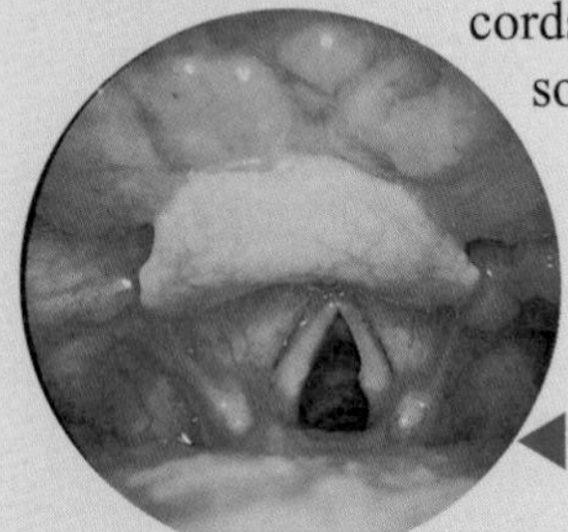

vibrating piano string

direction of sound waves

sound wave

▲ **Fig 2** A vibrating string creates sound waves.

◀ **Fig 3** Vocal cords.

ACTIVITY

On your own.
- List four musical instruments that do not have strings.
- How do these instruments produce sounds?

Hearing

Sound waves would mean nothing to us if we had no way of detecting them. Luckily, your ears can pick up the vibrations in the air and transmit them to your brain. The shape of your outer ear helps it to catch sound waves and direct them into a narrow tube behind your jaw. At the end of the tube there is a thin sheet of tissue called your **eardrum**. The sound waves make your eardrum vibrate.

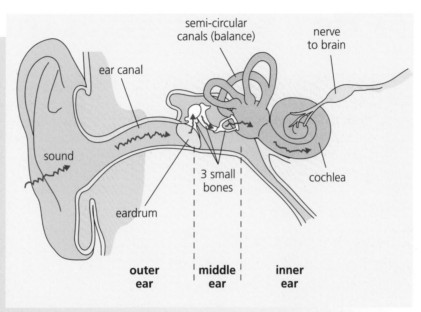

▲ **Fig 4** The human ear.

The vibration is passed on to three tiny bones deeper inside. They amplify the sound and transmit it even deeper, to a curly region called the **cochlea**. The cochlea contains fluid and nerves. Amplified sound makes the fluid vibrate. Finally, the nerves transmit vibration messages to your brain.

Turn it down

Some sounds are very quiet. Some sounds are so loud they can make our ears hurt. Whether we like a particular sound or not depends on many things. Regular, soft sounds are usually soothing. Irregular, loud sounds can be disturbing. We describe an unpleasant sound as a **noise**. The loudness of a sound can be measured in units called decibels. The sound of a jet plane taking off is about 110 decibels.

▶ **Fig 5** Loud sounds can damage your hearing.
People in noisy work places must protect their ears.

- In a group.
  - Make a list of all the devices in the home that are meant to create sound.
  - Make a separate list of devices that produce noise.
  - Do any of the devices on your lists vibrate?

🏠 Write a short article that explains how we can hear sounds from across a room.

75 How sound waves travel

In this section of the book you will have opportunities to:
- Describe how to find the speed of sound in air
- Explain how sound travels through different materials.

In a group.
Discuss why a sound becomes louder as you move nearer to the source of the sound. What happens if you put a wall between you and the sound? Why?

Sound energy

When you hear a sound, the air molecules that make your eardrum vibrate have not travelled all the way from the object that made the sound. **Sound energy** is passed from one molecule to another like a baton in a relay race.

the 'baton' (sound energy) the 'athletes' (air molecules)

Sound energy takes time to travel through the air. When you shout near a big building, you may hear an **echo** when the sound waves bounce back to you. You could even use an echo to measure the speed of sound (see below).

▲ **Fig 1** Sound energy is passed from air molecule to air molecule. The energy eventually makes air molecules near your ear vibrate.

Echo timing

Fig 2 shows a way to measure the speed of sound by timing an echo. Stand exactly 200 metres from a high, wide building. Clap your hands once and listen for the echo. The time between the clap and its echo is the time it took for the sound to travel to the wall and back again. Now try to clap in time with the echo, so that your next clap covers the sound of the echo from the previous clap. The time between your claps will allow somebody with a stopwatch to measure how long sound takes to travel to the wall and back.

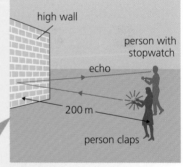

high wall

person with stopwatch

echo

200 m

person claps

distance one clap travels = 200 metres x 2
                                      = 400 metres
time between claps   = 1.2 seconds
therefore sound travels 400 m in 1.2 s
speed of sound in air   = distance ÷ time
                                        = 400 m ÷ 1.2 s
                                        = 333 m/s

▲ **Fig 2** This is not an easy experiment because it may be hard to find a suitable place to try it.

On your own.
- Compare the speed of sound with the speed of light.
- Why would it be difficult to calculate the speed of light in a similar way to the speed of sound?

Echo-sounding

Sound waves can be used to locate wrecks and submarines underwater. This is called echo-sounding or **sonar**. Sound waves from the ship travel through the water and bounce back from any sunken ships or submarines (see Fig 3). Echo-sounding can also be used to check whether the water is deep enough for a ship to proceed safely.

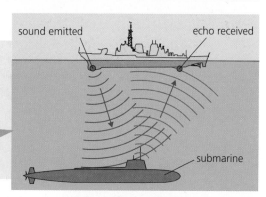

Fig 3 Echoes help to locate the sea bed and any objects above it.

Ultrasound

Very small sound waves called ultrasound are used to examine an unborn baby. The waves pass through the fluid in the womb and bounce back from the baby's body.

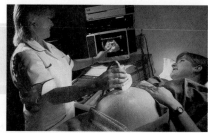

Fig 4 An ultrasound scan can show how well a baby is growing.

Sound and materials

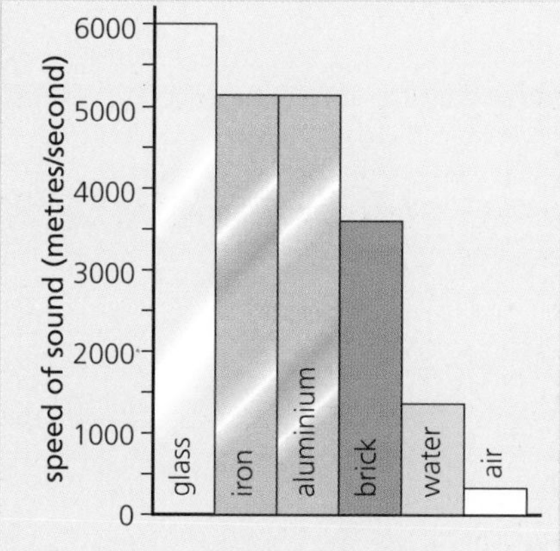

Sound travels through anything that can vibrate. This includes gases, liquids and solids (see Fig 5). We can hear sounds through walls and floors, in swimming pools and in the air. Sound waves travel well through water. Whales can call to each other over many kilometres. If you tap very softly on a long bench and ask a friend to place his/her ear to the other end of the bench he/she will hear the tap through the bench but not through the air. Sound travels very well through solids.

Fig 5

(bar chart: speed of sound (metres/second) vs material — glass ≈6000, iron ≈5100, aluminium ≈5100, brick ≈3600, water ≈1300, air ≈300)

- In a group.
  - Explain why walls with air spaces in the middle of them are more soundproof than solid walls.
  - What else can help to keep sound out of a building?

Research some of the ways that people are protected from loud noises. Write down how these methods of protection work.

76 Loudness and waves

Sound and a vacuum

We can hear a bell ringing inside a glass jar perfectly well. Sound travels through air and glass. Removing all the air from the jar makes a **vacuum** inside. If the bell is rung now, you will not be able to hear it. There are no air molecules inside to be vibrated by the bell. You can see the striker hitting the gong but you cannot hear the sound.

Sound cannot travel through a vacuum

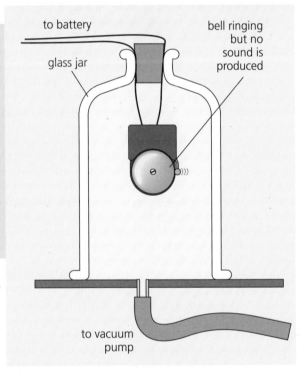

to battery

glass jar

bell ringing but no sound is produced

to vacuum pump

▶ **Fig I** Bell in a vacuum.

About waves

The energy from a vibrating object travels outward as waves (see Unit 74). If you have ever watched a ball floating on waves you will have noticed that the ball bobs up and down. The waves do not push the ball along. This is because the waves move but the water just moves up and down. Sound waves in air behave in a similar way but this time they move backwards and forwards. The wave moves but the air does not. Sound waves can be seen by attaching a microphone to a machine called an **oscilloscope**. This shows the wave on a small screen (see Fig 2).

Sound waves have crests and troughs just like a wave in a pond. As a wave becomes bigger it rises higher and higher above the normal (silent) level.

The distance above or below normal is called the **amplitude**. The amplitude of a wave is the distance from the crest (or the trough) to the middle. The larger the amplitude, the larger the wave. High waves in the sea have more energy. They can do more damage. This is also true of sound waves. A very large vibration will cause large sound waves. Large waves have a large amplitude. Waves with a large amplitude give a louder noise.

> Sound waves with a large amplitude produce loud sounds.

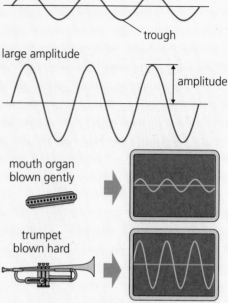

▶ **Fig 2**

ACTIVITY

With a partner.
- Which instrument do you think produces sound waves with the largest amplitude, a trumpet or a flute?
- Explain why.

Tuning forks and explosions

A tuning fork vibrates very fast. It is small and does not move very much air. The waves that the fork makes have a very small amplitude. The sound is not very loud. We can make it sound louder by pressing the base onto a hollow box. The vibration from the fork is **amplified** by the box. The box moves more air than the fork can.

A vast amount of air is moved by an explosion. The sound waves moving out from an explosion are very big. An explosion makes a very loud bang.

REVIEW

- In a group.
  - Discuss why many musical instruments have strings near a large hollow box or chamber.
  - What role does the chamber play?

 Use a washing-up bowl to create waves of different amplitudes. Which are the waves that require most energy from you? Write down your findings.

77 High and low notes

In this section of the book you will have opportunities to:
● Describe what wavelength is
● Explain the link between the pitch of a sound and the frequency of the wave causing it.

In a group.
Make a list of sounds you would call high pitched and those you would call low pitched. Where do these sounds come from?

Pitch of a sound

A guitar has strings of different thickness. The thinnest string vibrates very quickly when it is plucked. This creates sound waves that are close together.

A thin string produces a sound with a high **pitch**. The thickest string vibrates more slowly when it is plucked. This creates sound waves that are further apart than the ones made by the thin string. The thick string produces a sound with a low pitch.

The wave shapes produced by these two strings are shown in Fig 1.

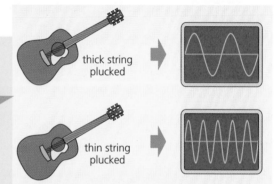

▲ **Fig 1** The thinnest string produces sound waves that are closer together.

The pitch of a sound depends on how quickly or slowly the object making the sound is vibrating.

Wavelength

The distance between waves can be measured. It is the distance between two neighbouring crests or troughs. This is called the **wavelength** (see Fig 2).

▶ **Fig 2**

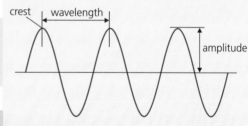

On your own.
● Which guitar string produces sound waves with the shortest wavelength? Explain why.

Frequency

The **frequency** of a sound is the number of vibrations per second. Frequency is measured in **Hertz** (Hz). The thin string of a guitar vibrates 660 times per second. The frequency of the sound it makes is 660 Hz. The thickest string of a guitar vibrates 165 times per second. Remember that the pitch of a sound depends on how quickly or slowly the object is vibrating. The thin string has the highest frequency because it vibrates faster than the thick string. It will give a higher pitched sound.

> The higher the frequency of a sound, the higher its pitch.

We can hear sounds that have a frequency between 20 Hz and 20 000 Hz (20 kHz). We say that these sounds are **audible**. A large drum produces a very low note. This could be as low as 20 Hz. A shrill whistle may produce a note as high as 20 kHz. A dog whistle produces a note above 20 kHz. We cannot hear a dog whistle, but dogs and many other animals can. Higher frequencies than we can hear are called **ultrasound**. Lower frequencies than we can hear are called **infrasound**.

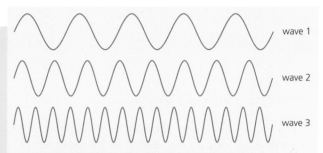

▲ **Fig 3** Waves that are closer together have a higher frequency. They make a higher pitched sound.

Changing the pitch of a string

▼ **Fig 4**

The pitch of a guitar string depends on its thickness. It can also be altered by changing the length of the string (see Fig 4).

A short string vibrates more quickly than a long string. A short string therefore makes a sound with a higher frequency. A high frequency makes a high pitch. All the strings of a guitar are the same length but a guitar player can make notes of many different pitches. The frets across the neck of the guitar allow the player to press down and shorten the vibrating part of any string (see Fig 5).

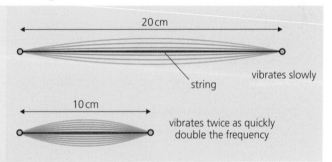

◀ **Fig 5**

↻ **Connections**

This unit builds on earlier work on changing sounds at Key Stage 2 and will support further work on sound at Key Stage 4.

REVIEW

- In a group.
  - Hold a ruler firmly on top of a desk so that it overhangs the edge. Twang the ruler so that it makes a sound. Experiment to see how the length of the ruler changes the sound.
  - What does this tell you about the frequency and the pitch of the sounds?
  - Discuss your findings with other groups.

Research how bats use echo location for hunting. Write down your findings.

Summary of Year 8 topics

Biology (pages 86–113)

After studying the first part of the Year 8 topics you should have learned about life processes and living things in greater detail.

Food and digestion

1. Name the six essential nutrients.
2. List five foods that are rich in protein.
3. Draw a diagram of the digestive system and label it.

Respiration

4. What are the functions of blood?
5. What are alveoli and why are they important?
6. Write down the word equation for aerobic respiration. Why is this respiration important?

Microbes and disease

7. How can bacteria be spread from person to person?
8. What are antibodies and how do they help to protect you from disease?
9. Explain why antibiotics are so useful but should be used carefully.

Ecological relationships

10. What is a quadrat and what is it used for?
11. Describe an example of a predator–prey relationship.
12. Draw a pyramid of number diagram for a food chain you might find in a garden.

Chemistry (pages 114–137)

The second part of the Year 8 topics should have helped you to gain a greater understanding of materials and their properties.

Atoms and elements

13. Name the three sub-atomic particles.
14. What are the symbols for lead, sodium, copper and chlorine?
15. Write a word equation for oxygen reacting with zinc to give zinc oxide.

Compounds and elements

16. List five examples of compounds.
17. Describe how you would separate sand from water.
18. Explain what happens to the particles in a solid as it melts.

Rocks and weathering

19. Explain how the properties of rocks are linked to their uses.

20. Describe the difference between weathering and erosion.

21. List three ways that rock particles can be transported.

The rock cycle

22. Name two igneous rocks and two sedimentary rocks.

23. How are metamorphic rocks made?

24. Draw and label a diagram that shows the rock cycle.

Physics (pages 138–165)

The third part of the Year 8 topics should have helped you to understand physical processes such as heating and cooling, magnetism, light and sound.

Heating and cooling

25. Which two points are used to set a thermometer?

26. Explain what happens to the particles in a metal as it expands.

27. List two examples of conduction and two examples of convection.

Magnets and electromagnets

28. Draw the field pattern around a bar magnet.

29. Write down three practical uses for electromagnets.

30. Describe two ways to increase the strength of an electromagnet.

Light

31. How would you show that light travels in straight lines?

32. Why does a swimming pool look shallower than it is?

33. Explain why a green cap looks black in blue light.

Sound and hearing

34. Sketch some sound waves to explain amplitude, wavelength and frequency.

35. How can whales many kilometres apart hear each other?

36. How can sound waves be used to find sunken ships?

Introduction to Year 9 topics

Biology (pages 170–195)

The first part of the Year 9 topics focuses on some very important aspects of life processes and living things. It is divided into four sections. Each section covers a unit from the Scheme of Work for Science.

Inheritance and selection

In this unit you will learn to recognise some inherited characteristics and describe how these are influenced by environmental conditions. You will study how genetic information from both parents is inherited through sexual reproduction and that this mixing of genetic material can result in variation. Asexual reproduction results in clones. The unit goes on to describe how the resulting characteristics can be desirable in certain circumstances and that this principle is used in selective breeding.

Fit and healthy

This unit covers ideas about health and lifestyle. You will learn how maintaining a healthy skeleton and muscles depends on eating the correct nutrients and that exercise is important for health. You will go on to study the effects of diet, smoking, alcohol and other drugs on health and be encouraged to consider the value of a healthy lifestyle.

Plants and photosynthesis

In this section you will learn that plants use carbon dioxide and water as the raw materials for photosynthesis. They also need light as the energy source. You will study how plants make glucose using photosynthesis and that this can be stored as starch. You will also be encouraged to understand that plants carry out both photosynthesis and respiration. The unit goes on to explain the vital functions of roots and leaves and how these parts of the plant are specially adapted to carry out their roles.

Plants for food

This section will give you opportunities to study humans as part of a complex food web. You will be helped to explore the factors affecting plant growth and learn about the ways that crop yields can be improved. The unit goes on to explain that some of the ways of increasing crop yield can have effects on the distribution and abundance of other plants and animals. Finally, you will study how toxic materials can accumulate in a food chain.

Chemistry (pages 196–219)

The second part of the Year 9 topics is designed to help you to understand materials and their properties. It is divided into four sections. Each section covers a unit from the Scheme of Work for Science.

Reactions of metals and metal compounds

In this section you will explore the properties of metals and non-metals and learn how acids react with metals, metal carbonates and metal oxides. You will study how salts are formed and review your understanding of the tests used to identify hydrogen and carbon dioxide. The unit will also encourage you to use symbols and formulae and combine these into symbol equations as a way of representing chemical reactions.

Patterns of reactivity

This section will give you opportunities to identify and describe similarities in chemical reactions. You will learn to identify differences in the reactivity of different metals. The unit encourages you to use these differences to explain some uses of metals and how they are found and extracted. You will learn about the reactivity series of metals and be able to use it to predict chemical reactions.

Environmental chemistry

This unit of work will help you to describe how acid rain is formed and how it affects the environment, buildings and the landscape. You will study how air pollution and water pollution is caused and how it is monitored. The unit encourages you to be aware of different environmental issues.

Using chemistry

In this section you will be able to learn more about how chemical reactions are used to make new products and as a source of energy. Exothermic and endothermic reactions are explained and some examples given. You will learn that mass is conserved when chemical reactions occur. The unit introduces you to some examples of useful chemicals made by chemical reactions.

Physics (pages 220–243)

The third part of the Year 9 topics is designed to help you to understand some important physical processes. It is divided into four sections.

Energy and electricity

In this section of the book you will have opportunities to describe some examples of energy transfers and transformations. You will learn how electricity is generated in power stations and be encouraged to consider some of the environmental effects of this. You will then study the efficient use

of energy and learn that in most energy transformations some energy is wasted.

Gravity and Space

This unit of work will allow you to develop your earlier ideas about the gravitational pull between bodies and understand that the force depends on the mass of the bodies and their distance apart. You will learn that the movement of planets around the Sun, and satellites around the Earth, relates to gravity. The unit goes on to explain the use of artificial satellites for communications, observing the Earth, and exploring the Solar System and beyond. You will also study the difference between mass and weight.

Speeding up

This unit helps you to build on your earlier work on speed and forces and how forces can be measured. You will study the relationship between speed, distance and time. You will also be encouraged to describe how streamlining reduces resistance to air and water and understand that the resistance increases with the speed of the object. You will learn that this is linked to the particle model.

Pressure and moments

This final unit will help you to understand key ideas about pressure and to explain the relationship between force, area and pressure. You will learn about examples of how pressure can be increased or decreased. You will also study pressure in liquids and how this has to be considered in designing dams or by divers. The unit also explains turning forces and the action of levers and you will learn how to apply the principle of moments to explain a range of situations.

78 Sexual and asexual reproduction

KEY IDEAS

In this section of the book you will have opportunities to:
- Explain that the nucleus of a cell contains genes that control the characteristics of an organism
- Explain that fertilisation produces a new set of genes.

STARTER

In a group.
Look at the different people in your group. Make a list of the ways that you look alike. In what ways are you different? Discuss which of these differences you are likely to have inherited from your parents.

Sexual reproduction

All living things get old and die. Replacements are made by the process of reproduction. Many animals reproduce by a process called **sexual reproduction**. This involves the joining of a female sex cell, or ovum, with a male sex cell, or sperm. Flowering plants also reproduce by sexual reproduction. The female sex cell, or ovule, is fertilised by a pollen grain which contains the male sex cell. The nucleus of the female sex cell, or gamete, joins with the nucleus of the male sex cell, or gamete.

The genetic material in a nucleus contains genes. These genes carry the information that determines the characteristics of the organism. During fertilisation the genes from both parents are mixed. This mixing of genetic material from both parents produces a new set of genes. The offspring will be a unique individual. It may have characteristics in common with its parents but it will not be identical. • • • • • • • • •

Sexual reproduction produces offspring that are similar to the parents but unique. This means that within a species there will always be variation. This is important. The variation can result in improved characteristics so individuals are better adapted to their habitat. They may be able to gather food better, run faster or fight for mates more effectively. These individuals are likely to breed more successfully and their offspring will inherit many of the improved characteristics. This can lead to a general improvement in the species.

cytoplasm

nucleus

membrane

before cell division the genetic material can be stained and seen under a microscope

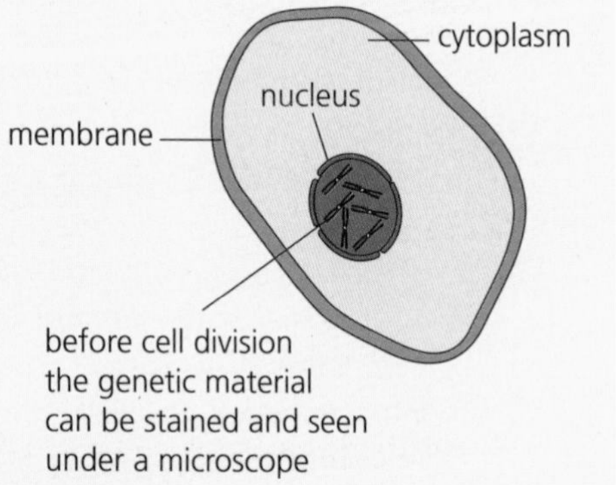

▲ **Fig 1** Cell showing genetic material within the nucleus.

▲ **Fig 2** Children inherit characteristics from their parents but are not identical to them.

With a partner.
- Discuss how sexual reproduction can lead to a species becoming better adapted to their habitat.
- Make a list of your ideas.

Asexual reproduction

Many organisms reproduce by **asexual reproduction**. This is the simplest form of reproduction. There are many different types but they have two things in common:

1 Only one parent is needed

2 The new individual is genetically identical to the parent.

A common type of asexual reproduction is **binary fission** (see Unit 2). The division of a cell by binary fission results in two identical cells. This is a quick and efficient form of reproduction but does not lead to any genetic mixing. The identical cells are sometimes called clones. There is little chance of the new cells being better adapted to their environment than the parent cell.

Vegetative reproduction

Some plants have developed a type of asexual reproduction called **vegetative reproduction**. This allows one part of the plant to develop into a new plant. There are many ways in which this can be done, but bulbs and tubers are examples you have probably seen. •••••••

Remember that the plants that grow from vegetative reproduction are genetically identical to the parent plant.

▼ **Fig 3** Bulbs and tubers.

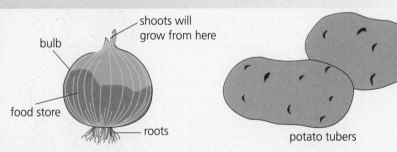

shoots will grow from here

bulb

food store

roots

potato tubers

- In a group.
  - Produce a large poster which shows the advantages and disadvantages of sexual reproduction and asexual reproduction.
  - Include some examples to illustrate your ideas.

  Research some of the ways that gardeners use vegetative reproduction to produce extra flowers and vegetables in their gardens.

79 The causes of variety

In this section of the book you will have opportunities to:
- Review that the characteristics of an organism are inherited from its parents
- Explain that variations can come from a number of causes.

In a group.
Look at the photograph in Fig 1. Make a list of the ways that the lettuce plants are similar. Make a list of the ways that the lettuce plants are different. Now compare the lettuce to the cabbage plants. How big are the differences between these?

The causes of variation

▼ Fig 1

When animals and plants reproduce sexually their offspring acquire a mixture of characteristics from both parents. New combinations of characteristics can be made. Mixing genetic material causes variation. If an organism survives long enough to reproduce, its characteristics can be **inherited**, or passed on to future generations. If a variation creates a weakness, the organism may not survive long enough to pass on its weakness.

Inherited characteristics do not always develop fully. A person who has inherited the ability to grow tall may not get enough to eat to grow properly. This person will not become as tall as possible. Factors such as food and lifestyle are called **environmental** factors.

Inherited variation

The information for all the characteristics of an organism is copied and then passed to the next generation in large molecules called **genes**. Genes are the coded instructions that make up our genetic material. You received half of your genes from each parent. Your own personal characteristics are therefore a selection from both of your parents. You have two genes for every characteristic and one comes from each parent. One may be stronger than its partner. If you inherit one gene for brown eyes and one for blue eyes, for example, you will have brown eyes. This is because the brown eye gene is stronger or **dominant**.
Family members, therefore, often look alike but can sometimes look completely different.

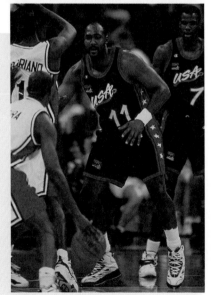

▶ **Fig 2** These players inherited the characteristics needed to grow tall, but they must also have eaten well and remained healthy.

On your own.
- Write down the words inherited, gene and dominant.
- Make your own dictionary definition for these words.
- Learn how to spell them and what they mean.

Sometimes a mistake occurs when the genetic code is being copied. Information might be lost, changed or added. If this happens a gene may not work at all or it may work differently. A change in a gene is called a **mutation**. This means there is always a chance of some completely new characteristic.

Most mutations simply cause problems, but once in a while something different and useful arises this way. Mutations can occur naturally but the rate of mutation can be speeded up. Radiation and some chemicals can increase the chance of mutations.

Environmental variation

Identical twins come from a single fertilised egg that divided in half before each half grew into a new baby. Because their genetic material is identical you would expect them to be exactly the same in every way.

Studying identical twins that were separated at birth and brought up in different situations can give us some idea of how important environment might be. If one twin has a healthy home life with good food and exercise and the other is less fortunate there can be a visible difference in their adult size and shape.

Plants can also show how the environment can affect inherited characteristics. Identical plants are easy to create from cuttings. When they are grown in different areas they can produce different yields, depending on sunshine, rainfall and soil fertility.

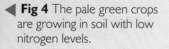

◀ **Fig 4** The pale green crops are growing in soil with low nitrogen levels.

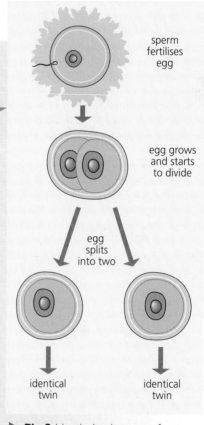

sperm fertilises egg

egg grows and starts to divide

egg splits into two

identical twin

identical twin

▶ **Fig 3** Identical twins come from a single fertilised egg.

- In a group.
  - Design an experiment using one packet of seeds and two plant pots of compost that shows how environmental factors can create variation among members of the same species.

80 Selective breeding

Selective breeding

Every new organism is unique. Characteristics inherited from both parents make it different from either of them. It is possible to mix characteristics deliberately to create special varieties of animals and plants.

One **variety** of plant may be very tall and strong but only produce small fruits. This plant might be very good at surviving wind and bad weather, but the food yield would be low.

Another variety of the same plant might be small and weak but produce very large fruits. This plant would be easily damaged but if it did survive it would give a good yield. The farmer would like to combine the good characteristics from both varieties to get a tall, strong plant with big fruits. If the farmer fertilises one plant with pollen from the other one the offspring will have a chance to combine some of the good characteristics. This is called **selective breeding**. Each step in selective breeding is called **cross breeding**.

▲ **Fig 1** These trees have been selectively bred for generations. They are disease resistant, strong, and give a high yield.

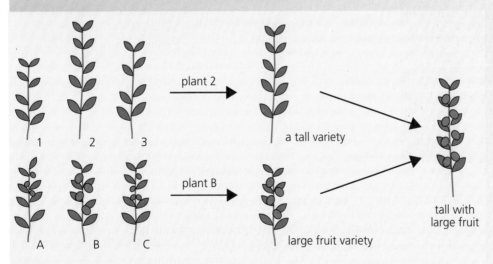

plant 2 → a tall variety

plant B → large fruit variety

tall with large fruit

◀ **Fig 2** Some variations can lead to useful characteristics.

ACTIVITY

With a partner.
- Study Fig 2. In you own words, write down how the tall plant with large fruit is produced.

It is important to realise that the perfect mixture of characteristics will not show in the first generation of offspring. The ones that seem most promising then are used as parents for the next generation. It takes many generations of breeding to arrive at a variety that can be grown commercially.

▲ **Fig 3** Selective breeding is not new. Ancient Egyptians began creating wheat from wild grasses three thousand years ago.

Garden varieties

Many modern garden plants are the result of selective breeding. Flowers can be made bigger and even be created in unnatural colours. Plant breeders also select for characteristics that make a new plant easier to grow, sturdier and resistant to disease.

Animal breeding

Selective breeding is used for animals as well as plants. Poultry and cattle have been selectively bred for many generations. Chickens can be bred to gain weight quickly or lay brown eggs, and cattle can be bred to give more milk or meat. Some people believe that selective breeding can be cruel. Animals may become too heavy to move comfortably. Even some pets have been bred for characteristics that make them uncomfortable.

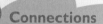 **Connections**

This work builds on your earlier work on reproduction and variation. It leads on to further work on plants for food, and inheritance and genetics.

REVIEW

- In a group.
  o Some scientists argue that selective breeding can be cruel and bad for the environment. What do the people in your group think?
  o Summarise your ideas as a few bullet points and prepare to present them to the class.

Choose five fruits or vegetables. Look at each in turn and make a list of the characteristics you think might have been improved by selective breeding.

81 Healthy skeleton

KEY IDEAS

In this section of the book you will have opportunities to:

- Explain that your skeleton is a frame of bones that supports and protects body organs
- Describe how joints between bones allow the skeleton to move and bend.

STARTER

In a group.
On a large piece of paper draw a human skeleton. Label as many bones as you can. Try to write down some ways that you can make sure your bones are healthy.

The human skeleton

The human skeleton contains more than 200 bones. Some parts of the skeleton protect organs. Other parts support our body and allow us to move. Bone is a mixture of soft living material and hard non-living mineral salts. This makes bone hard but prevents it from being brittle. Healthy bones need elements such as calcium and phosphorus. We obtain these elements from minerals and trace elements in foods such as milk, fruit and vegetables. Vitamins are also essential for healthy bones. Without vitamin D a disease called rickets (soft bones) results.

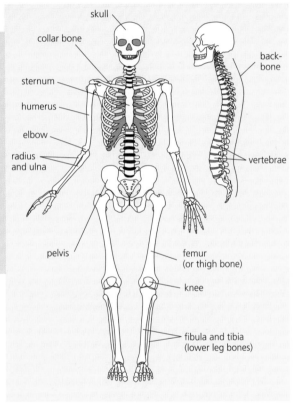

▲ **Fig 1** The human skeleton.

Labels: skull, collar bone, sternum, humerus, elbow, radius and ulna, pelvis, back-bone, vertebrae, femur (or thigh bone), knee, fibula and tibia (lower leg bones)

ACTIVITY

On your own.
- Write down why it is important to have minerals and vitamins in our diet.
- Which foods do you think would be especially important for healthy bones?

Parts of the human skeleton

The **skull** is a rigid box made up of plates of bone firmly joined together. They work like a crash helmet to protect the brain.

The **rib cage** is a flexible case around our heart and lungs. Each rib curves round the sides of the chest from the backbone and is joined in front to a plate of bone called the **sternum**. Ribs are connected to one another by the muscles that help us to breathe.

The backbone, also called the spine or **vertebral column**, is a chain of chunky bones called

vertebrae. It protects the spinal cord, which carries messages between your brain and body. It also supports the skull, ribs and limbs.

Arms and legs are limbs made of long bones with joints that allow them to move. They are mainly for support. Legs allow us to stand and walk. Arms allow us to move objects and take care of our body.

How do joints work?

Different joints work in different ways. There are three main types of joint:

1. hinge joints
2. ball and socket joints
3. gliding joints.

Hinge joints

A typical hinge joint is found in the knee. It allows the bones to move backwards and forwards like the hinge on a door. Hinge joints are not designed to move from side to side. The ends of the bones are coated with a smooth substance called **cartilage** which prevents them from grinding together. A slippery fluid inside the joint helps it to move easily.

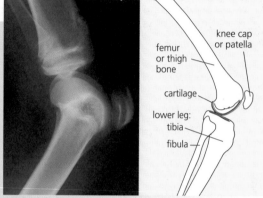

▲ **Fig 2** Unless the cartilage is damaged the bones will move smoothly.

knee cap or patella
femur or thigh bone
cartilage
lower leg:
tibia
fibula

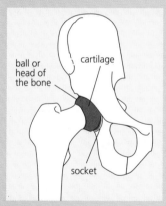

ball or head of the bone
cartilage
socket

▲ **Fig 3**

Ball and socket joint

Some parts of our body need to move more freely than a hinge would allow. For example, the shoulder can move in a full circle. The type of joint that permits a circular movement is called a ball and socket (see Fig 3).

Gliding joints

Some joints are designed to allow bones to slide a little way. The small bones inside our wrists (see Fig 4) and feet are arranged this way.

▼ **Fig 4**

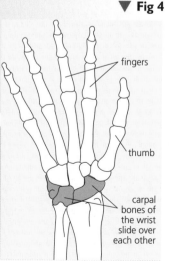

fingers
thumb
carpal bones of the wrist slide over each other

- In a group.
  - List the words that are in bold in this unit.
  - For each word write a definition.
  - Now write each word and its definition on a piece of card.
  - Carry these cards around and use them to learn the words.
  - You could try this technique for other words in science you must learn.

82 Bones on the move

In this section of the book you will have opportunities to:

- Explain that muscles pull on bones to make them move
- Describe how muscles often work in pairs called antagonistic muscle pairs.

In a group.
Some diseases cause muscles to waste away. Discuss the problems that this would cause to a sufferer of a disease like this. Make notes of your ideas so that you can discuss them with the rest of the class.

Muscles

A skeleton cannot move without muscles to work the joints. Muscle is an elastic meaty tissue that makes up a large part of your body. The kind of muscle that moves joints is called skeletal muscle. Muscles work by **contraction**, getting shorter and fatter. This uses up energy. Muscles are made of protein and it is vital that we have enough protein in our diets. We can obtain this protein from plant or animal sources.

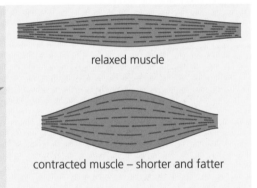

relaxed muscle

contracted muscle – shorter and fatter

▲ **Fig 1** A muscle will pull anything its tendons are attached to.

Muscles and joints

Muscles are attached to bones by strong fibres called **tendons**. When a muscle contracts, its tendons pull on the bones and make the joint move. Muscles cannot push. They can only pull. This means that one muscle can only move a joint in one direction (see Fig 2).

Your biceps can pull your hand towards your shoulder but it cannot push the bones apart again. Muscles on the other side of your arm, called the triceps, work the opposite way. They can pull the lower arm down but cannot push it up. Between them, the biceps and triceps can move the lower arm up and down. Muscles that work against one another like this are called **antagonistic muscle pairs** (see Fig 3).

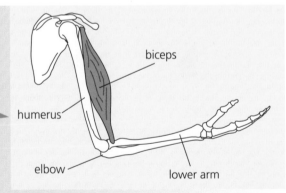

biceps

humerus

elbow

lower arm

▲ **Fig 2**

With a partner.
- Discuss why skeletal muscles work in pairs.
- Draw diagrams to show how this happens.

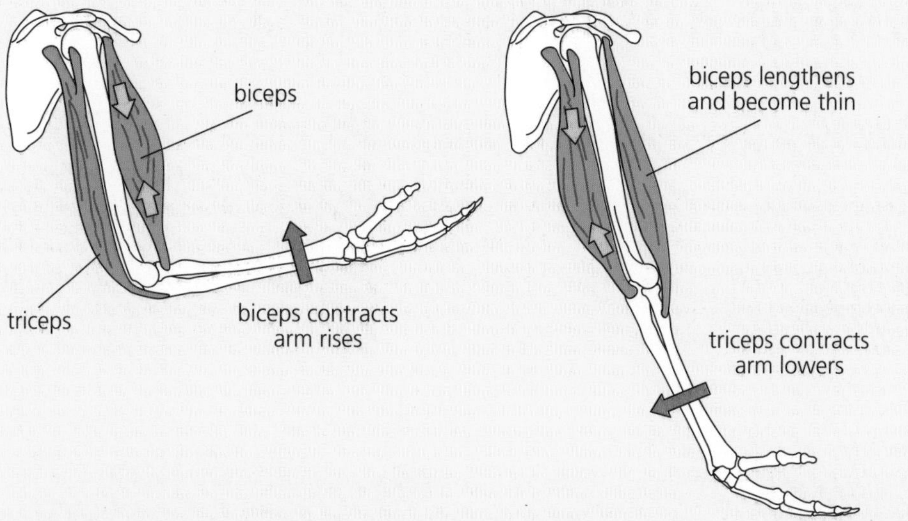

Fig 3 Muscles can only pull.

biceps

triceps

biceps contracts
arm rises

biceps lengthens
and become thin

triceps contracts
arm lowers

Fig 4 A body-builder learns to tense antagonistic muscle pairs at the same time to make them bulge.

Exercise is good for muscles. The muscles will become stronger. It is possible to over-exercise muscles and this can cause problems for the muscles and tendons. Sudden stretching or lifting very heavy weights can tear muscles and snap tendons. Warming up before exercise will help. This ensures a good supply of blood to the muscle.

Other jobs for muscle

We can decide when we want to move a joint. Our brain sends a message along nerves to the muscle and tells it to contract. Because we volunteer to do this the muscles are called **voluntary**.

Not all the muscles in your body are used to move joints.
Your diaphragm (see Unit 43) is a sheet of muscle that makes you breathe, even if you try not to. Another kind of muscle you cannot control is found in your heart. The walls of your intestines and blood vessels also contain muscles. This helps them to contract and push materials along. We do not tell these muscles to work. Our heart beats and the walls of our intestines carry on working when we are asleep. Because we do not volunteer to make these movements the muscles are called **involuntary**.

- In a group.
  - Use your knowledge of antagonistic muscle pairs to describe what happens to your leg muscles as you bend your ankle up and down.
  - Produce a poster to show what happens.

83 Smoking and lung disease

KEY IDEAS

In this section of the book you will have opportunities to:
- Describe that the lining of the windpipe has special cells that help to clean the air as it enters the lungs
- Explain that the chemicals in tobacco smoke can damage your health.

STARTER

In a group.
Try to recall your earlier work on breathing. Write down how breathing takes place and compare inhaled air with exhaled air.

Lungs

Lungs are where oxygen enters our blood. Without oxygen, a person dies very quickly. Anything that interferes with the way our lungs work is bad for our health. It is important to keep our lungs clean, undamaged and free from infection. Smoking causes serious damage and makes our lungs work less efficiently. Non-smokers who breathe in other people's smoke can suffer from the same health problems as smokers. This is called **passive smoking**.

The normal cleaning service

The cells lining your windpipe are adapted to remove particles from inhaled air before it reaches the bronchioles and alveoli. Some cells produce sticky mucus which traps dust and **bacteria**. Other cells have tiny hairs called **cilia** which beat in waves to push the mixture back up to your throat. If the mixture of mucus and dirt is swallowed it can be destroyed by acid in your stomach.

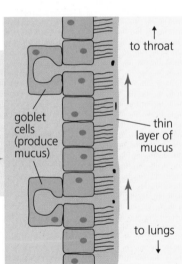

to throat

goblet cells (produce mucus)

thin layer of mucus

to lungs

▶ **Fig 1** The cilia beat to remove particles. The mucus traps particles and is then swallowed.

Cilia and smokers

The tar in tobacco smoke damages the cilia in the windpipe so that they stop working. This means that bacteria, dirt and mucus can build up deep inside the lungs. Bacteria in your lungs can cause infections such as bronchitis. Mucus and dirt in the bronchi and bronchioles make you cough. Eventually the alveoli become blocked and damaged. This reduces the working surface of the lungs and makes it harder to breathe (see Fig 2).

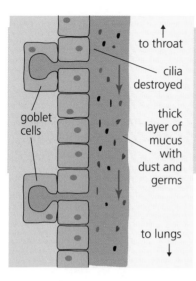

to throat

cilia destroyed

goblet cells

thick layer of mucus with dust and germs

to lungs

ACTIVITY

With a partner.

- Study Figs 1 and 2.
- In your own words explain what smoking can do to the lining of the windpipe.
- What problems can this cause?

◀ **Fig 2** Damaged and destroyed cilia cannot protect the lungs.

Blocking blood cells

One of the chemicals in tobacco smoke is a gas called carbon monoxide. This gas can pass through the lungs and into the blood. Carbon monoxide links to haemoglobin, as oxygen does, but unlike oxygen it does not easily let go. Once a red blood cell is full of carbon monoxide it cannot carry oxygen. This makes the blood of smokers less efficient.

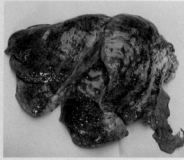

◀ **Fig 3** Which lung would you rather have inside you?

Lung cancer

Cells are always dividing to replace cells that become old and die. Sometimes this normal process can get out of control. If too many cells are made they can grow into a lump called a **tumour**. Tobacco smoke contains chemicals that can cause cells to divide and form tumours.

REVIEW

- In a group.
  - Design a leaflet that explains to people of your age why smoking causes illness.

84 Staying healthy

KEY IDEAS

In this section of the book you will have opportunities to:
- State the names of some drugs and solvents
- Explain how drugs, alcohol and solvents can damage your health.

STARTER

In a group.
Brainstorm a list of drugs you have heard about. Discuss the drugs and write about the harmful effects and dangers of taking them.

Effects of drugs on the body

The reason why the drugs you get from your doctor work is because they have an effect on your body. If you take them without medical advice you can damage your health. Some people take drugs in large doses because they enjoy one or two of the effects they have on their body. This is very dangerous because drugs have other effects that we do not notice. These are called **side-effects**. Side-effects can permanently damage your body. Side-effects can affect a person's personality and can cause brain damage. Side-effects can kill you.

Drug addiction

Many drugs are also addictive, which means that they start making you feel bad when your body wants them. At the same time they often stop making you feel good. When a person has become an addict it takes more and more of the drug to cause an effect. Many drug addicts, even young people, die before they can be given help. There are strict laws about the use of drugs. These laws are made to protect us from the danger of drug abuse.

The table shows some of the drugs that some people misuse.

▶ **Table 1**

Drug	Effects
Heroin	Sense of well being but is addictive and can lead to death.
Barbiturates	Can relax or slow people down. May cause death, especially if mixed with alcohol.
Cocaine	Feelings of excitement followed by depression. Can cause death.
Cannabis	Hallucinations and feelings of well being. May cause mental damage. Can lead to infertility in men (cannot produce sperm).
LSD	Hallucinations or 'trips' may cause serious mental derangement. The person may act in a wild manner.

Alcohol as a drug

Alcohol is very easy to buy and can be bought legally by people over 18 years of age. This does not mean it is safe. Alcohol can also damage health. It is sometimes difficult to work out how much alcohol some drinks contain. Alcohol is often measured in units. One unit of alcohol is half a pint of beer, a single measure of spirits, a glass of cider or a glass of wine. Table 2 shows how alcohol affects the way people behave.

Drinking a large amount of alcohol at one time can kill a person. People who drink too much alcohol may become addicted. A person addicted to alcohol is called an alcoholic.

Drinking too much alcohol can damage the brain and liver. Alcohol can also make some people aggressive. Even a small amount of alcohol can make people sleepy and slow down their reactions. It also causes them to make poor decisions. They may think they are capable of driving when they are not. This is why it is very dangerous for anyone to drive a car if they have been drinking alcohol. There are very strict drinking-and-driving laws to protect people from drink-drivers.

Units of alcohol	Effect on the body
1–3	skin flushed, talkative and confident
4–6	judgement slower, increased risk of having an accident
7–9	blurred vision, speech slurred
10–15	staggering, loss of balance, loss of memory
Over 20	clammy skin, dilated pupils
Over 30	coma, possible death

▲ **Table 2** Note: these figures are for an adult man. Women, and especially children, will show effects much sooner. One unit of alcohol is half a pint of beer, a single measure of spirits, a glass of cider or wine.

DRINKING AND DRIVING WRECKS LIVES

◀ **Fig 1** Drinking and driving can kill friends or strangers.

ACTIVITY

On your own.
- List some of the dangers of drinking too much alcohol.
- Do you think a ban on alcohol would be a good idea?
- Write down your reasons and be prepared to share them with the rest of the class.

 Connections

This work builds on earlier work on cells and health and fitness. It links closely to work on health covered in PHSE and leads on to further study of breathing and health issues.

Solvent abuse

Chemicals that dissolve other chemicals are called solvents. They have many uses in industry and the home. Our body uses water as a solvent. Solvents other than water can harm our body.

The vapour from a solvent can make a person light headed. This may feel funny but it means a person is not in control and may have an accident. Solvents can also cause damage to your body. Smelling, or 'sniffing' glues and solvents can damage your lungs and brain very badly. Even a small amount of solvent can kill. Some solvents can also be addictive. Once a person starts to abuse solvents it can be very difficult for them to stop.

REVIEW

- In a group.
  - Design a poster that aims to persuade young people to say no to drugs. Include the scientific arguments but also make it eyecatching.

85 How plants make food

Sources of food

Animals get their food by eating plants or other animals. Plants make their own food by joining together simple molecules. They need energy from the Sun to do this.

Energy from the Sun

During the day green plants use energy from the Sun to join together water and carbon dioxide molecules to make glucose. This is called **photosynthesis**. Photosynthesis takes place mainly in leaves and depends on a very important green pigment called chlorophyll. The chlorophyll is contained in **chloroplasts**.

Having a large surface helps a leaf to obtain as much sunlight as possible. Small holes called stomata allow gases to pass in and out of the leaf. Each leaf is thin and has a spongy structure of cells. This allows gases to reach all the cells.

Palisade cells contain a large number of chloroplasts. The cells are lined up in the leaf like a small fence. This helps the energy entering the surface of the leaf to travel a long way through the palisade cells. This allows as much light as possible to reach the chlorophyll in the chloroplasts.

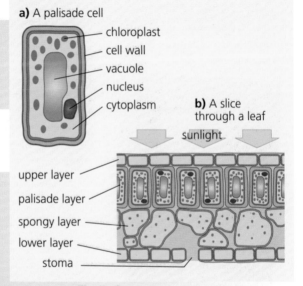

a) A palisade cell
- chloroplast
- cell wall
- vacuole
- nucleus
- cytoplasm

b) A slice through a leaf

sunlight

- upper layer
- palisade layer
- spongy layer
- lower layer
- stoma

▲ **Fig 1a** Plant cell showing chloroplasts.
b Leaf showing leaf structure and cells.

▶ **Fig 2** The pigment in the leaf looks green because blue and red light energy is absorbed, leaving the green light to be reflected back to the eyes of the observer.

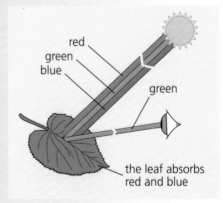

red
green
blue

green

the leaf absorbs red and blue

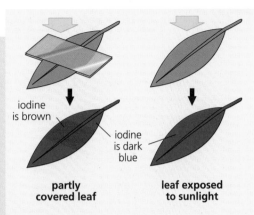

▼ Fig 3

iodine
is brown

iodine
is dark
blue

**partly
covered leaf**

**leaf exposed
to sunlight**

Biomass and photosynthesis

The glucose made by photosynthesis is sent around the plant to provide food. Cells in the root or stem can use the glucose to make energy. If the plant does not need to use all the glucose immediately then it has to be stored. Glucose is hard to store because it dissolves in water. Plants solve this problem by joining hundreds of glucose molecules together to make starch. Starch makes a better food store because it does not dissolve very well in water.

It is easy to test whether a plant has made some starch. Starch reacts with iodine solution by turning blue-black. Fig 3 shows some leaves that have been stained with iodine. Both plants were left in the Sun but one of them had part of a leaf covered up. You can see that this leaf only contains starch in the uncovered parts.

Glucose can provide energy or carbon. Carbon can be used to manufacture other molecules in the plant. In this way plants use the energy of the Sun to create new living matter from non-living matter. We call this material **biomass**.

Oxygen and photosynthesis

When glucose is made from water and carbon dioxide some oxygen is left over. It is easiest to test this on a submerged water-plant (see Fig 4) because any gases the plant makes can easily be collected.

When a glowing piece of wood meets the gas from the water-weed it begins to burn with a flame again. This shows that the gas produced during photosynthesis is oxygen.

ACTIVITY

With a partner.
● Discuss what plants do with the glucose they cannot use immediately.
● Why do they do this?
● Write your ideas down.

▼ **Fig 4** The gas is collected in a test tube.

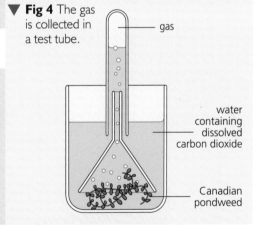

gas

water
containing
dissolved
carbon dioxide

Canadian
pondweed

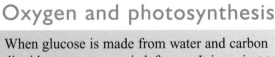

REVIEW

● In a group.
  ○ Discuss how plants are adapted to carry out photosynthesis.
  ○ Summarise your ideas in no more than six bullet points.
  ○ Produce an overhead projector transparency or powerpoint page of your ideas.
  ○ Prepare to discuss your ideas with the class.

🏠 Collect a few leaves from a plant. Take some from the top, some from the middle and some from the bottom. Place the leaves on graph paper and draw round them. Use the squares of the paper to estimate the surface area of each leaf. Can you see any trends? Use your knowledge of photosynthesis to explain any trends in leaf size.

86 Photosynthesis in detail

KEY IDEAS

In this section of the book you will have opportunities to:
- Explain that plants need carbon dioxide, water and light for photosynthesis
- Describe the word equation for photosynthesis
- Explain the difference between photosynthesis and respiration in plants.

STARTER

In a group.
Discuss your earlier work on photosynthesis. Make a list of the raw materials plants need in order to carry out photosynthesis. What are the products of photosynthesis?

The raw materials

▼ **Table 1** Composition of air.

Gas	Percentage
Nitrogen	78%
Oxygen	21%
Other gases (mainly carbon dioxide)	1%

A plant growing in air is in contact with a mixture of gases. These gases are shown in Table 1. In water, a plant is still in contact with these gases because of the air that is dissolved in the water.

If we try the iodine test (see Unit 85) on a plant growing in air that has had all the carbon dioxide removed, nothing happens. The iodine does not turn blue-black so we know there is no starch in the leaf. This tells us that a plant needs carbon dioxide to make starch. Because we know that starch is made from glucose, we can guess that the plant needs carbon dioxide to make glucose.

ACTIVITY

On your own.
- Write down how we know that carbon dioxide is a raw material of photosynthesis.
- Why do you suppose some plant growers try to increase the amount of carbon dioxide inside a greenhouse?

It is more difficult to test whether water is needed for photosynthesis because if you remove water from the plant it will die before your experiment is finished. Scientists have shown that water is a raw material for photosynthesis by watering a plant with **radioactive** water.

Building glucose

You now know that carbon dioxide, water and sunlight are needed for plants to make glucose. Next, we need to find out how they do this.

Glucose contains carbon, hydrogen and oxygen atoms. There are twice as many hydrogen atoms as oxygen atoms, as there are in water (see Unit 53). Glucose is a **carbohydrate**.

The atoms needed to make glucose come from carbon dioxide and water. These raw materials provide all the elements the plant needs to make glucose.

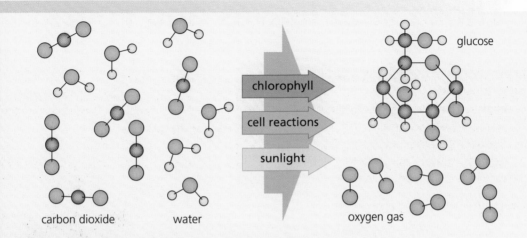

▲ **Fig I** Notice that the extra oxygen atoms are given off as a waste product.

This chemical reaction can be written down as a word equation.

$$\text{carbon dioxide} + \text{water} \xrightarrow[\text{chlorophyll}]{\text{light}} \text{glucose} + \text{oxygen}$$

This equation is exactly the reverse of the equation for **respiration**. Respiration (see Unit 44) is the process of breaking glucose down to release the energy that once came from the Sun. Photosynthesis and respiration are a very different series of reactions but overall they have the opposite effect.

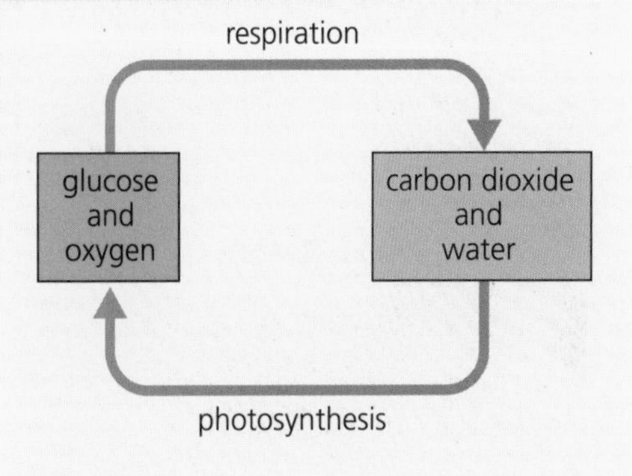

Connections

This work builds on earlier work on variation, classification and photosynthesis. It leads on to further study of plants as food.

▲ **Fig 2** Animals can only respire. Plants can make the equation go both ways. Remember that plants also respire.

- In a group.
  - Discuss why green plants use both respiration and photosynthesis.
  - What is the name of the gas given out by a green plant at night?
  - Discuss why flowers used to be removed from hospital wards at night.
  - Write your ideas down.

Write a short story explaining why taking plants on space missions would help to provide oxygen for the crew.

87 Those vital leaves and roots

KEY IDEAS

In this section of the book you will have opportunities to:

- Explain that specialised cells are essential for plant survival
- Explain that leaves and roots are adapted to carry out their functions.

STARTER

In a group.
Draw and label the parts of a flowering plant. Write down the functions of each part of the plant.

Plant organisation

Like animals, multicellular plants are made up of different types of cells. There is also division of labour in plants. Cells with the same function are gathered together into tissues. Plant tissues work together in organs. The major tissues and organs of a flowering plant (Fig 1) must all work together to carry out the seven functions of life and keep the organism alive.

Plants also need to move food and water from place to place. Instead of blood and a heart, they have a system of tubes called vascular tissue.

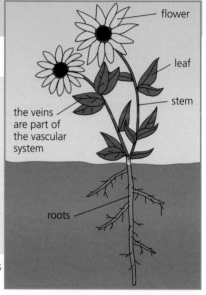

▶ **Fig 1** Plants have tissues and organs specialised to do different jobs.

Cells in leaves

Plants use energy from the Sun to turn water and carbon dioxide gas into sugar. This process is called photosynthesis and it takes place in the leaves (see Unit 86).

Palisade cells are especially well designed for photosynthesis. They contain many chloroplasts filled with chlorophyll and form a layer just beneath the upper protective covering of the leaf.
When the Sun shines on the leaf the energy from the sunlight passes directly into them. They are also tall and arranged in regular rows, to help the sunlight to shine deep inside.

▲ **Fig 2** Sunlight travels deeper into palisade cells because they are this way up.

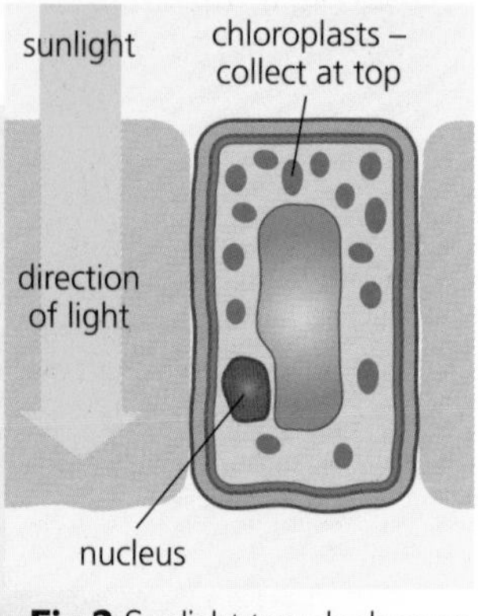

Guard cells are also very specialised leaf cells. They control the small pores called stomata on the underside of leaves. Full, fat, guard cells open a **stoma** and thin, empty ones close it. In this way the guard cells control the amount of water and gases that pass in and out of the leaf.

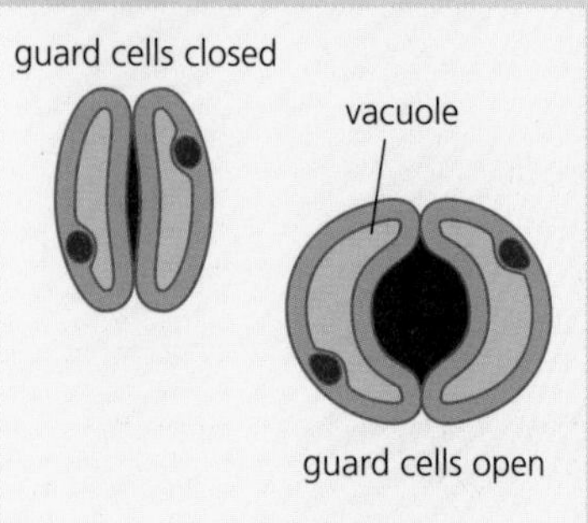

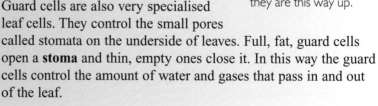

▲ **Fig 3** Hard, fat, guard cells open the stoma. Soft, flabby cells close it.

With a partner.
● Guard cells allow gases and water vapour to pass into and out of the leaf. Why is it vital that the stomata are able to open and close?

Those vital roots

The roots of a plant are normally under the soil. Roots fix a plant firmly in the soil so that it is not easily uprooted by animals or blown over by the wind. However, roots have other equally important jobs.

stem
leaf
some plants have a long, deep tap root
some plants have fibrous roots made up of many roots of the same size
main or tap root
side root
root cap

◄ **Fig 4** Plants have a variety of different roots, but most water and minerals are absorbed through the root hairs.

Root hairs

Root hairs are found on specially adapted cells on the outer surface of the root, just behind the root tip. The **root hair cells** have special outgrowths that push between the soil particles into the water there. The walls of root hairs are very thin. This makes it easy for water to pass from the soil into the root. Root hairs increase the surface area of the root and this increases the amount of water they can absorb.

Transport of water and minerals

Substances that enter the roots must next be transported to where they are needed. Water may have to travel all the way up to the leaves. Water, food and minerals are carried in a plant's **vascular system**. This contains a series of long cells connected together to make tubes. One set of tubes carries water and minerals upwards. Another set of tubes may carry food down from the leaves.

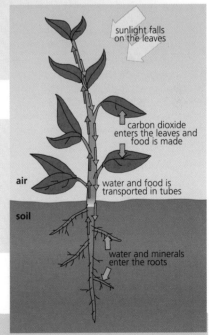

sunlight falls on the leaves
carbon dioxide enters the leaves and food is made
air
water and food is transported in tubes
soil
water and minerals enter the roots

▶ **Fig 5** We now know how plants obtain essential elements, make food by photosynthesis, and transport substances from one part to another.

● In a group.
  ○ Make a list of the ways that leaves and roots are adapted to do their jobs.
  ○ Write down your ideas and prepare to discuss them with other groups.

88 Nutrients needed by plants

KEY IDEAS

In this section of the book you will have opportunities to:

- Describe the raw materials needed by plants
- Explain how plants obtain these raw materials.

STARTER

In a group.
Imagine you are trying to grow vegetables in the classroom. Brainstorm what the plants would need for healthy growth. Write down your ideas.

Nutrients

A plant makes glucose from carbon dioxide and water, by photosynthesis. However, plant cells also contain protein. Protein contains nitrogen but glucose does not. The nitrogen must therefore come from somewhere else.

Essential elements

In addition to carbon, hydrogen and oxygen, plants also need other **essential elements**. One way to find out which elements are essential for healthy plant growth is to give them different diets and see how they grow.

This may sound easy but it is almost as difficult as working out an ideal diet for a person. A large number of plants must be grown in exactly the same conditions; the only difference is that one element is left out of the diet of half of them. This test has to be done all over again for each element tested, and then repeated many times to work out exactly how much of each element a plant needs. The same set of tests must be repeated for every different kind of plant a farmer or gardener wants to know about.

Element	Symptoms if lacking
Iron	poor leaves, no chlorophyll
Sulphur	poor growth, proteins not made
Nitrogen	poor growth, proteins not made
Calcium	cells do not divide properly
Potassium	poor growth, water lost
Magnesium	pale leaves, no chlorophyll
Phosphorus	poor growth, no energy molecules

▲ **Table 1** Essential elements.

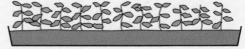

Growth medium with all essential elements
Growth medium with one essential element missing

▲ **Fig 1** Why are so many plants used in the test?

ACTIVITY

On your own.

- Describe why iron, sulphur, phosphorus and magnesium are essential elements for plants.

Nitrogen is needed to make proteins and enzymes. A plant cannot grow or repair itself without protein. Most plants cannot use nitrogen gas directly from the air or soil. They must use compounds of nitrogen such as nitrates. These compounds are made from **organic matter** when it is broken down by bacteria in soil. The organic matter could be dead plants, dead animals or waste materials such as manure. The bacteria recycle the nitrogen.

Some plants have bacteria living in their roots. These bacteria can use nitrogen gas and form nitrogen compounds. The plant provides a home, or **nodule**, for the bacteria. In return, the bacteria provide the nitrogen compounds for the plant to use. Plants of this type are called **legumes**. Examples include peas, beans and clover.

Sulphur is also essential for many proteins. Without sulphur these proteins could not be manufactured by the plant. A common source of sulphur in soil is in sulphates. In this form the sulphur can be absorbed by the roots and used by the plant.

Phosphorus is needed for proteins and energy storage molecules. Plant cells could not survive for more than a few seconds without phosphorus. Phosphorus is found in soil in the form of phosphates. As with nitrates and sulphates, the phosphates dissolve in water and can pass into the plant through the roots.

Magnesium is a vital part of chlorophyll. A shortage of magnesium slows down photosynthesis. A lack of magnesium kills the plant.

▲ **Fig 2** Root nodules.

  Study tip

You can remember the essential elements by learning the phrase: **I**n **S**ummer **N**ice **C**hildren **P**lay **M**any **P**uzzles. The first letter of each word in the phrase is the first letter of the name of the element. Try to make up your own.

REVIEW

• In a group.
  ○ Look back at your starter activity.
  ○ Discuss how you would improve your original ideas now you have studied more about plants.

How does a pot plant obtain its essential elements? How can the owners of the plant help?

89 Increasing crop yield

Fertile ground

Most plants get their essential nutrients from the soil. They absorb the nutrients as minerals dissolved in water. Soil with a good supply of essential elements is called fertile. The trees in a forest first take nutrients out of the soil and then, when they die, the nutrients are returned to the soil. This is how the soil of the forest remains fertile.

The plants we eat are removed from the soil where they grow. The essential elements in the plants are also removed. When the same land is used over and over again the soil becomes infertile. Plants will not grow well there because essential elements are missing. The **yield** will fall. There are two main solutions for this problem.

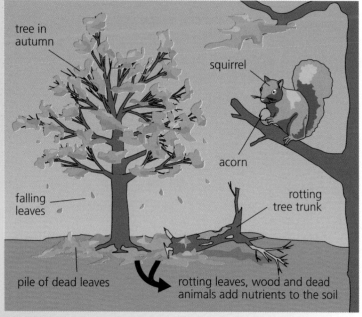

▲ **Fig 1** The essential elements in a forest return naturally to the soil.

1. Natural fertilisers can be added to the soil. Farmyard manure, compost or other organic material can restore essential nutrients. Natural fertilisers can be difficult to store and handle but they release essential elements slowly and well. They can also improve the physical texture of the soil.

2. Artificial fertilisers can be added to the soil. These are mixtures of chemicals made in factories. They work quickly and are easy to handle and store, but must be used carefully because rain can carry them into rivers and streams. Chemicals in water can make it bad to drink and damage the environment.

Fertiliser problems

Adding too much fertiliser to soils can cause problems. The fertilisers can be washed into streams, rivers and ponds. Here they can encourage microscopic plants in the water, such as algae, to grow. If this happens on a large scale it is called an algal bloom. When the large number of plants die they are broken down by bacteria. This uses up the oxygen in the water. The lack of oxygen can result in the death of fish and other animals. Natural fertilisers are less easily washed out of the soil.

▲ **Fig 2** These fish have died because of lack of oxygen.

ACTIVITY

With a partner.
- Fertilisers increase the yield of crops but they can cause problems in the environment. Discuss whether or not you think farmers should use fertilisers.

Connections

This work builds on earlier work on ecological relationships and photo-synthesis. The work links to inheritance, selection and environmental chemistry. This unit will help you to understand further work on the impact of humans on the environment at Key Stage 4.

Pesticides and herbicides

Another way to increase the yield of crops is to stop pests from eating them before they are harvested. Microorganisms, insects and other animals can all attack crops. For the animal the crop is just part of their natural food web. **Pesticides** are chemicals that will kill pests but not harm the crops. This will help to increase yields and provide more crops. However, pesticides can cause environmental damage. The pests being killed can be the food source for predators. This means the pesticide will have an impact on populations and food webs in the area. Some pesticides are also harmful to humans.

A weed is really a plant that is growing in the wrong place. Weeds will take up space, steal nutrients and may block light from crop plants. Removing weeds will increase yield. The weeds can be removed by hand or by using chemicals. Chemicals that kill unwanted plants are called weedkillers or **herbicides**. These must be used with great care so that other plants and animals are not affected.

REVIEW

- In a group.
  - Produce a leaflet to be given out at a local garden centre. The leaflet should give information about how gardeners could improve the health and yield of their plants, but in an environmentally friendly way.

Research some of the ways that organic farmers control weeds and pests.

90 Food chains and toxic materials

In this section of the book you will have opportunities to:
- Explain how toxic materials can enter food chains
- Describe how toxic materials can build up in food chains.

With a partner.
Write down an example of a food chain. Imagine the plant at the start of the chain had been sprayed with a pesticide. Discuss what could happen to the pesticide after the plant was eaten. Make a note of your ideas and be prepared to discuss them with the class.

Toxic substances

Many chemicals have been sprayed onto soil, ponds and rivers to control the spread of diseases in humans, farm animals and crops. These chemicals are designed to kill the organisms that spread the diseases. They are therefore poisonous or **toxic**.

Toxins that kill pests are called pesticides.

Toxic substances and food webs

Pesticide sprayed on a crop will land on everything. It may slow down poisoned insects and make them easier to catch. If it does not kill the insects quickly the insects may be eaten by birds or other secondary consumers. Each secondary consumer eats many primary consumers (see Unit 9).

Each time a bird eats a poisoned insect it will collect some more pesticide. If the bird cannot excrete a pesticide it will become more and more concentrated in the bird's body. If the bird is eaten by a predator all this poison will enter the predator's body. A hawk eating many smaller birds can collect an immense dose of pesticide. This might be enough to kill the hawk. Even if it is not enough to kill, it can upset the hawk's behaviour or chemistry badly enough to prevent it breeding.

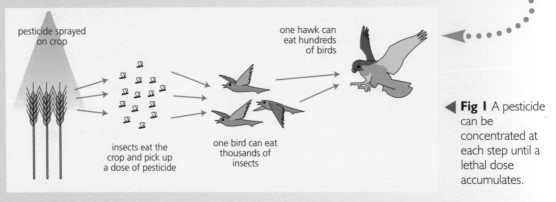

pesticide sprayed on crop

one hawk can eat hundreds of birds

insects eat the crop and pick up a dose of pesticide

one bird can eat thousands of insects

◀ **Fig I** A pesticide can be concentrated at each step until a lethal dose accumulates.

With a partner.
- Design another example of a food chain and show how a toxic substance can pass down the chain.

DDT was once used to poison all kinds of insects. As well as protecting crops, it worked very well on mosquitoes and helped to control the disease called malaria. DDT does not harm people but it is very toxic to many other animals. Eventually the damage to animals along the food chain became so serious that the use of DDT was banned in most countries. DDT is not broken down by the animals and builds up in fat tissue inside the body.

Reversing the effects

Evidence is sometimes hard to collect and to understand. It took a long time to discover that a particular type of pesticide caused some birds to lay eggs that were not fertile. Pesticides can also make eggshells so thin that the eggs break easily. These side effects caused a decrease in the population of birds of prey. Since the pesticides responsible for these and other side effects were banned, the bird populations have increased.

Other toxic chemicals

Many other toxins can enter the environment accidentally. Some of the waste products of industry can spill into rivers. When a **polluted** river enters the sea the toxins get into the food webs there. Some toxins, such as oil spilled from tankers or chemical cargoes washed overboard, enter the sea directly.

Heavy metals

▼ **Fig 2** Waste water containing mercury being discharged into Minamata bay.

Toxins can be simple chemical elements. Lead is toxic to people, and so is mercury. Mercury from a plastics factory by the sea in Japan poisoned cats and people in the nearby town of Minamata. First the cats became very ill and died. A few months later people in the town began to suffer from the same illness. By the time the disease was identified as mercury poisoning more than 40 people had died and 60 were permanently disabled. Many of the fish and birds near Minamata were also dead. Scientists found 20 to 60 times the normal amount of mercury in the shellfish from the sea there. Because the cats and people were the tertiary consumers they had received very large doses of mercury.

REVIEW

- In a group.
  - Try to show the Minamata story as a food chain.
  - Use this to explain how the cats and people in Minamata received high doses of mercury.

Research some examples of toxic substances entering food chains. You may need to look up old newspapers or articles on CD ROM or the Internet. Produce a summary of your findings.

91 The reactions of metals

KEY IDEAS

In this section of the book you will have opportunities to:
- Explain how metals react with oxygen, water and acids.

STARTER

In a group.
Make a list of the properties of metals that make them so useful. Compare your list with those from other groups.

The reactions of metals

Some metals are very unreactive. Gold stays shiny for thousands of years. If all metals were this unreactive we would not have to worry about rusting. This is not the case. Most metals are reactive. Some are very reactive indeed.

Metals and oxygen

Oxygen is all around us in the air. Most metals react with oxygen to form metal oxides. Here is an example:

sodium + oxygen ⟶ sodium oxide

Some metals react with oxygen more quickly than others. Sodium reacts with oxygen as soon as it is exposed to the air. Pure sodium metal is stored under oil to prevent it from oxidising. Some other metals such as zinc, iron and copper react quickly with oxygen when they are heated but only oxidise slowly at room temperature.

The oxides of reactive metals are called **bases**. If a base is soluble in water it makes an **alkaline** solution.

ACTIVITY

On your own.
- Explain the difference between a base and an alkali. Write down an example of each.

Metals and water

Water is a compound made of the elements hydrogen and oxygen. If a reactive metal is added to water the metal will 'steal' the oxygen. This leaves the hydrogen alone. Hydrogen atoms join up into pairs and fly away as a gas. The word equation for the reaction between magnesium and water is:

magnesium + water ⟶ magnesium oxide + hydrogen

Magnesium reacts very slowly with cold water. Only a few bubbles of hydrogen gas would be produced in several days. It reacts very quickly with steam.

Sodium reacts very quickly with water. The sodium is pushed around on the surface of the water by the hydrogen gas released in the reaction. The other product is sodium hydroxide. This makes an alkaline solution. The word equation for this reaction is:

sodium + water ⟶ sodium hydroxide + hydrogen

Metals such as gold, copper and silver will not react with water, even if it is heated into steam.

Metals and acids

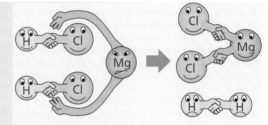

▶ **Fig I** Magnesium takes the hydrogen from hydrochloric acid to form the salt called magnesium chloride. Hydrogen gas is given off.

Acids contain hydrogen. When a metal reacts with an acid it replaces the hydrogen. This makes a **salt**. The hydrogen is given off as a gas. Not all metals react with acids. We can place metals into a table of reactivity (see Unit 94).

Here are some word equations for metals reacting with acids:

magnesium + hydrochloric acid ⟶ magnesium chloride + hydrogen
calcium + nitric acid ⟶ calcium nitrate + hydrogen

Each laboratory acid forms a special type of salt.

Hydrochloric acid forms **chlorides**. Sulphuric acid forms **sulphates**. Nitric acid forms **nitrates**.

Metal	Reaction with oxygen	Reaction with water	Reaction with dilute acid
Sodium	burns quickly to form an oxide	reacts with cold water to give off hydrogen	reacts quickly with acids to give off hydrogen
Calcium			
Magnesium			
Aluminium		reacts with steam to give off hydrogen	reacts slowly with acids to give off hydrogen
Zinc	burns less quickly to form an oxide		
Iron			
Lead	reacts slowly to form a layer of oxide	no reaction	reacts very slowly to give off hydrogen
Copper			no reaction
Silver	no reaction		
Gold			

◀**Table I** The reactions of metals.

REVIEW

● In a group.
  ○ Plan how you could safely make a pure sample of magnesium chloride from magnesium metal and an acid. Include a word equation.

92 Metal compounds and acids

Acids and carbonates

Limestone is a chemical compound called calcium carbonate. Other carbonates include copper carbonate, zinc carbonate and magnesium carbonate. These are called metal carbonates because they contain a metal as well as the carbonate.

An acid reacts with a carbonate by breaking it down into a salt, water and carbon dioxide gas. The carbon dioxide makes the reaction fizz.

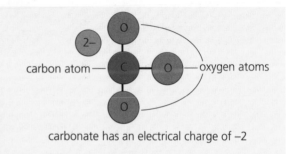

carbonate has an electrical charge of –2

▲ **Fig 1** Structure of carbonates.

This is one way to find out if a substance is a carbonate. The general word equation is:

acid + metal carbonate ⟶ metal salt + water + carbon dioxide

Word equations (see Unit 54) are a useful shorthand for writing down what happens in a chemical reaction, but they only go so far. To get more useful information we must use **symbol equations**.

Formulae of compounds

When atoms combine or join together they do so in very strict ways. Each atom has the ability to **bond** or join onto a specific number of other atoms. This is called its **valency** or combining power. Some common valencies are given in Table 1.

There are important rules to follow when writing the formula of a compound.

1. Write down the name of the compound. Be careful, some names are very similar.

2. Look up the symbols for the chemicals. Use a table of valencies like the one in Table 1.

3. Count the number of positive charges and the number of negative charges on the ions. Compounds do not have an electrical charge so these must eventually balance.

4. If you have too many positive charges, you must add more of the negative ions. If you have too many negative ions you must add more of the positive ions.

5. Once the charges are balanced you can write down the formula.

Positive ions		Negative ions	
Name	Symbol and charge	Name	Symbol and charge
Ammonium	NH_4^+	Chloride	Cl^-
Sodium	Na^+	Hydroxide	OH^-
Copper	Cu^{2+}	Nitrate	NO_3^-
Magnesium	Mg^{2+}	Carbonate	CO_3^{2-}
Zinc	Zn^{2+}	Oxide	O^{2-}
Aluminium	Al^{3+}	Sulphate	SO_4^{2-}

◀ **Table 1**
Valencies.

Let us see an example worked out for us. The compound is zinc chloride.

Name   zinc   chloride
Symbols Zn^{2+} Cl^-

There are more positive charges than negative
so we add extra chloride. Zn^{2+} Cl^-
                                    Cl^-
                           $ZnCl_2$

ACTIVITY

On your own.
- Write down the formulae for calcium carbonate and sodium carbonate.

Notice that a small 2 is used to show that there are two chloride atoms for every zinc atom.

Symbol equations

In a chemical reaction matter is not created and it is not destroyed. Therefore, every atom on one side of the equation must be found on the other. So, to write symbol equations you:

- Write down the correct word equation.
- Find the symbol for each atom and work out the formula for each compound.
- Write the formulae and symbols underneath the word equation.
- Balance the equation by making sure that every atom on one side can be found on the other.

Study tip

Once you have worked out the formula of each compound NEVER alter it. You can add more or less of the substance in order to balance the equation.

For example:

calcium + hydrochloric acid ⟶ calcium chloride + water + carbon dioxide
Ca   + HCl   ⟶ $CaCl_2$ + H_2O + CO_2
Ca   + 2HCl   ⟶ $CaCl_2$ + H_2O + CO_2

To balance the equation we needed to make sure we had exactly the same number of atoms on both sides.

REVIEW

- In a group.
  - Describe the reaction between sodium carbonate and hydrochloric acid in words, in a word equation and then as a symbol equation.

- Research and then write word and symbol equations for the reactions between copper oxide and hydrochloric acid and lead oxide and sulphuric acid.

93 Salts and their uses

KEY IDEAS

In this section of the book you will have opportunities to:
- Predict the names and formulae of salts formed from chemical reactions.

STARTER

In a group.
Use your prior knowledge to explain what the word salt means to a scientist. Write down some examples of salts.

Making salts

Fig 1 summarises the reactions of acids you have studied so far. Notice that in every case one of the products is a salt. Reacting substances with acids is often a very good way of making salts. However, it is not the only way.

We can also make salts we want from salts we already have. To do this we use displacement reactions. These are described in more detail in Unit 94. If we want some zinc chloride and we have some copper chloride and zinc, we can make zinc chloride by putting them together in water. The zinc will displace the copper and zinc chloride will form.

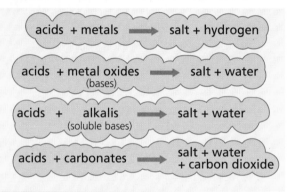

▲ **Fig 1** How acids react with four main groups of chemicals. Notice that salts are formed every time. Acid reactions are a very good way to make salts.

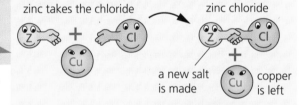

▶ **Fig 2** Zinc and copper chloride reacting.

Making copper sulphate

There are different ways to make a sample of the salt copper sulphate. For example:
- reacting copper oxide with sulphuric acid
- reacting copper carbonate with sulphuric acid.

When black copper oxide powder is added to sulphuric acid a chemical reaction takes place. The copper combines with the sulphate present in the solution to form copper sulphate. The hydrogen from the acid combines with the oxide and forms water.

copper oxide + sulphuric acid ⟶ copper sulphate + water

Any unreacted copper oxide can be removed by filtering. The filtrate is a blue colour. The copper sulphate can be obtained as crystals by evaporating the filtrate. It is clear from its appearance that copper sulphate is a new substance. It is a salt.

Connections

This work builds on earlier work on atoms, elements and compounds. It extends your understanding of reactions between acids and metal compounds and leads on to further work on patterns of reactivity.

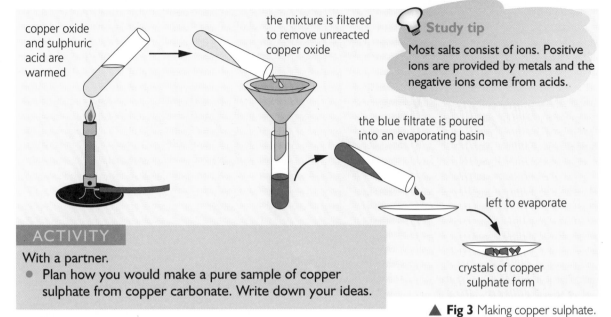

copper oxide and sulphuric acid are warmed

the mixture is filtered to remove unreacted copper oxide

the blue filtrate is poured into an evaporating basin

left to evaporate

crystals of copper sulphate form

ACTIVITY

With a partner.
- Plan how you would make a pure sample of copper sulphate from copper carbonate. Write down your ideas.

▲ **Fig 3** Making copper sulphate.

Properties of salts

Salts are all made of ions. This makes them similar in many ways.

Most salts dissolve in water

Salts are solids with crystal shapes

When dissolved in water they conduct electricity

When melted they conduct electricity

▶ **Fig 4** Crystals of salts in close up.

Uses of salts

Many salts occur naturally. Calcium flouride (flourite), calcium sulphate (gypsum) and rock salt are examples. If the salt dissolves in water then they can be washed into rivers and carried to the sea. This is why the sea is salty. Salts have many uses. Some are shown in Table 1.

▶ **Table 1** Uses of salts.

Salt	Formula	Uses
Sodium chloride	NaCl	food preservation and seasoning
Potassium nitrate	KNO$_3$	explosives, fertilisers
Sodium hydrogen carbonate	NaHCO$_3$	baking powder, making glass
Silver bromide	AgBr	photographic film
Sodium nitrate	NaNO$_3$	fertilisers

REVIEW

- In a group.
  - Plan how you would produce a pure sample of sodium nitrate. What could the product be used for?

Research and then make a list of the different salts that are dissolved in the sea. Which is the saltiest sea in the world?

94 The Reactivity Series

KEY IDEAS

In this section of the book you will have opportunities to:
- Explain that metals can replace other metals in salts
- Explain that these reactions depend on some metals being more reactive than others.

STARTER

In a group.
Make a list of all of the metal objects you can see in the room. Discuss which are shiny and which are tarnished or rusted. Try to explain why.

Metals and solutions

Crystals of copper sulphate are blue. They dissolve in water to make a blue solution. Zinc metal is bluish-grey.

When a lump of zinc is added to copper sulphate solution the blue colour of the solution fades and the zinc becomes darker. This is what we see. We cannot see the chemical reaction between the copper sulphate and the zinc but we can see the result. Zinc has **displaced** the copper. The solution becomes paler because zinc sulphate is not blue. The zinc looks darker because a thin layer of copper forms on its surface.

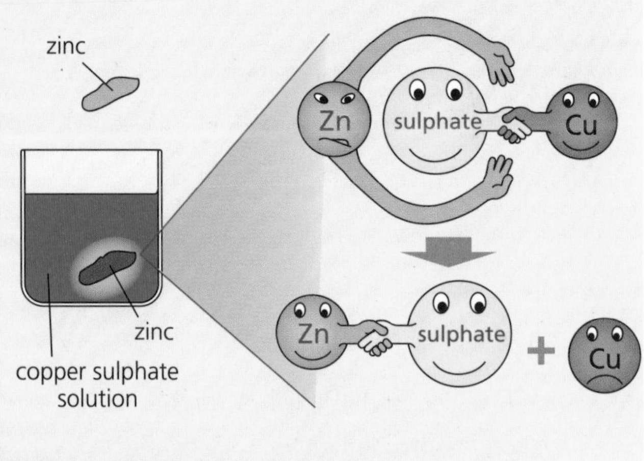

The word equation for this reaction is:

zinc

Zn sulphate Cu

zinc

copper sulphate solution

Zn sulphate **+** Cu

▲ **Fig 1** Zinc displaces copper from copper sulphate.

⚠ **Caution:** copper sulphate is poisonous.

zinc + copper sulphate ⟶ zinc sulphate + copper

We can use displacement reactions to make salts we want from salts we already have. If we want some magnesium chloride and we already have some lead chloride and some magnesium, we can make magnesium chloride by putting them together in water.

magnesium + lead chloride ⟶ magnesium chloride + lead

Competing metals

We cannot make copper from zinc sulphate and copper. A displacement reaction is the result of a competition between two metals. The most **reactive** metal always wins.

Zinc is more reactive than copper. Zinc holds onto chloride more firmly than copper does. We can arrange metals into an order of reactivity by comparing them, one by one, to find out which ones displace others from their salts.

Table 1 shows the reactivity for the four metals we have already mentioned. You can see that not all the mixtures result in reactions.

Metal	Solution			
	copper sulphate	zinc chloride	lead chloride	magnesium chloride
copper		no reaction	no reaction	no reaction
zinc	zinc sulphate forms		zinc chloride forms	no reaction
lead	lead sulphate forms	no reaction		no reaction
magnesium	magnesium sulphate forms	magnesium chloride forms	magnesium chloride forms	

▲ Table 1

ACTIVITY

With a partner.
● Discuss Table 1. Try to place the metals in order of reactivity.
● Place the most reactive metal at the top.

The Reactivity Series of metals

A list of metals could be arranged in alphabetical order. Another way of organising the list is shown in Table 2. This places the most reactive metal at the top and the least reactive at the bottom. The ones in between are arranged by comparing them with one another. Gold is at the bottom and potassium is at the top. This is the **Reactivity Series** of metals.

The order of reaction of these metals with oxygen and acids is exactly the same. Potassium reacts violently with water, oxygen and acids. Gold is the least reactive metal of all.

▶ **Table 2** Hydrogen and carbon are not metals. They are placed in the reactivity series to make it more useful.

potassium	metals above carbon cannot be extracted from ores by heating with carbon or carbon monoxide	metals above hydrogen will displace it from water, steam or dilute acids
sodium		
calcium		
magnesium		
aluminium		
carbon		
zinc	metals below carbon can be extracted from ores by heating with carbon or carbon monoxide	
iron		
lead		
hydrogen		
copper		metals below hydrogen will not displace it from water, steam or dilute acids
silver		
gold		

REVIEW

● In a group.
  ○ Use your knowledge of the Reactivity Series of metals to explain why some of the metals in your review survey were tarnished and rusty but others remained shiny.

95 Extracting and using metals

Extracting metals

A few metals do not react easily with oxygen. Gold and silver are unreactive metals. They can be found in the ground as pure metal. This is not true for most other metals. Metals are normally found as **ores**. Ores are metals combined with other elements. If we want to get a pure metal, we need to dig its ore out of the ground and separate it from other elements in the ore.

▲ **Fig 1** Iron comes from iron ore dug out of a quarry.

Metal ores

Many metal ores are oxides. Some common ores are shown in Table 1.

Metal	Common name of the ore	Chemical name of the ore	Method of extraction
copper	copper pyrites	copper iron sulphide	chemical reaction
aluminium	bauxite	aluminium oxide	electricity
iron	haematite	iron oxide	chemical reaction
tin	cassiterite	tin oxide	chemical reaction

◀ **Table 1** Some metals and their ores.

Many metals are extracted from their ores by reduction (reduction means removing oxygen). When carbon powder is heated with lead oxide, the carbon takes the oxygen and becomes carbon dioxide. The lead oxide is **reduced** to pure lead metal. This can be done in the laboratory.

⚠ **Caution**: Lead and all its compounds are poisonous. Never experiment with lead at home.

Iron from iron oxide

The iron ore called **haematite** is rusty red because it contains iron oxide. Pure iron is obtained from crushed haematite by reduction. Many metals react more strongly with oxygen than iron does. Aluminium or magnesium, for example, could be used to take oxygen from iron. These metals are not used because they are too expensive to extract.

Fortunately, carbon can also be used to reduce iron oxide. This reaction requires heat, but the heat can come from the same source as the carbon. This source is coke.

The reduction of iron oxide to iron is done in a **blast furnace**. The burning coke gives off carbon monoxide, and the carbon monoxide reacts with the iron oxide to make iron and carbon dioxide. The word equation for this is:

iron oxide + carbon monoxide ⟶ iron + carbon dioxide

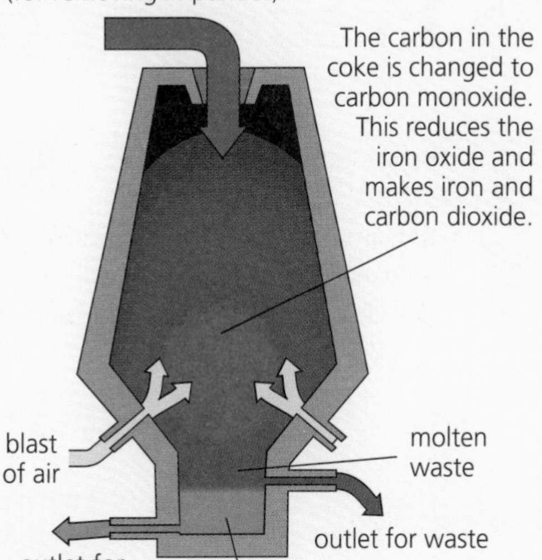

iron ore, coke and limestone (for removing impurities)

The carbon in the coke is changed to carbon monoxide. This reduces the iron oxide and makes iron and carbon dioxide.

blast of air

molten waste

outlet for waste

outlet for molten iron   molten iron

▲ **Fig 2** In a blast furnace, carbon monoxide from burning coke reduces iron oxide to pure iron.

Aluminium from bauxite

▼ **Fig 3**

Some metals cling to oxygen very firmly. They cannot be extracted from their ores by simple chemical reactions. Ores containing these metals require a great deal of energy to break them down. Electricity can provide this energy. Splitting a chemical with electricity is called **electrolysis**. Aluminium is extracted from its oxide, called **bauxite**, by electrolysis. It is a very expensive process.

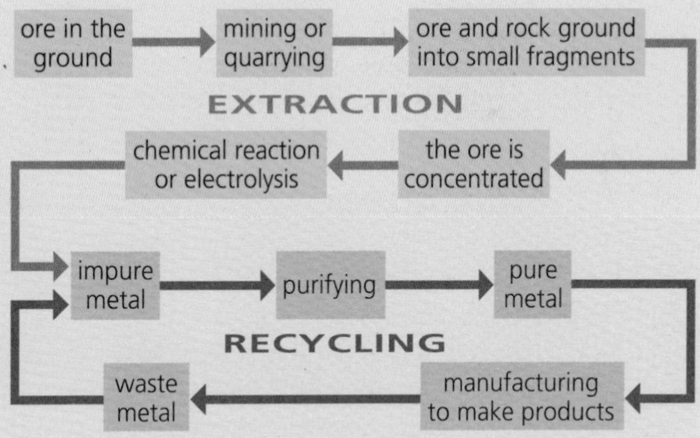

ore in the ground → mining or quarrying → ore and rock ground into small fragments

EXTRACTION

chemical reaction or electrolysis ← the ore is concentrated

impure metal → purifying → pure metal

RECYCLING

waste metal ← manufacturing to make products

- In a group.
  - Use your knowledge of the reactivity series to explain why:
    - gold is found naturally as pure metal
    - iron is extracted chemically from haematite
    - aluminium is extracted using electrolysis from bauxite.

Design and produce a poster to encourage people to recycle metals. Include on the poster the costs and environmental impact of extracting metals from their ores.

96 Predicting chemical reactions

KEY IDEAS

In this section of the book you will have opportunities to:
- Explain that the Reactivity Series can be used to predict chemical reactions.

STARTER

In a group.
How does zinc metal react with copper sulphate solution? Write your ideas down and predict the products.

Using the Reactivity Series

The Reactivity Series shows that potassium is a very reactive metal. If we add potassium to water we know there will be a violent reaction. The Reactivity Series is already helping us to **predict** what is going to happen. We can also use it to predict the way other reactions will go.

Predicting reactions

Carbon powder and lead oxide react together when they are mixed up and heated. Carbon can be added above lead in the Reactivity Series. It should therefore displace lead. This is exactly what happens.

lead oxide + carbon ⟶ lead + carbon dioxide

▶ **Fig 1** Lead oxide and carbon heated together produce lead and carbon dioxide.
⚠ **Caution:** Lead is poisonous to swallow or inhale.

Predicting speed

Calcium fizzes or **effervesces** gently in water as hydrogen gas is produced. The water becomes warm. Potassium comes above calcium in the Reactivity Series. It should therefore react more violently with water. Potassium reacts so violently with water that the hydrogen bursts into flames.

ACTIVITY

With a partner.
- Discuss how you could safely collect and test the gas that is given off when calcium reacts with water.
- Write down your ideas.

The distance between two metals in the Series gives us another way of predicting the result of an experiment.

▲ **Fig 2** Potassium reacts violently with water. It is useful to know in advance when an experiment might be violent.

Lead is only slightly more reactive than copper. Reactions between copper and lead compounds do not go very fast.

When copper oxide and powdered lead are heated together the lead displaces the copper and takes the oxygen to produce lead oxide. Because there is not much difference in reactivity between these two metals the reaction is slow and very gentle.

When magnesium powder is heated with copper oxide the reaction is violent. Magnesium is much more reactive than copper. It snatches the oxygen very quickly. Once this reaction starts it goes like a firework.

The Reactivity Series can also tell us how **stable** a chemical is likely to be. Metals higher in the Reactivity Series form compounds very easily because they hold onto other chemicals very firmly. Once they are part of a compound they are very difficult to remove. The compound is hard to **decompose**.

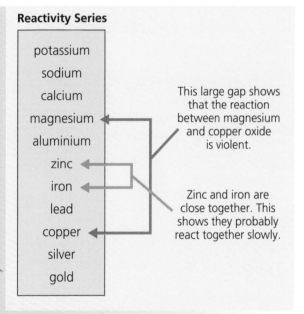

Reactivity Series

potassium
sodium
calcium
magnesium
aluminium
zinc
iron
lead
copper
silver
gold

This large gap shows that the reaction between magnesium and copper oxide is violent.

Zinc and iron are close together. This shows they probably react together slowly.

▲ **Fig 3** A small gap between metals gives a slow reaction between their compounds. A large gap can give a violent reaction.

Copper carbonate breaks down into copper oxide and carbon dioxide very easily when it is heated. Potassium is higher in the Reactivity Series. Potassium carbonate cannot be decomposed, even by very high temperatures.

$$\text{potassium carbonate} \xrightarrow{\text{heat}} \text{no reaction}$$

$$\text{copper carbonate} \xrightarrow{\text{heat}} \text{copper oxide} + \text{carbon dioxide}$$

Connections

This unit builds on your earlier work on atoms and elements, compounds and mixtures and reactions of metals and metal compounds. This work will lead on to work on environmental chemistry and using chemistry.

REVIEW

- In a group.
  - Discuss why metals that react violently form stable compounds.
  - Think of as many examples as you can, including food and biology.
  - Be prepared to share your ideas with other groups.

Explain why we do not have sodium water pipes and potassium money. Predict what would happen if we did and write chemical equations for any reactions you think may occur.

97 Air pollution and acid rain

KEY IDEAS

In this section of the book you will have opportunities to:
- Explain what causes acid rain.

STARTER

In a group.
Discuss the different ways that the environment could be damaged by acid rain. Write down your ideas and prepare to discuss them with other groups.

Acid rain

The oxides produced when fuels burn include some acid gases. Two of them are sulphur dioxide and nitrogen dioxide. An acid gas mixed with water is an acid. Clouds and rain are water. When acid gases from chimneys and exhaust pipes enter clouds they make acid. When it rains, acid gas falls from acid clouds.

Carbon dioxide is a normal part of the air. It is also an acid gas, so rainwater is normally slightly acidic. With acid rain the water becomes much more acidic than normal.

Acid rainwater falls on the soil and runs into streams, lakes and the sea. Some lakes in Sweden now contain so much acid that nothing can live there. Some of the acid that rains on Sweden comes from factories and cars in the UK. Air pollution and acid rain are international problems. Acid rain can be so acidic that the pH of rivers and lakes can be as low as pH 3. This is as acidic as vinegar. This is too acidic for many animals and plants and they die.

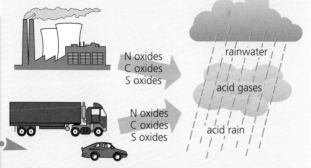

▲ **Fig 1** Acid rain damages buildings, pollutes water and poisons forest trees.

▲ **Fig 2** Nobody knows exactly how acid rain damages trees. All we know is that trees die where strong acid rain falls.

◀ **Fig 3** Some of the water in lakes can be as acidic as vinegar because of acid rain.

ACTIVITY

With a partner.
- Discuss why acid rain should be thought of as an international problem rather than just a problem in this country.
- Write down your ideas.

Buildings at risk

Concrete is strong but it is brittle. Concrete often has steel rods added to strengthen it. This is called **reinforced concrete**. If acid rain soaks between the joints in reinforced concrete it can reach the steel rods inside. The steel can slowly corrode until it is too weak to support the concrete. The concrete may look good on the outside, but it can break suddenly when the rods become too weak to work. Buildings and bridges made of reinforced concrete have to be regularly inspected for corrosion.

▶ **Fig 4** The steel that strengthens concrete can be weakened by acid rain.

Rocks at risk

Limestone, chalk and marble all contain calcium carbonate. This substance is attacked easily by acids. Acids in rain can help to keep the surface of these rocks very clean. This is because the surface is constantly washed away by acid in the rain. It is not washed but weathered. Buildings, walls and gravestones can all be damaged by acid rain.

Other kinds of air pollution

There are many other kinds of air pollution. Some of these are listed in Table 1.

Pollutant	Source
Carbon monoxide	burning fuels
Smoke	burning fuels
Lead compounds	cars
Sulphur dioxide	burning fuels
Carbon dioxide	burning fuels
Chlorofluorocarbons (CFCs)	refrigeration and aerosol cans

▶ **Table 1**

REVIEW

- In a group.
  - Look back at the ideas you had during the starter activity.
  - Add any new ideas you may have.
  - Now make a list of the ways that acid rain could be reduced.

  Write down some of the ways that you could change your lifestyle to help to reduce acid rain. How would you persuade others to join you?

98 Fuels and the environment

Fossil fuels

Coal comes from prehistoric plants that have been buried for millions of years. Oil comes from dead animals that have also been buried for millions of years. They are called **fossil fuels** because they are the remains of ancient life.

Burning fossil fuels

Burning is a chemical reaction. Burning fuel gives out energy and creates new chemicals.

Fossil fuels contain carbon, hydrogen, nitrogen and sulphur. When fuel is burned, these elements combine with oxygen to make oxides. Carbon oxidises to carbon dioxide and carbon monoxide. Hydrogen oxidises to water. Nitrogen oxidises to nitrogen dioxide. Sulphur oxidises to sulphur dioxide.

▲ **Fig 1** Burning fossil fuels releases five thousand million tonnes of carbon dioxide into the atmosphere every year. This could double by the year 2020.

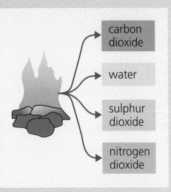

carbon dioxide

water

sulphur dioxide

nitrogen dioxide

◀ **Fig 2** Some of the gases created when coal burns.

ACTIVITY

With a partner.
- List the gases produced when coal burns.
- Which of these do you think will be the most harmful? Why?

The greenhouse effect

The sunny side of the Moon is baking hot. The dark side is freezing cold. This is because the Moon has no atmosphere. Carbon dioxide in the Earth's atmosphere helps to keep the Earth warm. Some of the daytime heat from the Sun is kept in at night by a blanket of

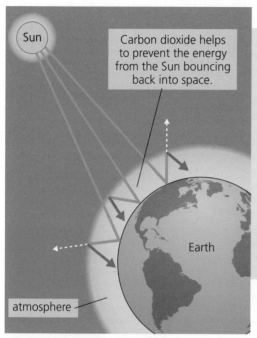

▲ **Fig 3** The greenhouse effect.

carbon dioxide. This is the **greenhouse effect**. Without our atmosphere the surface temperature of Earth would be −18 °C.

▲ **Fig 4** The Sun warms the air in the greenhouse and it is trapped. It is much warmer inside the greenhouse than outside.

▼ **Fig 5** This island could disappear if the sea level rises too high.

Global warming

Burning a tree that grew recently releases carbon dioxide it recently removed from the air. Burning fossil fuels releases carbon dioxide that has been locked in the ground for millions of years. This extra carbon dioxide increases the greenhouse effect. It makes the Earth warmer.

The Earth has become 2°C warmer in the last 100 years. This is evidence for the theory of **global warming**. Burning fossil fuels has also increased during this time. It is increasing all the time. If the temperature rises higher the Polar ice could melt and make sea levels rise. There will be less dry land to live on and grow food on.

The warming of the atmosphere can also change weather patterns. Places in the world may become much hotter and drier. Other places may experience great storms on a more regular basis.

REVIEW

- In a group.
  - Make a list of the possible causes of global warming.
  - Discuss whether it really matters if the planet is getting warmer.
  - Write down your ideas and prepare to discuss them with another group.

🏠 Imagine you live on a low-lying South Pacific island. Produce a piece of creative writing that describes your worries about global warming and suggest some ideas to reduce the problem.

99 Water pollution

KEY IDEAS

In this section of the book you will have opportunities to:
- Explain how water resources are affected by human activity.

STARTER

In a group.
List some of the vital uses of water. Discuss why it is important to have a clean and safe water supply. Write your ideas down and be prepared to discuss them with other groups.

Water

Water is a vital resource. It is essential for life and is used in the home and industry for a wide variety of purposes. Clean, unpolluted water is needed for health and we also use it for leisure. Animals and plants that live in water (**aquatic**) also need clean water.

▲ **Fig 1** Rivers and oceans were a common dumping ground for many chemicals and human waste.

Water pollutants

There are many different substances that can pollute water. These are called **pollutants**. Some of the most serious are listed here.

Sewage   Oil   Fertilisers   Detergents

Heavy metals such as lead and mercury   Pesticides

Sewage

Sewage is human waste that has been passed down toilets and into the sewers. Today, most of the sewage in the UK is treated before it enters rivers and the sea. Sewage must be treated as it contains many harmful bacteria and could be the cause of diseases. The chemicals in sewage can act as fertilisers. The sewage helps algae and bacteria to grow in the water. The algae and bacteria can use up all of the oxygen and this can cause other organisms to die. This is called **eutrophication**. Many years ago some rivers were so full of

▲ **Fig 2** A few years ago this river was so polluted it would have been dangerous to swim in it.

sewage that no fish could survive. Since then new laws have made our rivers much cleaner.

With a partner.

- Discuss why eutrophication is such a problem. Write down your ideas.

Oil

Oil can pass into rivers and seas in a number of ways (see Fig 3). The oil can cause a great deal of environmental damage. It can coat beaches and rocks and cover the feathers of sea birds. It is very expensive to clean up oil-spills. The detergents used to disperse the oil can also be harmful.

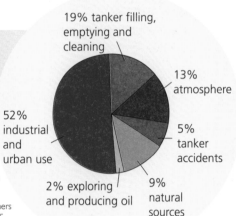

▶ **Fig 3** Sources of oil pollution.

Source: The International Tanker Owners Pollution Federation Ltd. London, 1995.

Fertilisers

Fertilisers contain chemicals that encourage plants to grow. In rivers this can cause eutrophication in the same way as sewage. Millions of tonnes of fertilisers are used by farmers and these can be washed into streams and rivers.

spraying fields

rain

streams flow into rivers and ponds

rain washes fertiliser into stream

▲ **Fig 4** Wash off of fertilisers into rivers and to the sea.

- In a group.
  - Imagine you are members of a Government Advisory Committee.
  - What advice would you give the Government about reducing water pollution?
  - Write down your ideas.

Research how heavy metals can enter rivers and the sea. Explain why they are harmful.

213

100 Chemical changes

KEY IDEAS

In this section of the book you will have opportunities to:
- Describe how atoms combine in new arrangements when chemical reactions occur
- Explain that no matter is lost or gained during chemical reactions.

STARTER

In a group.
Discuss some of the chemical reactions you have studied. Write down three examples. Name the chemicals that are added together and the new chemicals that are made.

Types of change

The change from water to ice is a physical change. It can easily be reversed. Many everyday changes cannot easily be reversed. Burned paper cannot be unburned. This is a permanent change. New substances have been made. This is an example of a chemical change.

▶ **Fig 1** The match will not reappear after it has cooled down. Burning is a chemical reaction.

Chemical reactions

As you will know from earlier work, a chemical change is a permanent change. **Chemical reactions** produce new substances. Some examples are:

- acids reacting with metals
- fuels burning
- food being digested.

Remember that the **reactants** are the chemicals that react together in a chemical reaction. The reactants combine together in new patterns to make the **products**.

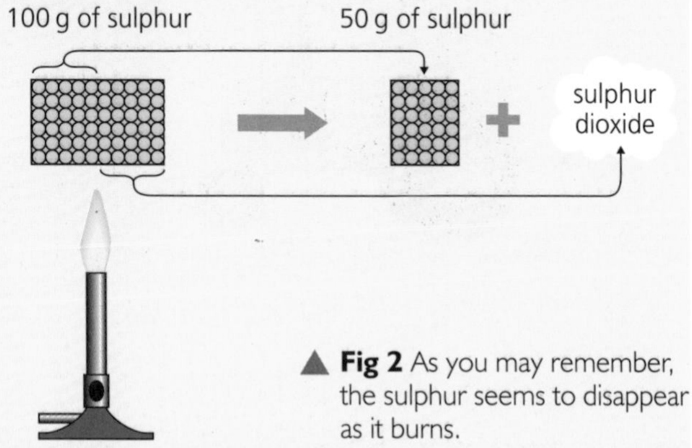

The new chemicals are made because the atoms in the reactants have been rearranged. All of the original atoms are present but they are in new combinations. Atoms are never broken down during chemical reactions (see Unit 52). As you may recall from earlier work, if you start out with 100 grams of sulphur and then burn half of it you will have 50 grams left. The chemical reaction has not made half of the sulphur disappear. The sulphur atoms have been rearranged and exist in a new chemical.

100 g of sulphur → 50 g of sulphur + sulphur dioxide

▲ **Fig 2** As you may remember, the sulphur seems to disappear as it burns.

With a partner.
- Discuss Fig 2.
- Explain what happens to all of the atoms of sulphur as it burns.

Conservation of mass

Atoms cannot be destroyed by a chemical reaction. The missing sulphur must therefore still exist somewhere.

Before the experiment began, all the sulphur atoms were packed together into a solid. When the sulphur burned, it reacted with oxygen in the air. Each atom of sulphur joined with two atoms of oxygen from the air to make a gas called sulphur dioxide. Because sulphur dioxide is a gas, it spread into the air. If you could collect all the sulphur dioxide gas you would find that it contained exactly 50 grams of sulphur. Sulphur atoms cannot be destroyed. The mass of sulphur stays the same throughout the experiment. It simply goes somewhere else.

Magnesium metal burns with a very bright flame. If we burn the magnesium inside a covered pot then we can measure any change in mass during the experiment. This experiment is shown in Fig 3. •••••••••••••

If we start with 24 grams of magnesium we end up with 40 grams of powder. The mass of magnesium is not reduced by burning. On the contrary, it is increased. The increase in mass occurred because the magnesium atoms joined with oxygen atoms from the air. The extra mass is the mass of the oxygen atoms that were added to the magnesium.

> During chemical reactions matter is not created or destroyed. The atoms are rearranged to make new substances.

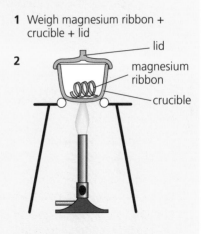

1 Weigh magnesium ribbon + crucible + lid

2 lid / magnesium ribbon / crucible

3 Weigh magnesium oxide + crucible + lid

▶ **Fig 3** Never watch magnesium burning. The bright light can damage your eyes.

- In a group.
  - Explain why charcoal has a smaller mass than the wood it is made from.
- Use the idea that matter cannot be created or destroyed during chemical reactions to explain what happens when a match burns.

101 Chemical reactions and heat

Chemical reactions and heat

As you know from earlier work, as methane gas burns we can see a number of changes. In the bunsen burner we can see that the gas flame is hot and blue. This means that when methane burns it gives out heat and light. We use the heat to cook food or keep us warm. The chemical reaction also changes methane gas into carbon dioxide and water. Chemicals that react with oxygen to give out heat are called **fuels**.

▶ **Fig 1** Bunsen burner on blue flame.

Exothermic reactions

As you may recall, the word equation for burning methane is:

methane + oxygen ⟶ carbon dioxide + water

There is a lot of energy stored in a methane molecule. Molecules of carbon dioxide and water contain less energy than methane molecules. This means that methane contains more energy than it needs to make carbon dioxide and water. The extra energy is released when a molecule of methane breaks down. Chemical reactions that give out heat are called **exothermic** reactions. • • • • • • • • • •

Other fuels we use are coal, wood, butane, propane, paraffin, petrol and diesel. They provide energy for heating, transport and industry. Energy does not have to be heat or light. It can also be sound, movement and electricity. The chemical reactions in a battery produce electrical energy.

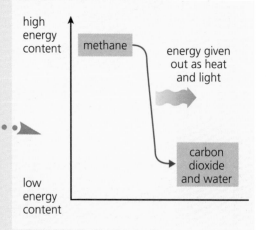

high
energy
content

methane

energy given
out as heat
and light

carbon
dioxide
and water

low
energy
content

▲ **Fig 2** Energy is released when methane burns. This is an exothermic reaction.

ACTIVITY

With a partner.
- Why are exothermic reactions so important to us?
- Write down your ideas.

As you know from earlier work, sherbet is a mixture of citric acid and sodium hydrogencarbonate. When water is added to this mixture, the two chemicals react to release carbon dioxide. The fizzing sherbet makes your mouth feel cold. This is because the chemical reaction needs heat. It takes the heat from your mouth. Reactions that require heat are called **endothermic** reactions.

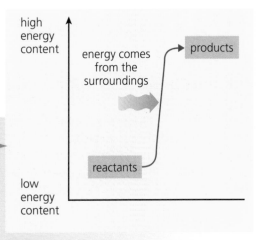

▲ **Fig 3** Fizzing sherbet takes in energy. This is an endothermic reaction.

citric acid + sodium hydrogencarbonate ⟶ sodium citrate + carbon dioxide + water

Fuels and engines

If we want to use energy for any kind of work we need to be able to control the way it is released. Petrol burns in air very quickly. The energy is rapidly lost as heat, light and sound. If we trap some petrol and air in a cylinder and then add a spark, there will be an explosion. In a petrol engine, this explosion moves a piston. The moving piston turns a rod that eventually turns a wheel. In this way, the chemical energy in the petrol is changed to movement energy.

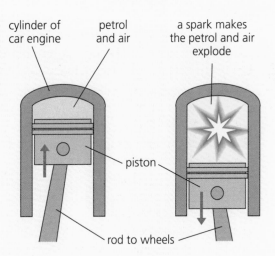

▶ **Fig 4** Chemical energy harnessed in a car engine to drive the wheels.

REVIEW

- In a group.
  - Make a list of all the different fuels mentioned above.
  - Describe how you have seen them used.
  - How is the burning of the fuels controlled?

Design a small poster that explains how important exothermic reactions are.

102 Important new chemicals

Chemicals

There are fewer than 100 natural chemical elements. There are more than a million known chemical compounds. Chemical compounds are made by combining atoms of elements. Most of the chemicals that we find and use on Earth must be created by chemical reactions.

Ammonia

Fertilisers are often added to soils to make them more fertile. They may come from natural sources, such as animals or plants, or be made in factories. One chemical that is important for making fertilisers is a gas called ammonia. This gas occurs naturally. It is also made in very large amounts by a chemical reaction in a factory. As well as helping to make fertilisers, ammonia is used to make cleaning materials, plastics and nitric acid.

Ammonia molecules are made of nitrogen atoms and hydrogen atoms. In a factory, these elements are mixed together and heated under high pressure. Each nitrogen atom combines with three hydrogen atoms (see Fig 1). This is called a **synthesis** reaction because a new chemical is made by joining other chemicals together. • • • • • • • •

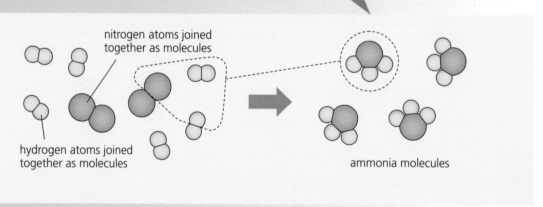

nitrogen atoms joined together as molecules

hydrogen atoms joined together as molecules

ammonia molecules

▲ Fig 1

Lime

Lime is the common name for the chemical called calcium oxide. This chemical is needed to make cement. It also helps to make water or soil less acidic. Lime is made from limestone. The chemical name for limestone is calcium carbonate. Limestone (calcium carbonate) is turned into lime (calcium oxide) by heating it in an oven or kiln until the molecules split into smaller ones. The smaller molecules are calcium oxide (lime) and carbon dioxide gas. This type of reaction is called a **decomposition** reaction because new chemicals are made by breaking down another chemical.

▲ **Fig 2** Millions of tonnes of limestone are quarried for roads and to make lime.

ACTIVITY

With a partner.
- Discuss the difference between a synthesis reaction and a decomposition reaction.
- Write down your ideas.

Living things and chemical reactions

Your body is a giant factory carrying out hundreds of chemical reactions. Chemical reactions are essential to life. Plants use energy from the Sun to **synthesise** glucose from water and carbon dioxide (see Unit 86). Animals and plants get that energy back by respiration.

Industry can use very high temperatures to make reactions go faster. These high temperatures would kill living things. Living things use enzymes instead of heat to speed up chemical reactions so that they do not need high temperatures. Enzymes are **catalysts**. Industry also uses catalysts to help chemical reactions. The production of ammonia (see Fig 1) is speeded up by having iron as a catalyst.

Connections

This work builds on earlier work on chemical reactions and patterns of reactivity and links to other ideas, such as photosynthesis and respiration. The work allows you to review your knowledge of even earlier work about atoms and chemical changes.

REVIEW

- In a group.
  - Look at the list of manufactured substances you created during the starter activity. Select one each from your list and find out what the substance was made from.
- Research how hand warmers for climbers and skiers work.

103 Energy transfers

KEY IDEAS

In this section of the book you will have opportunities to:
- Explain how energy moves from place to place
- Describe how energy can help us to do work.

STARTER

In a group.
Discuss how you get the energy that allows you to move your body. Write down your ideas.

Work and energy

Work is done whenever a force makes something move. When work is done by an object it loses energy. When work is done on an object it gains energy. • • • • • • • • • • ▶

Energy can exist in many different forms and can change between them. This is called **energy conversion**. It is important to recall that energy cannot be created or destroyed. This is the **law of conservation of energy**.

Some different forms of energy are:

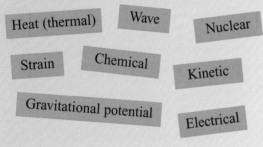

Heat (thermal) Wave Nuclear

Strain Chemical Kinetic

Gravitational potential Electrical

▲ **Fig 1** The work is being done *by* the person, she loses energy. The work is being done *on* the swing, it gains energy.

Energy transfers

As you may recall, the change from one form of energy to another can be shown as an energy transfer chain. You may have seen the one opposite, • • • • • • but some stages are missing.

▶ **Fig 2**

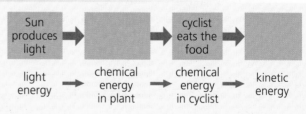

Sun produces light		cyclist eats the food	
light energy →	chemical energy in plant →	chemical energy in cyclist →	kinetic energy

ACTIVITY
With a partner.
- Discuss the energy transfer chain in Fig 2.
- Write down what should be in the blank boxes.

Electrical energy

Electrical energy is a convenient way of doing many things. The energy can be transferred around circuits. This electrical energy can be converted or transformed in components. In this way we can use electricity to provide other forms of energy. This is vital for industry and we use it in our daily lives, perhaps without even thinking about it.

▲ **Fig 3** Electrical energy is converted into light and sound in entertainment systems.

Energy stores

Energy is stored in food and fuels. Energy can also be stored in other ways, such as in compressed springs, batteries, flywheels and stretched elastic bands. Many toys use stored energy by converting it into other energy forms. For example, a clockwork toy converts the energy stored in the spring into kinetic (movement) and sound energy.

REVIEW
- In a group.
  - Draw an energy story to show all the energy transfers involved in making hydroelectricity.

 Draw or collect some pictures of electrical appliances. Now try to include them in some energy transfer chains.

 Study tip

Take some small pieces of coloured card. Write down a different form of energy on each card. Use page 220 to help you. You can now try to arrange the cards into different energy transfer chains. Every time you do this make sure that you give an example that you have seen.

104 Generating electricity

Smoke

Most of the 'smoke' you see coming from a power station is water vapour. Smoke and other gases that are produced when a fossil fuel burns come out of thinner, taller chimneys.

ACTIVITY

On your own.
- Write down some of the disadvantages of using fossil fuels in power stations.

▲ **Fig 1** Power stations generate electricity.

Inside a power station

Many power stations burn fossil fuels. Fig 1 shows a power station that uses coal. The coal arrives by train or truck and then it is stored. When it is needed, the coal is tipped into a large furnace. Inside the furnace the coal burns to give out heat. The heat is used to boil water. This turns the water to steam.

Jets of very hot steam travel along pipes until they hit the **turbine**. A turbine is like a water wheel for steam. Large fans on the turbine make it spin round when the steam hits them. The turbine is attached to the generator. When the turbine twists the generator, electricity is made (see Fig 2 opposite).

After hitting the turbine the steam is still very hot. It needs to be cooled before it can go back into the boiler. The steam is cooled in a cooling tower. Here, cold water is poured over the pipes that contain the steam. It is the cooling water that we see evaporating from the power station, not the steam that drives the turbines.

▼ **Fig 2**

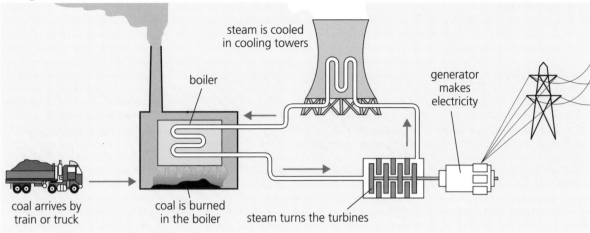

steam is cooled
in cooling towers

boiler

generator
makes
electricity

coal arrives by
train or truck

coal is burned
in the boiler

steam turns the turbines

Efficient use of resources

No machine or factory is perfectly efficient. There is always some waste. All power stations lose some of the energy they take from the energy resource they use. Most of the waste is in the form of heat lost through the cooling towers and in waste gases. Some power stations are more efficient than others. The efficiency of four different types of power stations is shown in Fig 3.

Coal power stations have a maximum efficiency of 40%. This means that for each kilogram of coal burned, the energy from at least 600 grams is wasted. Gas power stations have a maximum efficiency of 50%. This means that for each kilogram of gas burned, the energy from at least 500 grams is wasted.

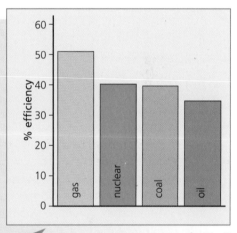

▲ **Fig 3**

Electricity where we need it

Electricity has to be sent from the power stations, where it is generated, to other places where it is needed. We have a network of power cables called the National Grid. You have probably seen parts of it. Many of the cables are carried across the countryside on tall **pylons**. When the cables reach your home they are much smaller. They may also be buried underground.

REVIEW

- In a group.
  - Produce a poster explaining how electricity is generated in a power station and then sent to factories and homes.

Find out the name of your nearest power station and the energy resource it uses. Write a short newspaper article arguing for cleaner fuels to be used to generate electricity.

105 Energy efficiency

KEY IDEAS

In this section of the book you will have opportunities to:
- Describe the law of conservation of energy
- Explain that energy is not lost during an energy transfer.

STARTER

In a group.
Think back to your earlier work on electrical circuits. Draw a circuit containing one cell (battery), wires and two bulbs in series. Discuss what happens to the electrical energy in the circuit.

Electrical circuits

In electrical circuits such as Fig 1, the battery pushes electrons around the circuit. The electrons leave the negative (−) terminal of the battery with energy that they carry to the bulbs or other appliances. The electrons lose all of this energy as they are forced through the wires of the bulbs.

Not all batteries are the same. As you will recall, a battery with a higher **voltage** will give the electrons more energy. The circuit in Fig 1 contains two bulbs. The voltmeters

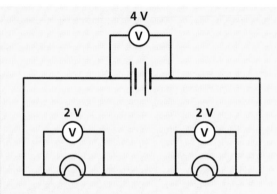

▲ **Fig I** Circuit with bulbs and voltmeters.

show how much energy the electrons lose as they pass through the bulbs. The higher the voltage reading across a bulb or other component in a circuit the more energy each electron loses as it pushes through. If you add up the voltage across the bulbs they will be equal to the voltage across the battery.

Power

When you plug an electric fire into the mains electricity in your house it starts to heat up. The electric fire is changing electrical energy into heat energy. The amount of energy the fire can change every second is known as the **power**. This is measured in **watts (W)** or **kilowatts (kW)**.

> A power of one watt shows that energy is being changed at a rate of one joule every second.

The power of the electric fire depends on two things. The current flowing through it and the voltage across it. The more voltage there is the more energy the electrons will have. The more current there is the more of these electrons there will be.

Appliance	Power rating
Kettle	2400 W
Lamp	60 W
Fire	3000 W
Iron	720 W

▲ **Table I** The power ratings of some common appliances.

With a partner.
● Try to place the appliances in Table 1 into a league table, with the one that would be the most expensive to run at the top.

The power for an appliance can be given by the **power equation**:

power = voltage x current
(watts)   (volts)   (amps)

Efficiency

We try to design machines so that they are as efficient as possible. This means they should transfer as much energy as possible to the job. The efficiency of an electric drill is shown in Fig 2.

The electric drill is inefficient. It wastes more than 40% of the electricity it uses. This means that it wastes more than 40% of the money we pay for the electricity it uses. All the equipment in our home wastes some energy. The more energy a piece of equipment wastes, the more money we waste buying energy for it.

Inefficient equipment costs us more than money. Electricity is made by burning fuels. Inefficient equipment wastes fuel at the power station. This also increases pollution.

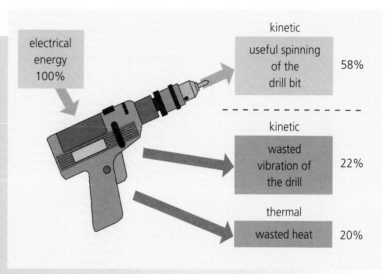

electrical
energy
100%

kinetic
useful spinning
of the
drill bit
58%

kinetic
wasted
vibration of
the drill
22%

thermal
wasted heat
20%

▲ Fig 2

Connections

This work builds on earlier work on energy resources, electricity and circuits, and burning fuels.

REVIEW

● In a group.
  ○ Make a list of as many ways as possible to use energy resources more efficiently in:
  a industry
  b transport
  c your home.

Write down how using more efficient appliances can help to make the air cleaner.

106 Gravitational forces

Gravity

Planets in the Solar System orbit the Sun (see Fig 2). But what prevents them from flying out into Space? They are held in position by gravity.

All objects have gravity. The pull of gravity is greater between massive objects than between small objects. The pull between you and the Earth is about 500 newtons but the pull between you and another person is about 500 million times smaller. Most of the gravity that holds us on the ground is due to the mass of the Earth. The Sun contains almost all of the mass in the Solar System. The Sun's mass is great enough to create a pull that holds the planets in their orbits.

▲ **Fig 1** Gravity pulls us down to Earth no matter how hard we try to escape. Gravity also pulls the Earth towards the Sun.

Orbits

The size of the Sun's gravitational pull on a planet depends on two things:
1. the distance between the planet and the Sun
2. the mass of the planet.

This means that:
- an inner planet will be pulled towards the Sun more strongly than an outer planet
- a massive planet like Jupiter will be pulled towards the Sun more strongly than a small planet.

Planets close to the Sun take less time to travel around it than planets further away. The Earth makes one complete orbit of the Sun in one year. Jupiter's 'year' is 12 of our years and Pluto takes 247 Earth years to go once round its orbit. Orbits are not usually perfect circles. Most of the planets have orbits that are **ellipses**.

ACTIVITY

On your own.
- Why does Pluto take much longer than the Earth to orbit the Sun?

▼ **Fig 2**

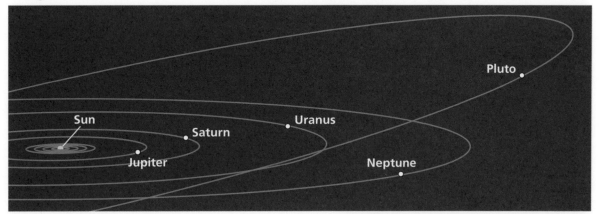

Comets

Comets move around the Sun in elongated orbits that are long ellipses or parabolas. Unlike the planets, the orbits do not have to be in the same plane. It may take many years for a comet to slowly orbit the Sun. Halley's comet comes close to the Sun and Earth every 76 years. As it approaches the Sun it speeds up. As it moves away it slows down.

A **comet** has a centre of dust and ice, called a nucleus, covered with layers of frozen gases. Out in Space, a comet has no tail. When it comes close to the Sun some of the frozen gases on its surface turn into vapour (see Fig 3). This is what we see as a comet's glowing tail. The tail always points away from the Sun, no matter which way the comet is moving.

Halley's comet is named after Sir Edmond Halley. Halley saw the comet in 1682, when he was a young man, and used his knowledge of gravitational forces and the movement of the planets to predict when it would be visible again. He was correct, although he did not live long enough to see the comet return.

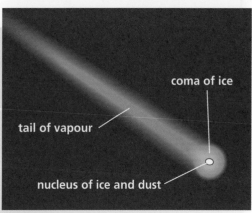

coma of ice

tail of vapour

nucleus of ice and dust

▲ **Fig 3**

▼ **Fig 4** Halley's comet.

REVIEW

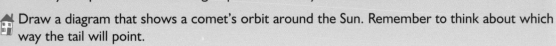

- In a group.
  - Imagine you are going to interview a scientist about the Solar System.
  - Design some questions to ask about gravity.
  - Pass your questions to another group and see if they can answer them.

🏠 Draw a diagram that shows a comet's orbit around the Sun. Remember to think about which way the tail will point.

107 Weight

Mass

All objects have a **mass**. This is the quantity of matter the object contains. It is the total of all of the atoms in the object. This will be the same wherever the object is. Mass is measured in kilograms (kg). Large masses are difficult to move, speed up or slow down. We know this if we have ever tried to push a car or move a large piece of furniture. It is also known that masses attract each other. Some examples of objects and their mass are given in Table 1.

Object	Mass in kg
Apple	0.1
Bag of sugar	2
Baby	3
Person	60–90
Car	1200
T. rex	10 000

▲ **Table 1** Some common masses.

Force

A force influences the direction, speed and shape of an object. It is the amount of push or pull and is measured in newtons (N). A large force is needed to crush concrete or bend metals. A small force is needed to open a bottle or fold paper.

Gravitational force is the force of attraction between masses. It is not known how or why this happens but we know it does. The greatest pull occurs with large masses that are close together. You may recall that it is gravitational force that holds the planets in orbit around the Sun. The gravitational force between objects with small masses is too small to measure. When one mass is large, for example a planet, the gravitational pull is important. This is why a thrown ball will soon be pulled down to the ground. It is attracted to the Earth.

▲ **Fig 1** Gravitational force will pull the hammer to Earth soon after it is thrown.

Weight

Weight is the gravitational force on an object. As weight is a force it is measured in newtons. A person with a mass of 60 kilograms will have a weight of 600 newtons on Earth. That is the amount of pull that the Earth has on the mass of the person's body. On the Moon the person will have a mass of 60 kilograms, but a weight of 100 newtons. This is because the Moon has less mass than the Earth and has less to attract the person with.

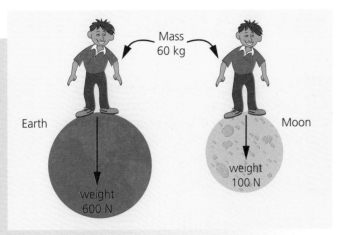

▲ **Fig 2** Weight of a person on the Earth and the Moon.

Measuring weight

When you stand on the bathroom scales it is the gravitational pull of the Earth that pulls you down onto the scales. It is your weight that is being measured and so the units should be newtons. Many scales show the units as kilograms. As you know, this is not a problem as long as people realise that this is their mass, not their weight. In reality, many people use mass and weight to mean the same thing, especially shops and supermarkets.

▶ **Fig 3**

108 Artificial satellites

KEY IDEAS

In this section of the book you will have opportunities to:
- Explain how the Moon and artificial satellites orbit the Earth.

STARTER

In a group.
Make a list of any satellites you have heard of. What are they used for?

Natural satellites

A **satellite** is a **body** in orbit around another body. The Earth is a satellite of the Sun. The Moon is a natural satellite of the Earth.

The Moon orbits the Earth once every month. We can see the Moon because it reflects light from the Sun. Nothing lives on the Moon but it has been visited by humans. The view of Earth from the Moon in Fig 1 is very clear. The Moon has no clouds or atmosphere to spoil the view.

▲ **Fig 1** Astronauts on the Moon get a wonderful view of Earth.

Artificial satellites

The Moon is 380 000 kilometres from Earth. It gives a good view of the Earth but it is a long way away. Artificial satellites can give a closer view of Earth. The first one was sent into space in 1957. Since then thousands more have been placed into orbit.

Some satellites can take detailed photographs of people and structures on Earth. They are sometimes called spy satellites. The information they provide is used to find out about what is happening in other countries.

Satellites are used for weather forecasting. Weather satellites can detect cloud movements and gathering storms and send pictures down to Earth (see Fig 2).

These pictures can be used to forecast the weather. Weather forecasts do much more than help us to decide when to go on a picnic or hang out the washing. The lives of those who work at sea may depend on knowing when a storm is coming. Farmers also rely on accurate weather forecasting.

▲ **Fig 2**

ACTIVITY

On your own.
- Why are weather satellites important?

Space exploration

Satellites are not only used to look at the Earth.
Telescopes placed on satellites can give a much clearer
view of stars than a telescope on Earth. The pictures are
not spoiled by dust and dirt in the Earth's atmosphere.
The Hubble Space Telescope (see Fig 3), which was
launched in 1990, can see seven times as far as
telescopes on Earth.

Satellites have even been sent millions of miles away to
orbit other planets in the Solar System. Our knowledge
of Mars, Venus and the outer planets has been improved
by pictures and other information from exploration
satellites.

▶ **Fig 3**

Communications satellites

We also use satellites to pass telephone, radio and television messages around the world.
Communications satellites in orbit above the Earth (see Fig 4) can receive and pass on
messages very quickly, to and from almost anywhere in the world, without wires or cables.
Although a satellite is very expensive to make and launch, the cost can be shared among
many different organisations. Once it is in place it can be used for a long time.

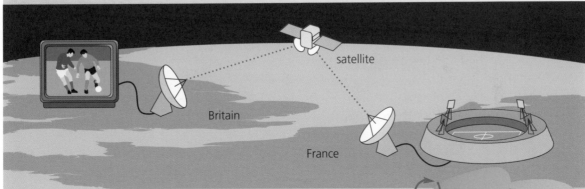

satellite

Britain

France

▲ **Fig 4** Live concerts and sporting events can be seen around the world.

Connections

This unit builds on earlier
work on forces and the
Solar System in Year 7. It
is linked to a unit of work
on speeding up.

REVIEW

- In a group.
  - Look back at your list from the starter activity.
  - Add any new ideas to the list.
  - Which ones did you not have at the beginning?

🏠 Count how many items of information on television or radio come to your home via satellite
during one single evening. Watch out especially for sports, news reports and 'live' interviews
with people in other countries.

109 Distance and time

KEY IDEAS

In this section of the book you will have opportunities to:
- Explain the relationship between speed, time and distance.

STARTER

In a group.
Discuss some of the ways that you could determine the speed of a runner in a race. Write your ideas down.

Distance and time

As you may recall, speed is determined by measuring the time taken for an object to travel a specific distance.

Remember the equation for calculating average speed:

Average speed = distance travelled ÷ time taken

$$v = \frac{d}{t}$$

Cover up the one you are trying to find.

d

$\div$ $\div$

t $\times$ v

◀ **Fig 2**

If you need to work out how long a journey will take you can simply change this equation around. If you want to see how far you have travelled at any time on a journey you can change the same equation round another way, see Fig 2.

▲ **Fig I** These runners are all running at different speeds

Distance–time graphs

The relationship between distance and time can be drawn on a graph. This is called a distance–time graph. The graph is made by plotting how much distance is covered during each stage or leg of the journey.

The diagram (see Fig 3 opposite) shows the distance–time graph for a girl walking to school. A steep line shows where she was walking quickly and went a long way in a short time. A flat line shows where she was standing still. We can use the graph to find out her speed at any time during the walk.

▶ **Fig 3** A distance–time graph.

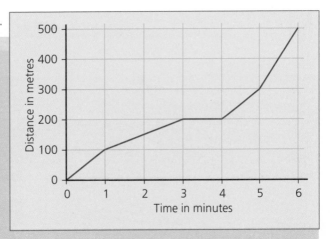

ACTIVITY

With a partner.

● Study the graph in Fig 3 and then answer the questions below.

a How long did the total journey take?

b When did the girl stop to wait for a friend?

c Where do you think she may have been walking downhill?

d Where do you think she might have been walking up a steep hill?

If the speed of an object is constant, we say that the object is moving with **uniform speed**. The speed and direction of an object is known as **velocity**. Care must be taken when measuring velocity. It can be misleading if two objects are moving relative to each other. Imagine you are in a car travelling at a velocity of 30 m/s in one direction and a car is approaching you at 40 m/s in the opposite direction. The car will appear to be moving towards you at 70 m/s. This is known as the **relative velocity**.

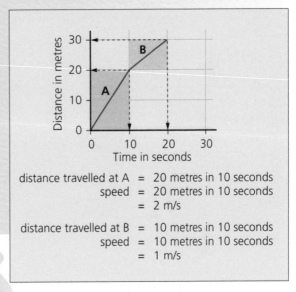

distance travelled at A = 20 metres in 10 seconds
speed = 20 metres in 10 seconds
= 2 m/s

distance travelled at B = 10 metres in 10 seconds
speed = 10 metres in 10 seconds
= 1 m/s

▲ **Fig 4** How to calculate speed from distance and time on a graph.

Study tip

When studying distance–time graphs remember that a steep line on the graph shows that the object or person is moving faster than when the line is not steep. A level section of the graph shows the object or person is not moving at all.

REVIEW

● In a group.

○ For one person in the group, draw a distance–time graph for their journey to school.

a Where and when are the fastest and slowest parts of the journey?

b What is the average speed during the journey?

⌂ Explain why distance–time graphs give a more accurate picture of a journey than the average speed.

110 Forces and speed

KEY IDEAS

In this section of the book you will have opportunities to:
- Study the effects of forces on speed.

STARTER

In a group.
Discuss why only knowing the average speed of a car does not give an accurate view of a journey. Write down your ideas.

Acceleration

At the start of a journey the speed of a vehicle changes. The drag racer can reach a speed of 60 metres per second (m/s) in less than 10 seconds. This means that the car has gained speed very quickly. This increase in speed in a certain time is known as **acceleration**.

To calculate acceleration we use the equation below:

$$\text{Acceleration} = \frac{\text{increase in speed}}{\text{time taken}}$$

▲ **Fig 1** This car is certainly accelerating!

The drag racer is increasing speed from 0 to 60 m/s in 10 seconds.

$$\text{Acceleration} = \frac{60 \text{ m/s}}{10 \text{ s}} = 6 \text{ m/s per second}$$

The drag racer is gaining in speed by 6 m/s every second. This is written as 6 m/s^2

Deceleration

This is the opposite of acceleration. If a car reduces speed from 30 m/s to 10 m/s in 10 seconds then it has a deceleration of 2 m/s^2. The speed of the car is falling by 2 m/s every second.

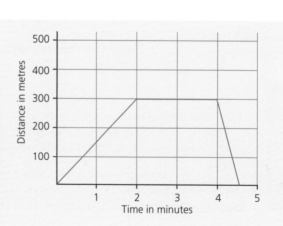

▶ **Fig 2** Distance–time graph.

► **Fig 3** This space probe will move forever, even with the engines off.

ACTIVITY

With a partner.
- Study Fig 2. Which part of the graph shows the vehicle:
  a accelerating
  b decelerating
  c moving at uniform speed?

Force and movement

If there are no forces on it, a moving object will continue to move at a steady speed in a straight line. This is what happens to deep space probes (see Fig 3). Even with all engines turned off the space probe will continue to move forever. There is no force of gravity, or objects to collide with.

In order to accelerate, the probe must fire its rockets. A large, powerful rocket will give a greater force than a small rocket. This will give greater acceleration. The greater the force on an object, the greater the acceleration. • • • • • • • • • • • • • • ►

The mass of the object is also important. With the same size of rocket engine, a probe with greater mass would have less acceleration. This can be shown in an equation:

Force	=	mass	x	acceleration
(newtons)		(kg)		(m/s²)

▶ **Fig 4** Probe firing rocket and accelerating.

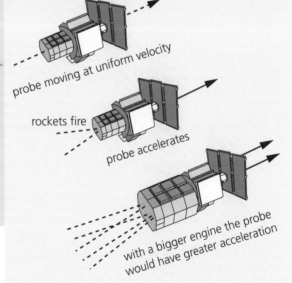
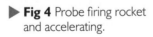

probe moving at uniform velocity

rockets fire

probe accelerates

with a bigger engine the probe would have greater acceleration

REVIEW
- In a group.
  - Design a poster explaining the links between mass, force and acceleration. Include some examples.

  Produce some creative writing that describes what happens to two astronauts when the engine of their spacecraft is damaged and turns on and off without warning.

III Streamlining

KEY IDEAS

In this section of the book you will have opportunities to:
- Explain how streamlining can reduce the effects of air and water resistance.

STARTER

In a group.
Discuss why a rocket in space will keep moving forever, even with its engines off. Now write down your ideas why objects on Earth will not keep moving in this way.

Friction

If the engine of the racing bike is switched off, the motorbike will slow down and stop. The motorcycle is slowed by **friction**. You may recall that friction is a force that acts to slow down objects as they rub past each other.

▲ **Fig 1** Even a streamlined motorcycle will be slowed by friction.

Air resistance

Air resistance is an example of friction. Although air is made of molecules of gases these can still cause friction. As objects move through the air the molecules rub against the object and slow it. Objects with large surface areas will cause the most air resistance as they will collide with more air molecules (see Fig 2).

Faster objects create more air resistance than slower objects. If we want an object to move faster we must reduce this air resistance. If we want an object to move slowly through air then one way to do it is to increase air resistance. Objects that are designed to reduce air resistance are **streamlined**. The objects are smooth and surfaces are shaped to cut through the air more easily. Animals can also use streamlining to travel quickly through air.

Connections

This work builds on earlier work on forces and their effects. It is linked to some ideas covered in the work on gravity and space and leads on to work on pressure and moments.

small cardboard sheet has some air resistance

large cardboard sheet has a great deal of air resistance

▲ Fig 2

Terminal velocity

When an object is dropped it accelerates as it falls through the air. As the object speeds up it has to move more and more air out of the way. The air resistance increases with the speed of the object. Eventually the upward force of the air resistance equals the force of gravity on the object. The object no longer accelerates. It falls at uniform speed. This is known as the **terminal velocity**. At terminal velocity the forces are balanced.

▶ **Fig 3** At terminal velocity the forces on the skydivers are balanced. The velocity will be constant.

ACTIVITY

With a partner.
- Discuss what would happen to the velocity of the skydivers when they open their parachutes.
- Write down your ideas.

Water resistance

Water molecules are closer together than the molecules in air. Objects moving through water have to push past these molecules. This causes friction. This is known as **water resistance**. Streamlined shapes will move through water with less resistance than other shapes. Machines such as submarines are streamlined. Many animals that have to move quickly through water have evolved to be streamlined (see Fig 4).

▲ **Fig 4** Sharks are very streamlined to help them to hunt their prey.

REVIEW

- In a group.
  - Design five questions that test knowledge and understanding of speed, friction, air resistance and water resistance.
  - Pass the questions on to another group and see how well they do.
- Research some examples of reducing and increasing friction. Write down your findings.

112 Forces and pressure

KEY IDEAS

In this section of the book you will have opportunities to:
- Explain the relationship between force and pressure.

STARTER

In a group.
Discuss how you would walk on soft snow without sinking in. Write down your ideas.

Pressure

You can easily sink into soft mud because all your weight is on the small area covered by your feet. Walking on boards spreads the weight. The **pressure** on each square centimetre of the ground is much smaller. Boards are often used to protect busy paths from being damaged by people walking on them.

Reducing pressure

▶ **Fig 1**

Caterpillar tracks spread the weight of a heavy vehicle (see Fig 1) over a larger area than wheels would. This reduces the pressure and helps to prevent the vehicle from getting bogged down. Snowshoes also help to reduce pressure and prevent a person from sinking into soft snow.

Many animals have feet designed to spread pressure. A camel's large flat feet help it to walk across soft sand. Birds that live in muddy places often have webbed feet.

▼ **Fig 2** If the force spreads out over a large area the pressure is low. If the force is concentrated on a small area the pressure is high.

Increasing pressure

A drawing pin can be pushed into wood quite easily. Your thumb will not go into the wood even if you press down with enough force to make a drawing pin go in. The force of the drawing pin is concentrated in one small area. Pressure describes how concentrated a force is. Nails, drawing pins and sharp knives

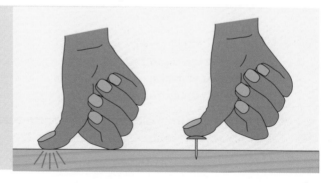

are the opposite of snowshoes and webbed feet. They concentrate force in a small area. This is why they can pierce or cut hard materials.

Calculating pressure

▶ **Fig 3**

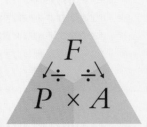

Pressure is defined as the force per unit area. It can be calculated by using this equation:

pressure = force ÷ area

Fig 3 shows an easy way to remember the equation as a triangle.

ACTIVITY

On your own.
- Use Fig 3 to help you to explain why large, flat surfaces are used to spread loads.
- Write down your ideas.

If you use your thumb to press on wood with a force of 100 N, the force is spread over one square centimetre. If you press on a drawing pin the force is concentrated on an area one hundred times smaller. The pressure on the point of the drawing pin is therefore 100 times larger than the pressure of your thumb.

Thumb	**Drawing pin**
pressure = force ÷ area	pressure = force ÷ area
pressure = 100 N ÷ 1 cm^2	pressure = 100 N ÷ 0.01 cm^2
pressure = 100 N per metre^2	pressure = 10 000 N per metre^2

Study tip

Try to place different values into the equation for calculating pressure. See what happens when you have a large force and a very small area. Next, try a small force and a very large area. This will give you valuable practice in using the equation.

REVIEW

- In a group.
  - Use graph paper to work out the area of your feet.
  - Find out your mass in kg.
  - Calculate the pressure you each put on the ground when you stand on one leg and on two legs (1 kg = 10 newtons).

 List as many examples as you can of forces being spread over a large area to reduce pressure. Draw some of the examples and show how the pressure is reduced.

113 Pressure in liquids

KEY IDEAS

In this section of the book you will have opportunities to:
- Explain the relationship between pressure, force and area in liquids and gases.

STARTER

In a group.
Imagine trying to push a balloon underwater in a swimming pool. Explain what would happen and try to give a scientific explanation.

Pressure in liquids

When you pour a liquid into a container it falls to the bottom. This is because the force of gravity is pulling the liquid downwards. This causes pressure on the container. It also causes pressure on any object placed into the water.

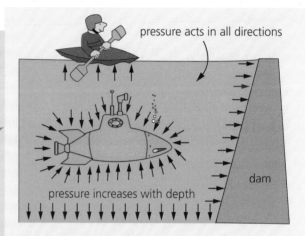

pressure acts in all directions

pressure increases with depth

dam

▲ **Fig 1** Pressures acting on a submarine and dam.

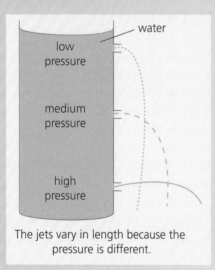

water

low pressure

medium pressure

high pressure

The jets vary in length because the pressure is different.

▲ **Fig 2** Water pressure can.

Pressure increases with depth. This is because there is more water pushing down on the water lower down the container. Every molecule of water is under pressure. A liquid will push on every surface that it is in contact with. The pressure acts in all directions. Dams have to be thicker at the base than at the top. This is because they have to withstand much higher pressure from the water at the bottom of the reservoir.

Hydraulics

Hydraulic brakes and machines use liquids under pressure. This is because liquids are not easily compressed. Any force is passed through the liquid. Car brakes work hydraulically. A small downward force from a driver creates a larger force at the brake pads. This is because the pedal pushes down a narrow tube filled with brake fluid. This puts the brake fluid under

high pressure. This high pressure brake fluid is used to
move the brakes. •••••••

force caused
(Y)
by brake pedal

The force at (X) is greater than the
force at (Y). The brake shoe presses
against the drum and stops the wheel.

brake shoe
brake fluid
brake drum

ACTIVITY

With a partner.
• Discuss why bubbles of air would be so dangerous in a car hydraulic brake system.

Diving and pressure

When a diver descends into the water the water pressure
increases. The pressure causes the air in the diver's lungs, inner
ears and other body spaces to contract. This is because the air
molecules are pushed closer together. To allow the diver to
breathe underwater the air in the air tanks must be delivered at a
pressure equal to the water pressure. The air is compressed and
released to the diver through a special valve.

This means that if a diver takes a breath of air at 10 metres depth
and then surfaces without breathing out, the air in his/her lungs
will double in volume. This could damage the diver's lungs.

Depth under water in metres	Pressure in atmospheres
surface	1
10	2
20	3
30	4
40	5

▲ **Table 1** Atmospheric
pressure and depth. At 5
atmospheres, the pressure is
5 times greater than
atmospheric pressure.

If a diver rises to the surface too quickly the gases that are dissolved in his/her blood cannot
escape through the lungs at all. Bubbles of gas, especially nitrogen, form in the blood. These
bubbles can be trapped in joints and cause great pain. Bubbles in the heart and brain can
cause even greater problems, even death. This is called decompression sickness or the 'bends'.

REVIEW

• In a group.
  ○ Design a toy with legs that move by hydraulics.
  🏠 Research what pneumatics means. Give some examples.

114 Turning forces

KEY IDEAS

In this section of the book you will have opportunities to:

- Explain that forces can make objects turn and that objects turn around a pivot.

STARTER

In a group.
A spanner is used to tighten nuts onto bolts. Discuss why spanners are more effective at tightening nuts than hands are.

Turning forces

Car wheels are attached firmly by tight nuts that cannot be loosened by hand. We need a wheel spanner to turn them. The nuts on the wheel turn around a point in the middle called the **pivot**. Many other tools also work by increasing the turning force a person can produce.

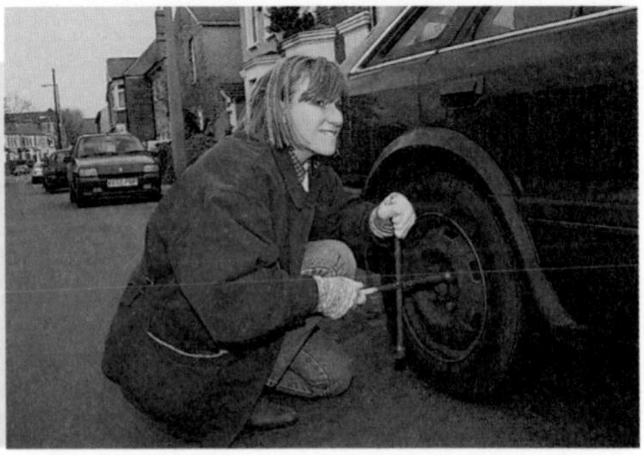

▶ **Fig 1** Turning force comes from the handle of the spanner.

Moment of force

Both people on the seesaw in Fig 2 are pushing down with the same force. Each person is also the same distance from the pivot point. The force around a pivot is called the **moment**. The moment is a combination of the length of a **lever** and the force on it. A seesaw is balanced when the moment is the same on both sides of the pivot.

We can show this as a calculation.

moment of force
= force x distance from the pivot

Each child is sitting two metres (m) from the pivot and pressing down with a force of 300 newtons (N) so the moment on each side is:

300 N x 2 m = 600 N m (newton metres)

This means that both sides cancel each other out.

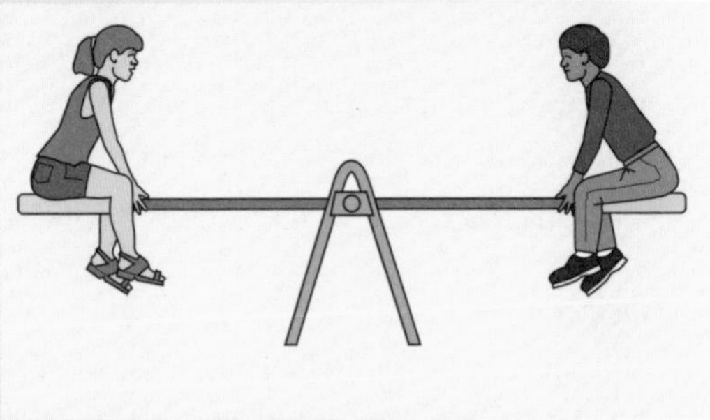

▲ **Fig 2** When two people the same weight sit on a seesaw it is balanced.

When the anti-clockwise moment is the same as the clockwise moment the object will balance.

The child in Fig 3 still pushes down with a force of 300 newtons but the adult is twice as big and pushes down with twice the force. The seesaw can still be balanced if the moments are made the same on both sides. We cannot make the adult smaller but we can adjust the distance. Halving the length of the adult's end of the seesaw can make up for the adult weighing twice as much. • • • • •

child $= 300\,\text{N} \times 2\,\text{m} = 600\,\text{Nm}$
adult $= 600\,\text{N} \times 1\,\text{m} = 600\,\text{Nm}$

With a partner.
● What would be the moment created by a force of 200 N placed 0.5 metres from the pivot of a seesaw?

▲ **Fig 3** An adult and a child need to allow for their difference in weight.

Levers

The child on the seesaw lifts the heavy adult by being further away from the pivot. This is how levers work. A long lever can move a boulder more easily than a short one. A longer lever has a larger moment. The lever can also be made to lift larger objects by using more force. This means pushing down on the lever with more effort.

Two ways of producing more leverage, turning effect or moment are:

1. to have a longer handle or lever
2. to increase the force on the handle or lever.

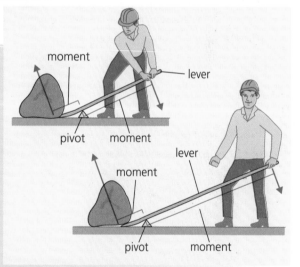

▲ **Fig 4** Increasing the length of a lever between the pivot and downward force increases the upward force on the boulder.

● In a group.
  ○ Think back to the starter activity.
  ○ Use the law of moments to explain why the spanner can turn a nut more tightly than bare hands.

🏠 Using a ruler with a pivot made from a pencil and some 2p coins, work out three different ways of balancing the seesaw if:
  a 3 coins are placed 6 centimetres away from one side of the pivot
  b 4 coins are placed 2 centimetres away from one side of the pivot.

Summary of Year 9 topics

Biology (pages 170–195)

After studying the first part of the Year 9 topics you should have learned some very important aspects of life processes and living things.

Inheritance and selection

1. Explain the differences between sexual and asexual reproduction.
2. What are clones?
3. How does selective breeding lead to better crops?

Fit and healthy

4. Which bones protect the heart and lungs from damage?
5. Explain why most muscles have to work in pairs.
6. Explain how alcohol is harmful.

Plants and photosynthesis

7. Write a word equation for photosynthesis.
8. How do gases move in and out of the leaves of a plant?
9. What are the three main functions of roots?

Plants for food

10. List three essential elements needed by plants.
11. Describe some of the advantages and disadvantages of using fertilisers to increase crop yield.
12. Explain how toxic materials can enter food chains.

Chemistry (pages 196–219)

The second part of the Year 9 topics should have helped you to understand more about chemical reactions and the environmental impact and uses of some important chemicals.

Reactions of metals and metal compounds

13. Describe how magnesium and copper react with acids.
14. Name the salt produced when hydrochloric acid reacts with copper oxide.
15. Write a word and symbol equation for the reaction between sodium and water.

Patterns of reactivity

16. What is the least reactive metal in the Reactivity Series?

17. What is the most reactive metal in the Reactivity Series?

18. Use the Reactivity Series to predict what happens when aluminium powder is heated with copper oxide.

Environmental chemistry

19. List two examples of gases that can cause acid rain.

20. Explain the Greenhouse effect.

21. List four examples of water pollutants and describe how they can enter waterways and the sea.

Using chemistry

22. Describe one example of an exothermic reaction. Write the word equation for the reaction.

23. What is meant by the term 'conservation of mass'?

24. List five important chemicals made by chemical reaction.

Physics (pages 220–243)

The third part of the Year 9 topics should have helped you to understand some more important physical processes.

Energy and electricity

25. Describe how the chemical energy in coal can be used to generate electricity.

26. Why are power ratings on electrical appliances so important to us?

27. Describe why an electric drill is inefficient in energy terms.

Gravity and Space

28. The size of the Sun's gravitational pull on a planet depends on two things. What are these?

29. On Earth an object has a weight of 6000 N. What would be its weight on the Moon?

30. List three uses of artificial satellites.

Speeding up

31. Why do distance–time graphs give a more accurate picture of a journey than average speed?

32. Write down the relationship between acceleration, speed and time.

33. Explain how streamlining reduces air and water resistance.

Pressure and moments

34. Explain why tractors have very large wheels.

35. Describe how you could prove that pressure in liquids increases with depth.

36. Why do we unscrew a nut with a spanner rather than with our fingers?

Useful formulae and tables

Photosynthesis

carbon dioxide + water $\xrightarrow[\text{chlorophyll}]{\substack{\text{energy from}\\\text{sunlight}}}$ glucose + oxygen

Respiration

glucose + oxygen $\longrightarrow$ carbon dioxide + water + energy

Reactivity Series

most reactive
potassium
sodium
calcium
magnesium
aluminium
zinc
iron
lead
copper
silver
gold
least reactive

Reactions of acids

acids + metals $\longrightarrow$ salt + hydrogen

acids + metal oxides (bases) $\longrightarrow$ salt + water

acids + alkalis (soluble bases) $\longrightarrow$ salt + water

acids + carbonates $\longrightarrow$ salt + water + carbon dioxide

Velocity, distance and time

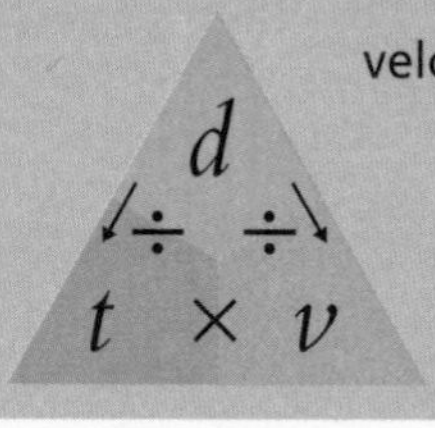

velocity = distance travelled ÷ time taken

$$v = \frac{d}{t}$$
$$t = \frac{d}{v}$$
$$d = t \times v$$

Moment of force

moment of force = force × distance from the pivot

Pressure, force and area

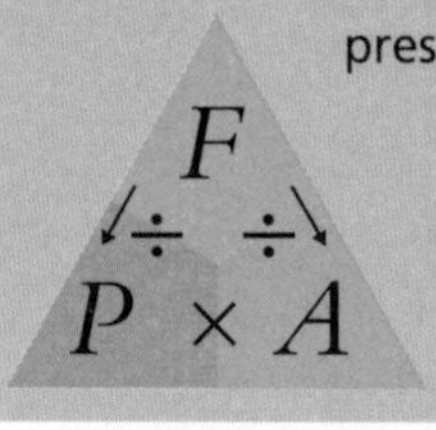

pressure = force ÷ area

$$P = \frac{F}{A}$$
$$F = P \times A$$
$$A = \frac{F}{P}$$

The Periodic Table

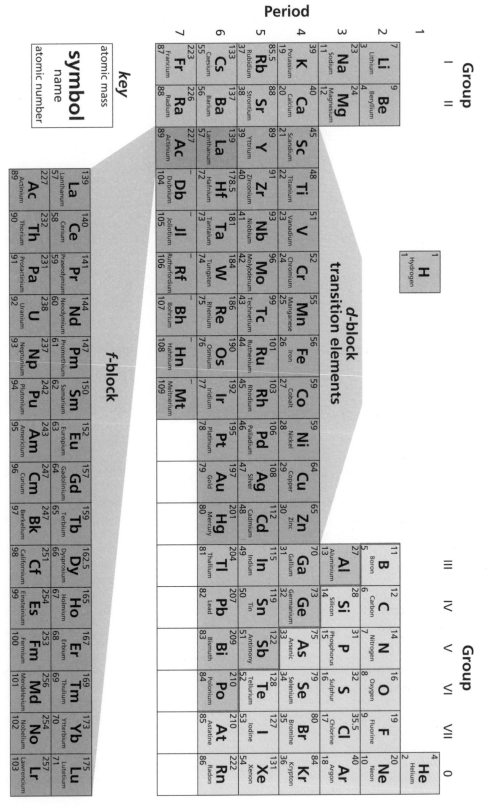

Group

	Group I	II				III	IV	V	VI	VII	0

Period

key

atomic mass
symbol
name
atomic number

d-block transition elements

f-block

Glossary

A

abiotic factors – the physical factors in a habitat e.g. pH, temperature and light intensity

absorption – the passage of nutrients from the gut to the blood

acceleration – the rate of change of the velocity of a moving body

acellular – made of one cell. Also unicellular

acid indigestion – pain due to too much acid in the stomach

acid rain – rainwater that is more acid than normal

aerobic respiration – using oxygen to get energy from glucose

air resistance – friction caused by air molecules

alkali – a solution made by dissolving a metal oxide in water

alloy – a mixture of metals

alternative energy – a renewable energy resource

alveolus (plural: alveoli) – a tiny air sac in a lung

amino acids – the basic building blocks of proteins

ammeter – a meter for measuring current

amniotic fluid – the fluid surrounding the foetus inside the womb

ampere – the unit for measuring current, also amp or A

amplify – to make a bigger wave with a louder sound

amplitude – the height of a wave

anaerobic respiration – respiration that takes place without oxygen

angle of incidence – the angle between an incoming ray (incident ray) of light and the normal line where it meets a plane mirror

angle of reflection – the angle between an outgoing ray (reflected ray) of light and the normal line where it leaves a plane mirror

aquatic – living in water

ascorbic acid – another name for Vitamin C

asexual reproduction – the process of cells dividing to produce exact copies of themselves

antagonistic muscle pair – two muscles working in opposite directions

anther – the part of a flower where pollen is made

antibiotic – a chemical that kills bacteria

antibody – a protein produced by your body to fight disease

antioxidant – preventing oxidation

armature – the metal arm carrying the clapper that hits the gong in an electric bell

artery – a blood vessel that carries blood from the heart

atom – the smallest particle of an element

atomic number – the number of protons in an atom

audible – a sound that a person can hear

axis – the (nearly vertical) centre of the Earth's spin

B

bacteria – a very large group of microorganisms. Some produce infectious diseases

balanced diet – a diet that contains the range of nutrients needed to stay healthy

base – oxide or hydroxide of a reactive metal

bauxite – the common name for aluminium ore (aluminium oxide)

bimetal strip – a strip made from two metals joined together

binary fission – the division of one cell into two identical daughter cells

biomass – the total amount of living material in any object or area

biotic factors – the factors linked to the plants and animals in a habitat

birth rate – the number of animals born or seeds germinating at one time

blast furnace – a furnace for extracting iron from iron ore

blood cells (red/white) – the cells found in the plasma of blood

boiling point – the temperature at which gas bubbles form in a liquid

bond – the link between one atom and another

breathing – the process by which air is drawn into and then expelled from the lungs

breccia – a sedimentary rock made up of large angular rock fragments

bronchiole – a small air tube in a lung

bronchus (plural: bronchi) – one of two main tubes branching off the windpipe

C

camouflaged – blending into the background or looking like something else

capillary – a tiny thin-walled blood vessel

carbohydrate – a high energy molecule containing carbon, hydrogen and oxygen

carbon dioxide – a combination of carbon and oxygen created by burning or respiration

cartilage – a strong smooth material, also called gristle

catalyst – a substance that helps a chemical reaction without becoming a product

cell – the basic building block of living things or the part of a battery where chemical energy becomes electrical energy

cell division – the splitting of a cell into two cells

cell membrane – flexible covering of the cell

cell wall – the hard, protective outer layer of some organisms, such as plants and bacteria

cervix – the neck of the uterus where it enters the vagina

change of state – a change between a solid, liquid or gas

chemical change – a change into a new substance not easily reversed

chemical energy – the energy stored

in chemicals such as fuels

chemical reaction – substances joining together to make new substances

chloride – a salt of hydrochloric acid

chlorophyll – the green pigment in plants that traps the energy in sunlight

chloroplast – a structure in a plant cell that contains chlorophyll

chromatography – a method of separation using a solvent

cilia – tiny moving hairs attached to cells

circuit – a complete ring of conducting materials

circulatory system – the system that includes the heart and blood vessels

classification – an attempt to organise a large quantity of information into a logical order

cochlea – part of the inner ear where vibrations become nerve messages

comet – a body made of dust and frozen gases

community – the collection of animals and plants that share a habitat

competition – one or more living things requiring the same food, mate or shelter

compound – a chemical substance made of different elements

condense – change from a gas to a liquid

conduction – the movement of heat energy along a material

conductor – a substance that transmits heat and electricity

conservation of mass – no alteration in mass during a change

constellation – a named 'shape' among the stars

consumer – an animal that feeds on plants or other animals

contact force – the force between colliding objects

contraction – shrinkage caused by cooling

convection – a way in which heat energy is transferred in liquids and gases

convection currents – the rising and falling of liquids and gases as convection occurs

core – the iron or steel rod in the centre of an electromagnet

corrosive – able to attack other materials

cross breeding – encouraging or forcing one variety of an organism to breed with a different variety

crystal – a solid which is made up of a regular arrangement of particles

current – the flow of electricity

cytoplasm – the liquid part of a cell

D

death rate – the number of animals or plants dying at one time

decanting – carefully pouring the liquid part of a mixture from the solid part

decompose – to break down into smaller parts

decomposition reaction – a reaction where a chemical is broken down into smaller chemicals, often by heating

dietary fibre – indigestible carbohydrates (roughage)

diffusion – the movement of one substance through another substance

digestion – chemically breaking down food into smaller molecules

digestive system – the organs of the body (mouth, stomach, small and large intestines, etc) that are responsible for the breaking down and absorption of food

dilute – mixed with water

displace – take the place of another element in a chemical compound

distillation – a method of separation using evaporation

diurnal – belonging to the day

division of labour – sharing out the functions needed to maintain life

dominant gene – a gene that is stronger than its opposite number

dormant – resting

dyke – a vertical crack filled with magma

E

eardrum – a membrane that transmits sound waves from the air

echo – a sound bouncing back from a solid surface

ecosystem – a self-contained community interacting with the environment

egested – unused food and fibre passed out of the anus

electrical potential energy – the electrical energy produced by a battery or other power source

electrolysis – splitting chemicals with electricity

electromagnet – an electric wire coiled around a metal core

electron – a small negatively charged sub-atomic particle

element – a substance made of one type of atom

ellipse – a slightly flattened circle shape

embryo – the first two months of development of a new baby

endothermic – taking in heat

energy conversion – changing one form of energy into another form

energy transfer – the movement of energy from one place to another

environment – geographical, geological and biological surroundings

enzymes – chemicals found in the digestive system that are used to break down larger particles into smaller pieces. They act as biological catalysts

equation – a shorthand description for a chemical reaction

equator – a (nearly horizontal) imaginary line around the Earth's middle

erosion – the movement of weathered rock

essential elements – elements necessary for healthy plant growth

eutrophication – a shortage of oxygen caused by the overgrowth and later death of aquatic plants

evaporation – changing from a liquid to a gas

excretion – the removal of waste products from living things

exhalation – breathing out

exothermic – giving out heat

expansion – growth caused by heating

F

fallopian tube – tube carrying ovum to uterus

fertilisation – the point when a sperm cell enters an egg and genetic material is combined

filament – very thin wire in a light bulb

filter – a substance that holds back part of what lands on it

filtrate – the part of a mixture that passes through a filter

filtration – separating a mixture by passing it through a filter

foam – a mixture of a gas in a liquid

foetus – a human embryo after two months

food web – a network of food chains

formula – the shorthand name of a compound

fossil – evidence of living things preserved in rocks

fossil fuels – fuels, e.g. coal, crude oil and natural gas, that are produced by the action of high temperatures and high pressures on plant and animal material over millions of years

fractional distillation – a method of separating liquid mixtures by evaporation

freezing point – the temperature at which a liquid becomes a solid

frequency – the number of vibrations per second

friction – the force that opposes the relative motion of two bodies in contact

fuel – a substance that combines with oxygen to give out heat in a way we can use

G

galaxy – a cluster of millions of stars

gamete – male or female sex cell (animal or plant)

gas exchange – the process of oxygen entering the blood and carbon dioxide leaving the blood

gene – a very large molecule carrying a code for one characteristic

genetic material – the material carrying the genetic code for the reproduction of cells

genus – a group of organisms just above species level

global warming – an increase in the Earth's average temperature

gravity – the force of attraction between any object in the Earth's gravitational field and the Earth itself

greenhouse effect – how carbon dioxide keeps the Earth warm

growth – the increase in the size and dry weight of an organism

H

habitat – the home for a living thing that provides everything it needs

haematite – one of the common ores of iron (iron oxide)

haemoglobin – the red pigment inside red blood cells

heat – a form of energy

hemisphere – one-half of the Earth between the equator and a Pole

herbicide – a chemical that kills plants

herbivore – an animal that only eats plants

Hertz (Hz) – the unit for measuring frequency

hibernation – winter sleep

hydroelectric power – electricity generated by flowing water

hydrogen – a chemical element that combines with oxygen to make water

I

igneous – rock formed when magma cools

immune system – the system that protects our body from disease

impurity – any unwanted substance mixed with another substance

incident ray – a ray of light hitting a surface

indicator – a chemical that indicates pH

inert – does not react with other substances

infection – the result of disease-causing bacteria entering the body

infrasound – a sound too low for a person to hear

inhalation – breathing in

inherited – characteristics transmitted genetically from a parent

insoluble – unable to dissolve in a liquid

insulator – a material that does not transmit heat and electricity

invertebrate – an animal without a backbone

involuntary – muscle that is worked by the body automatically

J

joules (J) – the SI unit of work and energy

K

key – a table or chart that helps you to identify living things

kinetic energy – energy of movement

kingdom – one of the five major divisions of living things

L

law of conservation of energy – the law that states that energy cannot be created or destroyed, but can be changed from one form to another

lever – a rod used with a pivot to increase force

light year – the distance light travels in one year

lime – calcium oxide or hydroxide

liver – a very important organ in your body

lubricate – cover a surface with a slippery substance

luminous – an object that emits light

M

magma – hot liquid rock

magnetic field – the shape and size of the area affected by a magnet

mammary glands – the milk-producing gland in a mammal

mass – a measure of how much matter is in an object

melting point – the temperature at

which a solid becomes a liquid

menstrual cycle – the monthly cycle of the female sex organs

metal carbonate – a compound of a metal and a carbonate

metamorphic rock – rock changed by heat or pressure

microhabitat – a small area within a larger habitat, e.g. under a stone

migration – regularly travelling to a different region

mineral – an element needed to make some body chemicals

mixture – substances mixed but not chemically joined

molecule – a group of atoms chemically joined

moment – the turning effect produced by a force

moraine – the piles of rock fragments associated with glaciers

multicellular – made of more than one cell

mutation – a sudden change in the structure of a gene

N

natural selection – survival of well-adapted organisms and death of badly adapted ones

natural (substance) – occurs in nature; not manufactured

neutral – having no charge

neutral – pH 7, neither acidic nor alkaline

neutron – a sub-atomic particle with no electrical charge

nitrate – a salt produced from nitric acid

nocturnal – belonging to the night

nodule – a rounded lump found on some plant roots (see legumes)

noise – an unpleasant sound

non-aqueous – a solvent not based on water

non-renewable – something that cannot be replaced

normal – a line at right angles to the surface

normal distribution – a pattern on a graph that shows the normal range of differences within one species

north-seeking pole – the end of a magnet that points northwards

nucleus – the central core of an atom or comet, or the control centre of the cell

nutrient – any food substance needed by the body

O

opaque – not allowing light to pass through

orbit – the path of a planet around the Sun

ore – a natural metal compound

organ – a group of tissues working together

organism – any plant, animal, fungus or bacterium

organ system – a group of organs working together

organic matter – material that has been produced by living things

oscilloscope – a machine to show the shape of waves

ovary – part of the female reproductive system producing eggs or the female reproductive organ of flowering plants

ovules – the parts of the female part of a flower that will eventually become seeds

ovum/ova – female sex cells

oxide – an element chemically combined with oxygen

P

palisade cells – cells found near the surface of leaves, containing a large number of chloroplasts

passive smoking – breathing in someone else's tobacco smoke

Periodic Table – a useful chart of elements

pesticide – a poison intended to kill an annoying animal

pH number – a measurement of acidity or alkalinity

photosynthesis – the process of making glucose by using energy from the sun

physical change – a change affecting the appearance of a substance but not its chemistry

pitch – how high or low a note is

pivot – the point around which an object turns

placenta – the structure made by an embryo to obtain food and oxygen from its mother

plane – a very flat, smooth surface

plankton – tiny plants and animals found in surface waters of oceans

platelets – small components of blood that are essential to clotting

Pole – one end of the Earth's axis

pollen – the male sex cell of a flowering plant

pollen tube – the tube down which the male sex cell (pollen) will travel to fertilise the female sex cell in flowering plants

pollutant – any unwanted or harmful substance

pollute – spoil by adding a damaging substance

population – the number of individuals of one species in one area at one time

porous – a material with tiny holes or pores within it that gases and liquids can pass through

potential difference – the difference between the energy at the start of its journey around a circuit and at the end

potential energy – stored energy

power – the rate at which work can be done or energy converted

predator – an animal that eats other animals

predict – to know or guess in advance

pressure – force in newtons (N) exerted on a measured area

prey – a specific animal eaten by a predator

primary colour – a pure colour containing no other colours

primary consumer – animals that feed off plants to obtain the energy and raw material needed for life

producer – a green plant making food by photosynthesis

product – a substance produced by a chemical reaction

property – any characteristic of a substance, such as colour or shape

protein – a body building material

protease – an enzyme that is capable of digesting proteins

proton – a positively charged sub-atomic particle

puberty – the time when sex organs begin to work

pylon – a tall tower carrying electrical cables

pyramid of biomass – a diagram showing the mass of organisms at each stage of a food chain

pyramid of numbers – a diagram showing the number of organisms at each stage of a food chain

Q

quadrat – a square structure used for counting the number of plants or animals within a given area

R

radiation – the way in which heat energy is transferred from a hotter to a cooler place without needing any other material

radioactive – the ability to give out radiation

reactant – a substance changed by a chemical reaction

reaction – the point when a chemical change occurs

reactive – readily reacts with other substances

Reactivity Series – the league table of metals that shows how reactive each one is

reduced – having oxygen taken away

reflect – to bounce off the surface of an object

reflected ray – a ray of light reflected from a surface

refracted ray – the bending of light when it passes from one medium to another

refraction – light bending at the surface of a transparent substance

reinforced concrete – concrete with steel rods inside

relative velocity – the velocity of an object when viewed from another moving object e.g. two trains moving towards each other

renewable – something that can be replaced

reproduction – the process whereby a living organism produces another organism similar to itself

reproductive system – the organs in females and males needed for reproduction

residue – the part of a mixture that is trapped by a filter

resistance – a component that reduces the flow of current

respiration – the process of breaking down foods for energy

reversible – able to go both ways

rib cage – the flexible cage protecting your heart and lungs

rock cycle – the repeated breaking and building of rocks

rocks – substances made up from minerals

root hair cells – root cells adapted to take in water

S

salt – a compound formed when a metal replaces hydrogen in an acid

sampling – the process of choosing and collecting a sample

satellite – a body in orbit around another body

scale – solid calcium carbonate from 'hard' water

scree – sharp fragments of loose rock on mountain slopes

scrotum – the bag of skin that holds the testes outside the body

secondary consumers – animals that feed off other animals to obtain the energy and raw materials they need for life

secondary sexual characteristics – body changes that develop during adolescence

sediment – small particles of rock

sedimentary – rock formed from sediment

selective breeding – breeding to produce a combination of desired characteristics

selectively or partially permeable – allowing only some chemicals through

sensitivity – the ability to detect the surroundings

series circuit – components that electricity passes through in turn

sewage – waste material, including some from toilets, that must be purified before it goes into rivers and the sea

sex hormones – chemicals that cause the changes of puberty

sex organs – the parts of the body responsible for sexual reproduction

sexual reproduction – a process that requires the union or fertilisation of two gametes (an egg cell and a sperm call) to form a zygote

sexually transmitted disease – a disease passed on by sexual contact

shadow – an area where light is blocked

short circuit – a wire that gives the current an easier route

side-effect – unwanted effect of a drug

sill – a horizontal crack filled with magma

skull – a round bony box protecting your brain

Solar System – the Sun and all the planets and asteroids that move around it

solubility – how well a substance dissolves

soluble – able to dissolve in a liquid

solute – the substance that dissolves in a liquid

solution – a mixture of a solute in a solvent

solvent – a chemical that dissolves other chemicals

sonar – a way of finding objects by listening for echoes

sound energy – energy transmitted in sound waves

south-seeking pole – the end of a magnet that points southwards

specialised – adapted to do a special job

species – an organism that is genetically distinct

spectrum – the range of colours in white light

speed – distance divided by time

stable – not easily changed or broken

stamen – the male reproductive organ of a flowering plant

sternum – a plate of bone at the front of the chest

stoma (plural: stomata) – a pore in the lower surface of a leaf

streamlined – shaped to reduce air or water resistance

sulphate – the product of a metal, metal oxide or metal carbonate reacting with sulphuric acid

suspension – a mixture of very small solid particles in a liquid

symbol – the short version of an element's name

symbol equations – a shorthand way of writing a chemical reaction that shows the symbols of elements and formulae of compounds involved

synthesis – building up

synthetic – manufactured, not natural

T

tap root – a plant's main deep root

taxonomy – the dividing of animals and plants into groups or taxa

temperature – how hot or cold a substance is

tendon – a tough strand that joins a muscle to a bone

terminal velocity – the maximum velocity reached by an object falling through a gas or liquid

tertiary consumer – animals that eat secondary consumers to obtain the energy and raw materials they need to survive

testis – the part of the male reproductive system that produces sperm

texture – the appearance and feel of a substance

thermal decomposition – chemical breakdown caused by heating

thermal energy (**heat energy**) – the energy that flows from one place to another because of a difference in temperature

thermal insulator – a substance that will not allow heat energy to pass through easily

thermostat – equipment to keep temperature constant

tissue – a group of similar cells grouped together

toxic – poisonous

trophic level – the position of a species in a food chain

tumour – a lump made by cells dividing too quickly

turbine – a wheel that is turned by jets of steam

U

ultrasound – a sound too high for a person to hear

umbilical cord – the connection between embryo and placenta

unbalanced – when forces in one direction are greater than the forces in other directions

unicellular – organisms made up of only one cell

uniform speed – when the speed of an object is constant (not changing)

Universe – the total amount of material and energy in existence

uterus – womb

V

vacuum – an area empty of free molecules

vacuole – a fluid-filled cavity inside a cell

valency – the maximum number of bonds an atom can form with other atoms

valve – a mechanism that allows a liquid to flow in one direction only

vapour – a gas at the same temperature as its liquid state

variation – a small difference between members of the same species. A larger difference between members of different species

variety – an organism of a single species that has distinctive features

vascular system – the plant's transport system

vascular tissue – the circulation system of a plant

vector – an animal that carries disease

vegetative reproduction – when one part of a plant is able to develop into a new plant

vein – a blood vessel that carries blood back to the heart

velocity – speed (v)

vertebrae – spinal joint

vertebral column – the spine or backbone

vertebrate – an animal with a backbone

villi – small folds in the lining of the small intestine wall

virus – a type of microorganism that can cause disease

vitamin – a ready-made chemical essential for health

voltage – a shorthand way of writing potential difference

volts – the units used to measure voltage

voluntary – muscle that we can move when we wish

W

water – a colourless, odourless liquid with the formula H_2O. It is essential for life

water resistance – a substance or substances that prevent water from passing through

watts (W) – the unit of power. One watt represents one joule of energy being changed into another form of energy per second

wavelength – the distance between neighbouring wave crests

weathering – physical and chemical breakdown of rocks

weight – the force of gravity pulling an object down

work – the movement of an object by a force

Y

yield – the edible amount of a plant produced from an area of land

Index